COMPLEX ANALYSIS

International Series in Pure and Applied Mathematics

William Ted Martin and E. H. Spanier
Consulting Editors

Ahlfors Complex Analysis
Bellman Stability Theory of Differential Equations
Buck Advanced Calculus
Busacker and Saaty Finite Graphs and Networks
Coddington and Levinson Theory of Ordinary Differential Equations
Dettman Mathematical Methods in Physics and Engineering
Epstein Partial Differential Equations
Golomb and Shanks Elements of Ordinary Differential Equations
Graves The Theory of Functions of Real Variables
Greenspan Introduction to Partial Differential Equations
Griffin Elementary Theory of Numbers
Hamming Numerical Methods for Scientists and Engineers
Hildebrand Introduction to Numerical Analysis
Householder Principles of Numerical Analysis
Lass Elements of Pure and Applied Mathematics
Lass Vector and Tensor Analysis
Lepage Complex Variables and the Laplace Transform for Engineers
Nehari Conformal Mapping
Newell Vector Analysis
Ralston A First Course in Numerical Analysis
Rosser Logic for Mathematicians
Rudin Principles of Mathematical Analysis
Saaty and Bram Nonlinear Mathematics
Simmons Introduction to Topology and Modern Analysis
Sneddon Elements of Partial Differential Equations
Sneddon Fourier Transforms
Stoll Linear Algebra and Matrix Theory
Struble Nonlinear Differential Equations
Weinstock Calculus of Variations
Weiss Algebraic Number Theory
Zemanian Distribution Theory and Transform Analysis

COMPLEX ANALYSIS

an introduction to the theory of analytic functions of one complex variable

Lars V. Ahlfors

Professor of Mathematics
Harvard University

second edition

McGraw-Hill Book Company

new york st. louis san francisco toronto london sydney

Complex Analysis

Library of Congress Catalog Card Number 65-20106

00656

234567890 MP 7321069876

to the memory of

Ernst Lindelöf

PREFACE

This text is a rigorous introduction on an elementary level to the theory of analytic functions of one complex variable. At American universities it is intended to be used by first-year graduate and advanced undergraduate students.

Since the time the first edition was published there has been a marked change in the quality of American students of mathematics. They enter college better prepared, and they are confronted with true mathematical reasoning at an earlier stage. To a lesser degree the same is true abroad.

In preparing the second edition the author has striven to adjust to this greater maturity of the readers. At the same time the essentially elementary character of the exposition has not been sacrificed. Indeed, nothing could be gained by addressing only the ablest students. Therefore, as in the first edition, the presentation is comparatively broad in the beginning, except for condensed reviews of familiar material, and rises only slowly to a higher level of conciseness. The author has tried to emphasize economy of thought in order to make the reader aware of the intrinsic unity which is so characteristic of the subject.

We enumerate the most important changes from the first edition:

1. The exponential and trigonometric functions are now defined by means of power series. In order to do so it was necessary to introduce an early elementary section on complex power series, a procedure that is not without didactic value in itself.

2. The introduction to point set topology has been rewritten. It now includes the fundamental properties of metric spaces and a more detailed discussion of compactness.

3. Normal families are approached in a more direct manner, and the connection with compactness is emphasized.

4. The Riemann mapping theorem has been combined with a section on the Schwarz-Christoffel formula.

5. A short chapter on elliptic functions has been added. It is deliberately very concentrated in an effort to spare the reader from the customary maze of notations that are needed only by specialists.

6. The exercise sections have been enlarged, and some starred exercises with generous hints for their solution have been included. The latter are to be regarded as part of the text, and students should be encouraged to compose complete proofs.

I should like to take this opportunity to reaffirm my indebtedness to my late teacher Ernst Lindelöf. The whole structure of the book is also deeply influenced by Emil Artin's idea to base elementary homology theory on winding numbers.

I am very grateful to a number of mathematicians who have pointed out errors in the first edition. I can only express a pious hope that no new ones have crept in.

Lars V. Ahlfors

CONTENTS

CHAPTER 8: GLOBAL ANALYTIC FUNCTIONS 275

COMPLEX ANALYSIS

1 COMPLEX NUMBERS

1. THE ALGEBRA OF COMPLEX NUMBERS

It is fundamental that real and complex numbers obey the same basic laws of arithmetic. We begin our study of complex function theory by stressing and implementing this analogy.

1.1. Arithmetic Operations. From elementary algebra the reader is acquainted with the *imaginary unit* i with the property $i^2 = -1$. If the imaginary unit is combined with two real numbers α, β by the processes of addition and multiplication, we obtain a *complex number* $\alpha + i\beta$. α and β are the *real* and *imaginary part* of the complex number. If $\alpha = 0$, the number is said to be *purely imaginary;* if $\beta = 0$, it is of course *real*. Zero is the only number which is at once real and purely imaginary. Two complex numbers are equal if and only if they have the same real part and the same imaginary part.

Addition and multiplication do not lead out from the system of complex numbers. Assuming that the ordinary rules of arithmetic apply to complex numbers we find indeed

$$(\alpha + i\beta) + (\gamma + i\delta) = (\alpha + \gamma) + i(\beta + \delta) \tag{1}$$

and

$$(\alpha + i\beta)(\gamma + i\delta) = (\alpha\gamma - \beta\delta) + i(\alpha\delta + \beta\gamma). \tag{2}$$

In the second identity we have made use of the relation $i^2 = -1$.

It is less obvious that division is also possible. We wish to show that $(\alpha + i\beta)/(\gamma + i\delta)$ is a complex number, provided that $\gamma + i\delta \neq 0$. If the quotient is denoted by $x + iy$, we must have

$$\alpha + i\beta = (\gamma + i\delta)(x + iy).$$

By (2) this condition can be written

$$\alpha + i\beta = (\gamma x - \delta y) + i(\delta x + \gamma y),$$

and we obtain the two equations

$$\alpha = \gamma x - \delta y$$
$$\beta = \delta x + \gamma y.$$

This system of simultaneous linear equations has the unique solution

$$x = \frac{\alpha\gamma + \beta\delta}{\gamma^2 + \delta^2}$$

$$y = \frac{\beta\gamma - \alpha\delta}{\gamma^2 + \delta^2},$$

for we know that $\gamma^2 + \delta^2$ is not zero. We have thus the result

$$\frac{\alpha + i\beta}{\gamma + i\delta} = \frac{\alpha\gamma + \beta\delta}{\gamma^2 + \delta^2} + i\,\frac{\beta\gamma - \alpha\delta}{\gamma^2 + \delta^2}. \tag{3}$$

Once the existence of the quotient has been proved, its value can be found in a simpler way. If numerator and denominator are multiplied with $\gamma - i\delta$, we find at once

$$\frac{\alpha + i\beta}{\gamma + i\delta} = \frac{(\alpha + i\beta)(\gamma - i\delta)}{(\gamma + i\delta)(\gamma - i\delta)} = \frac{(\alpha\gamma + \beta\delta) + i(\beta\gamma - \alpha\delta)}{\gamma^2 + \delta^2}.$$

As a special case the reciprocal of a complex number $\neq 0$ is given by

$$\frac{1}{\alpha + i\beta} = \frac{\alpha - i\beta}{\alpha^2 + \beta^2}.$$

We note that i^n has only four possible values: $1, i, -1, -i$. They correspond to values of n which divided by 4 leave the remainders 0, 1, 2, 3.

EXERCISES

1. Find the values of

$$(1 + 2i)^3, \qquad \frac{5}{-3 + 4i}, \qquad \left(\frac{2 + i}{3 - 2i}\right)^2, \qquad (1 + i)^n + (1 - i)^n.$$

2. If $z = x + iy$ (x and y real), find the real and imaginary parts of

$$z^4, \quad \frac{1}{z}, \quad \frac{z-1}{z+1}, \quad \frac{1}{z^2}.$$

3. Show that

$$\left(\frac{-1 \pm i\sqrt{3}}{2}\right)^3 = 1 \quad \text{and} \quad \left(\frac{\pm 1 \pm i\sqrt{3}}{2}\right)^6 = 1$$

for all combinations of signs.

1.2. Square Roots. We shall now show that the square root of a complex number can be found explicitly. If the given number is $\alpha + i\beta$, we are looking for a number $x + iy$ such that

$$(x + iy)^2 = \alpha + i\beta.$$

This is equivalent to the system of equations

$$\begin{aligned} x^2 - y^2 &= \alpha \\ 2xy &= \beta. \end{aligned} \tag{4}$$

From these equations we obtain

$$(x^2 + y^2)^2 = (x^2 - y^2)^2 + 4x^2y^2 = \alpha^2 + \beta^2.$$

Hence we must have

$$x^2 + y^2 = \sqrt{\alpha^2 + \beta^2},$$

where the square root is positive or zero. Together with the first equation (4) we find

$$\begin{aligned} x^2 &= \tfrac{1}{2}(\alpha + \sqrt{\alpha^2 + \beta^2}) \\ y^2 &= \tfrac{1}{2}(-\alpha + \sqrt{\alpha^2 + \beta^2}). \end{aligned} \tag{5}$$

Observe that these quantities are positive or zero regardless of the sign of α.

The equations (5) yield, in general, two opposite values for x and two for y. But these values cannot be combined arbitrarily, for the second equation (4) is not a consequence of (5). We must therefore be careful to select x and y so that their product has the sign of β. This leads to the general solution

$$\sqrt{\alpha + i\beta} = \pm\left(\sqrt{\frac{\alpha + \sqrt{\alpha^2 + \beta^2}}{2}} + i\frac{\beta}{|\beta|}\sqrt{\frac{-\alpha + \sqrt{\alpha^2 + \beta^2}}{2}}\right) \tag{6}$$

provided that $\beta \neq 0$. For $\beta = 0$ the values are $\pm\sqrt{\alpha}$ if $\alpha \geqq 0$, $\pm i\sqrt{-\alpha}$

if $\alpha < 0$. It is understood that all square roots of positive numbers are taken with the positive sign.

We have found that the square root of any complex number exists and has two opposite values. They coincide only if $\alpha + i\beta = 0$. They are real if $\beta = 0$, $\alpha \geqq 0$ and purely imaginary if $\beta = 0$, $\alpha \leqq 0$. In other words, except for zero, only positive numbers have real square roots and only negative numbers have purely imaginary square roots.

Since both square roots are in general complex, it is not possible to distinguish between the positive and negative square root of a complex number. We could of course distinguish between the upper and lower sign in (6), but this distinction is artificial and should be avoided. The correct way is to treat both square roots in a symmetric manner.

EXERCISES

1. Compute

$$\sqrt{i}, \qquad \sqrt{-i}, \qquad \sqrt{1+i}, \qquad \sqrt{\frac{1-i\sqrt{3}}{2}}.$$

2. Find the four values of $\sqrt[4]{-1}$.

3. Compute $\sqrt[4]{i}$ and $\sqrt[4]{-i}$.

4. Solve the quadratic equation

$$z^2 + (\alpha + i\beta)z + \gamma + i\delta = 0.$$

1.3. Justification. So far our approach to complex numbers has been completely uncritical. We have not questioned the existence of a number system in which the equation $x^2 + 1 = 0$ has a solution while all the rules of arithmetic remain in force.

We begin by recalling the characteristic properties of the real-number system which we denote by **R**. In the first place, **R** is a *field*. This means that addition and multiplication are defined, satisfying the *associative, commutative,* and *distributive laws.* The numbers 0 and 1 are neutral elements under addition and multiplication, respectively: $\alpha + 0 = \alpha$, $\alpha \cdot 1 = \alpha$ for all α. Moreover, the equation of subtraction $\beta + x = \alpha$ has always a solution, and the equation of division $\beta x = \alpha$ has a solution whenever $\beta \neq 0$.†

One shows by elementary reasoning that the neutral elements and the results of subtraction and division are unique. Also, every field is an *integral domain:* $\alpha\beta = 0$ if and only if $\alpha = 0$ or $\beta = 0$.

† We assume that the reader has a working knowledge of elementary algebra. Although the above characterization of a field is complete, it obviously does not convey much to a student who is not already at least vaguely familiar with the concept.

These properties are common to all fields. In addition, the field **R** has an *order relation* $\alpha < \beta$ (or $\beta > \alpha$). It is most easily defined in terms of the set $\mathbf{R}^+$ of *positive* real numbers: $\alpha < \beta$ if and only if $\beta - \alpha \in \mathbf{R}^+$. The set $\mathbf{R}^+$ is characterized by the following properties: (1) 0 is not a positive number; (2) if $\alpha \neq 0$ either α or $-\alpha$ is positive; (3) the sum and the product of two positive numbers are positive. From these conditions one derives all the usual rules for manipulation of inequalities. In particular one finds that every square α^2 is either positive or zero; therefore $1 = 1^2$ is a positive number.

By virtue of the order relation the sums $1, 1 + 1, 1 + 1 + 1, \ldots$ are all different. Hence **R** contains the natural numbers, and since it is a field it must contain the subfield formed by all rational numbers.

Finally, **R** satisfies the following *completeness condition:* every increasing and bounded sequence of real numbers has a limit. Let $\alpha_1 < \alpha_2 < \alpha_3 < \cdots < \alpha_n < \cdots$, and assume the existence of a real number B such that $\alpha_n < B$ for all n. Then the completeness condition requires the existence of a number $A = \lim_{n\to\infty} \alpha_n$ with the following property: given any $\varepsilon > 0$ there exists a natural number n_0 such that $A - \varepsilon < \alpha_n < A$ for all $n > n_0$.

Our discussion of the real-number system is incomplete inasmuch as we have not proved the existence and uniqueness (up to isomorphisms) of a system **R** with the postulated properties.† The student who is not thoroughly familiar with one of the constructive processes by which real numbers can be introduced should not fail to fill this gap by consulting any textbook in which a full axiomatic treatment of real numbers is given.

The equation $x^2 + 1 = 0$ has no solution in **R**, for $\alpha^2 + 1$ is always positive. Suppose now that a field **F** can be found which contains **R** as a subfield, and in which the equation $x^2 + 1 = 0$ can be solved. Denote a solution by i. Then $x^2 + 1 = (x + i)(x - i)$, and the equation $x^2 + 1 = 0$ has exactly two roots in **F**, i and $-i$. Let **C** be the subset of **F** consisting of all elements which can be expressed in the form $\alpha + i\beta$ with real α and β. This representation is unique, for $\alpha + i\beta = \alpha' + i\beta'$ implies $\alpha - \alpha' = -i(\beta - \beta')$; hence $(\alpha - \alpha')^2 = -(\beta - \beta')^2$, and this is possible only if $\alpha = \alpha'$, $\beta = \beta'$.

The subset **C** is a subfield of **F**. In fact, except for trivial verifications which the reader is asked to carry out, this is exactly what was shown in Sec. 1.1. What is more, the structure of **C** is independent of **F**. For if **F**′ is another field containing **R** and a root i' of the equation $x^2 + 1 = 0$,

† An *isomorphism* between two fields is a one-to-one correspondence which preserves sums and products. The word is used quite generally to indicate a correspondence which is one to one and preserves all relations that are considered important in a given connection.

the corresponding subset $\mathbf{C}'$ is formed by all elements $\alpha + i'\beta$. There is a one-to-one correspondence between $\mathbf{C}$ and $\mathbf{C}'$ which associates $\alpha + i\beta$ and $\alpha + i'\beta$, and this correspondence is evidently a field isomorphism. It is thus demonstrated that $\mathbf{C}$ and $\mathbf{C}'$ are isomorphic.

We now define the field of *complex numbers* to be the subfield $\mathbf{C}$ of an arbitrarily given $\mathbf{F}$. We have just seen that the choice of $\mathbf{F}$ makes no difference, but we have not yet shown that there exists a field $\mathbf{F}$ with the required properties. In order to give our definition a meaning it remains to exhibit a field $\mathbf{F}$ which contains $\mathbf{R}$ (or a subfield isomorphic with $\mathbf{R}$) and in which the equation $x^2 + 1 = 0$ has a root.

There are many ways in which such a field can be constructed. The simplest and most direct method is the following: Consider all expressions of the form $\alpha + i\beta$ where α, β are real numbers while the signs $+$ and i are pure symbols ($+$ does *not* indicate addition, and i is *not* an element of a field). These expressions are elements of a field $\mathbf{F}$ in which addition and multiplication are defined by (1) and (2) (observe the two different meanings of the sign $+$). The elements of the particular form $\alpha + i0$ are seen to constitute a subfield isomorphic to $\mathbf{R}$, and the element $0 + i1$ satisfies the equation $x^2 + 1 = 0$; we obtain in fact $(0 + i1)^2 = -(1 + i0)$. The field $\mathbf{F}$ has thus the required properties; moreover, it is identical with the corresponding subfield $\mathbf{C}$, for we can write

$$\alpha + i\beta = (\alpha + i0) + \beta(0 + i1).$$

The existence of the complex-number field is now proved, and we can go back to the simpler notation $\alpha + i\beta$ where the $+$ indicates addition in $\mathbf{C}$ and i is a root of the equation $x^2 + 1 = 0$.

EXERCISES (For students with a background in algebra)

1. Show that the system of all matrices of the special form

$$\begin{pmatrix} \alpha & \beta \\ -\beta & \alpha \end{pmatrix},$$

combined by matrix addition and matrix multiplication, is isomorphic to the field of complex numbers.

2. Show that the complex-number system can be thought of as the field of all polynomials with real coefficients modulo the irreducible polynomial $x^2 + 1$.

1.4. Conjugation, Absolute Value. A complex number can be denoted either by a single letter a, representing an element of the field $\mathbf{C}$, or in the form $\alpha + i\beta$ with real α and β. Other standard notations are $z = x + iy$, $\zeta = \xi + i\eta$, $w = u + iv$, and when used in this connection it is tacitly understood that x, y, ξ, η, u, v are real numbers. The real and imaginary part of a complex number a will also be denoted by $\mathrm{Re}\, a$, $\mathrm{Im}\, a$.

In deriving the rules for complex addition and multiplication we used only the fact that $i^2 = -1$. Since $-i$ has the same property, all rules must remain valid if i is everywhere replaced by $-i$. Direct verification shows that this is indeed so. The transformation which replaces $\alpha + i\beta$ by $\alpha - i\beta$ is called *complex conjugation*, and $\alpha - i\beta$ is the *conjugate* of $\alpha + i\beta$. The conjugate of a is denoted by $\bar{a}$. A number is real if and only if it is equal to its conjugate. The conjugation is an *involutory* transformation: this means that $\bar{\bar{a}} = a$.

The formulas

$$\mathrm{Re}\, a = \frac{a + \bar{a}}{2}, \qquad \mathrm{Im}\, a = \frac{a - \bar{a}}{2i}$$

express the real and imaginary part in terms of the complex number and its conjugate. By systematic use of the notations a and $\bar{a}$ it is hence possible to dispense with the use of separate letters for the real and imaginary part. It is more convenient, though, to make free use of both notations.

The fundamental property of conjugation is the one already referred to, namely, that

$$\overline{a + b} = \bar{a} + \bar{b}$$
$$\overline{ab} = \bar{a} \cdot \bar{b}.$$

The corresponding property for quotients is a consequence: if $ax = b$, then $\bar{a}\bar{x} = \bar{b}$, and hence $\overline{(b/a)} = \bar{b}/\bar{a}$. More generally, let $R(a,b,c, \ldots)$ stand for any rational operation applied to the complex numbers a, b, c, $\ldots$. Then

$$\overline{R(a,b,c, \ldots)} = R(\bar{a},\bar{b},\bar{c}, \ldots).$$

As an application, consider the equation

$$c_0z^n + c_1z^{n-1} + \cdots + c_{n-1}z + c_n = 0.$$

If ζ is a root of this equation, then $\bar{\zeta}$ is a root of the equation

$$\bar{c}_0z^n + \bar{c}_1z^{n-1} + \cdots + \bar{c}_{n-1}z + \bar{c}_n = 0.$$

In particular, if the coefficients are *real*, ζ and $\bar{\zeta}$ are roots of the same equation, and we have the familiar theorem that the nonreal roots of an equation with real coefficients occur in pairs of conjugate roots.

The product $a\bar{a} = \alpha^2 + \beta^2$ is always positive or zero. Its nonnegative square root is called the *modulus* or *absolute value* of the complex number a; it is denoted by $|a|$. The terminology and notation are justified by the fact that the modulus of a real number coincides with its numerical value taken with the positive sign.

We repeat the definition

$$a\bar{a} = |a|^2,$$

where $|a| \geqq 0$, and observe that $|\bar{a}| = |a|$. For the absolute value of a product we obtain

$$|ab|^2 = ab \cdot \overline{ab} = ab\bar{a}\bar{b} = a\bar{a}b\bar{b} = |a|^2|b|^2,$$

and hence

$$|ab| = |a| \cdot |b|$$

since both are $\geqq 0$. In words:

The absolute value of a product is equal to the product of the absolute values of the factors.

It is clear that this property extends to arbitrary finite products:

$$|a_1a_2 \cdots a_n| = |a_1| \cdot |a_2| \cdots |a_n|.$$

The quotient a/b, $b \neq 0$, satisfies $b(a/b) = a$, and hence we have also $|b| \cdot |a/b| = |a|$, or

$$\left|\frac{a}{b}\right| = \frac{|a|}{|b|}.$$

The formula for the absolute value of a sum is not as simple. We find

$$|a + b|^2 = (a + b)(\bar{a} + \bar{b}) = a\bar{a} + (a\bar{b} + b\bar{a}) + b\bar{b}$$

or

(7) $$|a + b|^2 = |a|^2 + |b|^2 + 2 \operatorname{Re} a\bar{b}.$$

The corresponding formula for the difference is

(7′) $$|a - b|^2 = |a|^2 + |b|^2 - 2 \operatorname{Re} a\bar{b},$$

and by addition we obtain the identity

(8) $$|a + b|^2 + |a - b|^2 = 2(|a|^2 + |b|^2).$$

EXERCISES

1. Verify by calculation that the values of

$$\frac{z}{z^2 + 1}$$

for $z = x + iy$ and $z = x - iy$ are conjugate.

2. Find the absolute values of

$$-2i(3 + i)(2 + 4i)(1 + i) \qquad \text{and} \qquad \frac{(3 + 4i)(-1 + 2i)}{(-1 - i)(3 - i)}.$$

3. Prove that

$$\left|\frac{a-b}{1-\bar{a}b}\right| = 1$$

if either $|a| = 1$ or $|b| = 1$. What exception must be made if $|a| = |b| = 1$?

4. Find the conditions under which the equation $az + b\bar{z} + c = 0$ in one complex unknown has exactly one solution, and compute that solution.

5. Prove Lagrange's identity in the complex form

$$\left|\sum_{i=1}^{n} a_i b_i\right|^2 = \sum_{i=1}^{n} |a_i|^2 \sum_{i=1}^{n} |b_i|^2 - \sum_{1\leqq i<j\leqq n} |a_i\bar{b}_j - a_j\bar{b}_i|^2.$$

1.5. Inequalities. We shall now prove some important inequalities which will be of constant use. It is perhaps well to point out that there is no order relation in the complex-number system, and hence all inequalities must be between real numbers.

From the definition of the absolute value we deduce the inequalities

$$\begin{aligned} -|a| &\leqq \operatorname{Re} a \leqq |a| \\ -|a| &\leqq \operatorname{Im} a \leqq |a|. \end{aligned} \tag{9}$$

The equality $\operatorname{Re} a = |a|$ holds if and only if a is real and $\geqq 0$.

If (9) is applied to (7), we obtain

$$|a + b|^2 \leqq (|a| + |b|)^2$$

and hence

$$|a + b| \leqq |a| + |b|. \tag{10}$$

This is called the *triangle inequality* for reasons which will emerge later. By induction it can be extended to arbitrary sums:

$$|a_1 + a_2 + \cdots + a_n| \leqq |a_1| + |a_2| + \cdots + |a_n|. \tag{11}$$

The absolute value of a sum is at most equal to the sum of the absolute values of the terms.

The reader is well aware of the importance of the estimate (11) in the real case, and we shall find it no less important in the theory of complex numbers.

Let us determine all cases of equality in (11). In (10) the sign of equality holds if and only if $a\bar{b} \geqq 0$ (it is convenient to let $c > 0$ indicate that c is *real* and *positive*). If $b \neq 0$ this condition can be written in the form $|b|^2(a/b) \geqq 0$, and it is hence equivalent to $a/b \geqq 0$. In the general case we proceed as follows: Suppose that equality holds in (11); then

$$|a_1| + |a_2| + \cdots + |a_n| = |(a_1 + a_2) + a_3 + \cdots + a_n| \\ \leqq |a_1 + a_2| + |a_3| + \cdots + |a_n| \leqq |a_1| + |a_2| + \cdots + |a_n|.$$

Hence $|a_1 + a_2| = |a_1| + |a_2|$, and if $a_2 \neq 0$ we conclude that $a_1/a_2 \geqq 0$. But the numbering of the terms is arbitrary; thus the ratio of any two nonzero terms must be positive. Suppose conversely that this condition is fulfilled. Assuming that $a_1 \neq 0$ we obtain

$$|a_1 + a_2 + \cdots + a_n| = |a_1| \cdot \left|1 + \frac{a_2}{a_1} + \cdots + \frac{a_n}{a_1}\right| \\ = |a_1|\left(1 + \frac{a_2}{a_1} + \cdots + \frac{a_n}{a_1}\right) = |a_1|\left(1 + \frac{|a_2|}{|a_1|} + \cdots + \frac{|a_n|}{|a_1|}\right) \\ = |a_1| + |a_2| + \cdots + |a_n|.$$

To sum up: *the sign of equality holds in* (11) *if and only if the ratio of any two nonzero terms is positive.*

By (10) we have also

$$|a| = |(a - b) + b| \leqq |a - b| + |b|$$

or

$$|a| - |b| \leqq |a - b|.$$

For the same reason $|b| - |a| \leqq |a - b|$, and these inequalities can be combined to

$$|a - b| \geqq ||a| - |b||. \tag{12}$$

Of course the same estimate can be applied to $|a + b|$.

A special case of (10) is the inequality

$$|\alpha + i\beta| \leqq |\alpha| + |\beta| \tag{13}$$

which expresses that the absolute value of a complex number is at most equal to the sum of the absolute values of the real and imaginary part.

Many other inequalities whose proof is less immediate are also of frequent use. Foremost is *Cauchy's inequality* which states that

$$|a_1b_1 + \cdots + a_nb_n|^2 \leqq (|a_1|^2 + \cdots + |a_n|^2)(|b_1|^2 + \cdots + |b_n|^2)$$

or, in shorter notation,

$$\left|\sum_{i=1}^{n} a_ib_i\right|^2 \leqq \sum_{i=1}^{n} |a_i|^2 \sum_{i=1}^{n} |b_i|^2.\dagger \tag{14}$$

† i is a convenient summation index and, used as a subscript, cannot be confused with the imaginary unit. It seems pointless to ban its use.

To prove it, let λ denote an arbitrary complex number. We obtain by (7)

$$(15)\qquad \sum_{i=1}^{n} |a_i - \lambda \bar{b}_i|^2 = \sum_{i=1}^{n} |a_i|^2 + |\lambda|^2 \sum_{i=1}^{n} |b_i|^2 - 2 \operatorname{Re} \bar{\lambda} \sum_{i=1}^{n} a_i b_i.$$

This expression is $\geqq 0$ for all λ. We can choose

$$\lambda = \frac{\sum_1^n a_i b_i}{\sum_1^n |b_i|^2},$$

for if the denominator should vanish there is nothing to prove. This choice is not arbitrary, but it is dictated by the desire to make the expression (15) as small as possible. Substituting in (15) we find, after simplifications,

$$\sum_1^n |a_i|^2 - \frac{\left|\sum_1^n a_i b_i\right|^2}{\sum_1^n |b_i|^2} \geqq 0$$

which is equivalent to (14).

From (15) we conclude further that the sign of equality holds in (14) if and only if the a_i are proportional to the $\bar{b}_i$.

Cauchy's inequality can also be proved by means of Lagrange's identity (Sec. 1.4, Ex. 4).

EXERCISES

1. Prove that

$$\left|\frac{a - b}{1 - \bar{a}b}\right| < 1$$

if $|a| < 1$ and $|b| < 1$.

2. Prove Cauchy's inequality by induction.

3. If $|a_i| < 1$, $\lambda_i \geqq 0$ for $i = 1, \ldots, n$ and $\lambda_1 + \lambda_2 + \cdots + \lambda_n = 1$, show that

$$|\lambda_1 a_1 + \lambda_2 a_2 + \cdots + \lambda_n a_n| < 1.$$

4. Show that there are complex numbers z satisfying

$$|z - a| + |z + a| = 2|c|$$

if and only if $|a| \leqq |c|$. If this condition is fulfilled, what are the smallest and largest values of $|z|$?

2. THE GEOMETRIC REPRESENTATION OF COMPLEX NUMBERS

With respect to a given rectangular coordinate system in a plane, the complex number $a = \alpha + i\beta$ can be represented by the point with coordinates (α,β). This representation is constantly used, and we shall often speak of the *point* a as a synonym of the *number* a. The first coordinate axis (x-axis) takes the name of *real axis*, and the second coordinate axis (y-axis) is called the *imaginary axis*. The plane itself is referred to as the *complex plane*.

The geometric representation derives its usefulness from the vivid mental pictures associated with a geometric language. We take the point of view, however, that all conclusions in analysis should be derived from the properties of real numbers, and not from the axioms of geometry. For this reason we shall use geometry only for descriptive purposes, and not for valid proof, unless the language is so thinly veiled that the analytic interpretation is self-evident. This attitude relieves us from the exigencies of rigor in connection with geometric considerations.

2.1. Geometric Addition and Multiplication. The addition of complex numbers can be visualized as *vector addition*. To this end we let a complex number be represented not only by a point, but also by a vector pointing from the origin to the point. The number, the point, and the vector will all be denoted by the same letter a. As usual we identify all vectors which can be obtained from each other by parallel displacements.

Place a second vector b so that its initial point coincides with the end point of a. Then $a + b$ is represented by the vector from the initial point of a to the end point of b. To construct the difference $b - a$ we draw both vectors a and b from the same initial point; then $b - a$ points from the end point of a to the end point of b. Observe that $a + b$ and $a - b$ are the diagonals in a parallelogram with the sides a and b (Fig. 1).

An additional advantage of the vector representation is that the length of the vector a is equal to $|a|$. Hence the distance between the points a and b is $|a - b|$. With this interpretation the triangle inequality $|a + b| \leqq |a| + |b|$ and the identity $|a + b|^2 + |a - b|^2 = 2(|a|^2 + |b|^2)$ become familiar geometric theorems.

The point a and its conjugate $\bar{a}$ lie symmetrically with respect to the real axis. The symmetric point of a with respect to the imaginary axis is

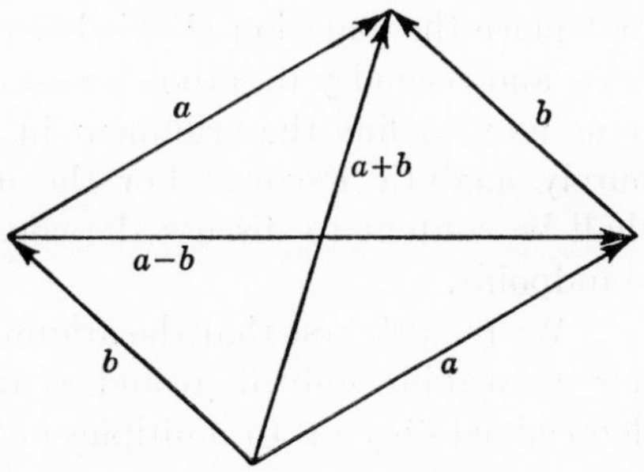

FIG. 1. Vector addition.

$-\bar{a}$. The four points a, $-\bar{a}$, $-a$, $\bar{a}$ are the vertices of a rectangle which is symmetric with respect to both axes.

In order to derive a geometric interpretation of the product of two complex numbers we introduce polar coordinates. If the polar coordinates of the point (α,β) are (r,φ), we know that

$$\alpha = r \cos \varphi$$
$$\beta = r \sin \varphi.$$

Hence we can write $a = \alpha + i\beta = r(\cos \varphi + i \sin \varphi)$. In this *trigonometric form* of a complex number r is always $\geqq 0$ and equal to the modulus $|a|$. The polar angle φ is called the *argument* or *amplitude* of the complex number, and we denote it by arg a.

Consider two complex numbers $a_1 = r_1(\cos \varphi_1 + i \sin \varphi_1)$ and $a_2 = r_2(\cos \varphi_2 + i \sin \varphi_2)$. Their product can be written in the from $a_1a_2 = r_1r_2[(\cos \varphi_1 \cos \varphi_2 - \sin \varphi_1 \sin \varphi_2) + i(\sin \varphi_1 \cos \varphi_2 + \cos \varphi_1 \sin \varphi_2)]$. By means of the addition theorems of the cosine and the sine this expression can be simplified to

$$a_1a_2 = r_1r_2[\cos (\varphi_1 + \varphi_2) + i \sin (\varphi_1 + \varphi_2)]. \tag{16}$$

We recognize that the product has the modulus r_1r_2 and the argument $\varphi_1 + \varphi_2$. The latter result is new, and we express it through the equation

$$\arg (a_1a_2) = \arg a_1 + \arg a_2. \tag{17}$$

It is clear that this formula can be extended to arbitrary products, and we can therefore state:

The argument of a product is equal to the sum of the arguments of the factors.

This is fundamental. The rule that we have just formulated gives a deep and unexpected justification of the geometric representation of complex numbers. We must be fully aware, however, that the manner in which we have arrived at the formula (17) violates our principles. In the first place the equation (17) is between *angles* rather than between numbers, and secondly its proof rested on the use of trigonometry. Thus it remains to define the argument in analytic terms and to prove (17) by purely analytic means. For the moment we postpone this proof and shall be content to discuss the consequences of (17) from a less critical standpoint.

We remark first that the argument of 0 is not defined, and hence (17) has a meaning only if a_1 and a_2 are $\neq 0$. Secondly, the polar angle is determined only up to multiples of 360°. For this reason, if we want to interpret (17) numerically, we must agree that multiples of 360° shall not count.

By means of (17) a simple geometric construction of the product a_1a_2 can be obtained. It follows indeed that the triangle with the vertices $0, 1, a_1$ is similar to the triangle whose vertices are $0, a_2, a_1a_2$. The points $0, 1, a_1$ and a_2 being given, this similarity determines the point a_1a_2 (Fig. 2).

In the case of division (17) is replaced by

$$\arg \frac{a_2}{a_1} = \arg a_2 - \arg a_1. \tag{18}$$

The geometric construction is the same, except that the similar triangles are now $0, 1, a_1$ and $0, a_2/a_1, a_2$.

Remark: A perfectly acceptable way to define angles and arguments would be to apply the familiar methods of calculus which permit us to express the length of a circular arc as a definite integral. This leads to a correct definition of the trigonometric functions, and to a computational proof of the addition theorems.

The reason we do not follow this path is that complex analysis, as

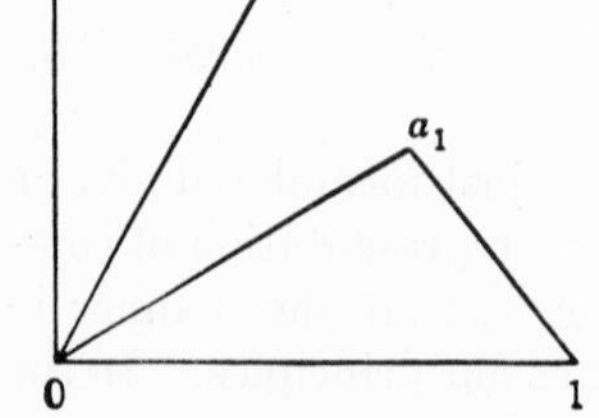

FIG. 2. Vector multiplication.

opposed to real analysis, offers a much more direct approach. The clue lies in a direct connection between the exponential function and the trigonometric functions, to be derived in Chap. 2, Sec. 5. Until we reach this point the reader is asked to subdue his quest for complete rigor.

EXERCISES

1. Find the symmetric points of a with respect to the lines which bisect the angles between the coordinate axes.

2. Prove that the points a_1, a_2, a_3 are vertices of an equilateral triangle if and only if $a_1^2 + a_2^2 + a_3^2 = a_1a_2 + a_2a_3 + a_3a_1$.

3. Suppose that a and b are two vertices of a square. Find the two other vertices in all possible cases.

4. Find the center and the radius of the circle which circumscribes the triangle with vertices a_1, a_2, a_3. Express the result in symmetric form.

2.2. The Binomial Equation. From the preceding results we derive that the powers of $a = r(\cos\varphi + i\sin\varphi)$ are given by

$$a^n = r^n(\cos n\varphi + i\sin n\varphi). \tag{19}$$

This formula is trivially valid for $n = 0$, and since

$$a^{-1} = r^{-1}(\cos\varphi - i\sin\varphi) = r^{-1}[\cos(-\varphi) + i\sin(-\varphi)]$$

it holds also when n is a negative integer.

For $r = 1$ we obtain *de Moivre's formula*

$$(\cos\varphi + i\sin\varphi)^n = \cos n\varphi + i\sin n\varphi \tag{20}$$

which provides an extremely simple way to express $\cos n\varphi$ and $\sin n\varphi$ in terms of $\cos\varphi$ and $\sin\varphi$.

To find the nth root of a complex number a we have to solve the equation

$$z^n = a. \tag{21}$$

Supposing that $a \neq 0$ we write $a = r(\cos\varphi + i\sin\varphi)$ and

$$z = \rho(\cos\theta + i\sin\theta).$$

Then (21) takes the form

$$\rho^n(\cos n\theta + i\sin n\theta) = r(\cos\varphi + i\sin\varphi). \tag{22}$$

This equation is certainly fulfilled if $\rho^n = r$ and $n\theta = \varphi$. Hence we obtain the root

$$z = \sqrt[n]{r}\left(\cos\frac{\varphi}{n} + i\sin\frac{\varphi}{n}\right),$$

where $\sqrt[n]{r}$ denotes the positive nth root of the positive number r.

But this is not the only solution. In fact, (22) is also fulfilled if $n\theta$ differs from φ by a multiple of the full angle. If angles are expressed in radians the full angle is 2π, and we find that (22) is satisfied if and only if

$$\theta = \frac{\varphi}{n} + k\cdot\frac{2\pi}{n},$$

where k is any integer. However, only the values $k = 0, 1, \ldots, n-1$ give different values of z. Hence the complete solution of the equation (21) is given by

$$z = \sqrt[n]{r}\left[\cos\left(\frac{\varphi}{n} + k\frac{2\pi}{n}\right) + i\sin\left(\frac{\varphi}{n} + k\frac{2\pi}{n}\right)\right],\quad k = 0, 1, \ldots, n-1.$$

There are n nth roots of any complex number $\neq 0$. They have the same modulus, and their arguments are equally spaced.

Geometrically, the nth roots are the vertices of a regular polygon with n sides.

The case $a = 1$ is particularly important. The roots of the equation $z^n = 1$ are called nth roots of unity, and if we set

$$\omega = \cos\frac{2\pi}{n} + i\sin\frac{2\pi}{n} \tag{23}$$

all the roots can be expressed by $1, \omega, \omega^2, \ldots, \omega^{n-1}$. It is also quite evident that if $\sqrt[n]{a}$ denotes any nth root of a, then all the nth roots can be expressed in the form $\omega^k\cdot\sqrt[n]{a}$, $k = 0, 1, \ldots, n-1$.

EXERCISES

1. Express $\cos 3\varphi$, $\cos 4\varphi$, and $\sin 5\varphi$ in terms of $\cos\varphi$ and $\sin\varphi$.

2. Simplify $1 + \cos\varphi + \cos 2\varphi + \cdots + \cos n\varphi$ and $\sin\varphi + \sin 2\varphi + \cdots + \sin n\varphi$.

3. Express the fifth and tenth roots of unity in algebraic form.

4. If ω is given by (23), prove that

$$1 + \omega^h + \omega^{2h} + \cdots + \omega^{(n-1)h} = 0$$

for any integer h which is not a multiple of n.

5. What is the value of

$$1 - \omega^h + \omega^{2h} - \cdots + (-1)^{n-1}\omega^{(n-1)h}?$$

2.3. Analytic Geometry. In classical analytic geometry the equation of a locus is expressed as a relation between x and y. It can just as well be expressed in terms of z and $\bar{z}$, sometimes to distinct advantage. The thing to remember is that a complex equation is ordinarily equivalent to two real equations; in order to obtain a genuine locus these equations should be essentially the same.

For instance, the equation of a circle is $|z - a| = r$. In algebraic form it can be rewritten as $(z - a)(\bar{z} - \bar{a}) = r^2$. The fact that this equation is invariant under complex conjugation is an indication that it represents a single real equation.

A straight line in the complex plane can be given by a parametric equation $z = a + bt$, where a and b are complex numbers and $b \neq 0$; the parameter t runs through all real values. Two equations $z = a + bt$ and $z = a' + b't$ represent the same line if and only if $a' - a$ and b' are real multiples of b. The lines are parallel whenever b' is a real multiple of b, and they are equally directed if b' is a positive multiple of b. The direction of a directed line can be identified with $\arg b$. The angle between $z = a + bt$ and $z = a' + b't$ is $\arg b'/b$; observe that it depends on the order in which the lines are named. The lines are orthogonal to each other if b'/b is purely imaginary.

Problems of finding intersections between lines and circles, parallel or orthogonal lines, tangents, and the like usually become exceedingly simple when expressed in complex form.

An inequality $|z - a| < r$ describes the inside of a circle. Similarly, a directed line $z = a + bt$ determines a right half plane consisting of all points z with $\text{Im}\,(z - a)/b < 0$ and a left half plane with $\text{Im}\,(z - a)/b > 0$. An easy argument shows that this distinction is independent of the parametric representation.

EXERCISES

1. When does $az + b\bar{z} + c = 0$ represent a line?

2. Write the equation of an ellipse, hyperbola, parabola in complex form.

3. Prove that the diagonals of a parallelogram bisect each other and that the diagonals of a rhombus are orthogonal.

4. Prove analytically that the midpoints of parallel chords to a circle lie on a diameter perpendicular to the chords.

5. Show that all circles that pass through a and $1/\bar{a}$ intersect the circle $|z| = 1$ at right angles.

2.4. The Spherical Representation. For many purposes it is useful to extend the system **C** of complex numbers by introduction of a symbol ∞ to represent infinity. Its connection with the finite numbers is established by setting $a + \infty = \infty + a = \infty$ for all finite a, and

$$b \cdot \infty = \infty \cdot b = \infty$$

for all $b \neq 0$, including $b = \infty$. It is impossible, however, to define $\infty + \infty$ and $0 \cdot \infty$ without violating the laws of arithmetic. By special convention we shall nevertheless write $a/0 = \infty$ for $a \neq 0$ and $b/\infty = 0$ for $b \neq \infty$.

In the plane there is no room for a point corresponding to ∞, but we can of course introduce an "ideal" point which we call the *point at infinity*. The points in the plane together with the point at infinity form the *extended complex plane*. We agree that every straight line shall pass through the point at infinity. By contrast, no half plane shall contain the ideal point.

It is desirable to introduce a geometric model in which all points of the extended plane have a concrete representative. To this end we consider the unit sphere S whose equation in three-dimensional space is $x_1^2 + x_2^2 + x_3^2 = 1$. With every point on S, except $(0,0,1)$, we can associate a complex number

$$z = \frac{x_1 + ix_2}{1 - x_3}, \tag{24}$$

and this correspondence is one to one. Indeed, from (24) we obtain

$$|z|^2 = \frac{x_1^2 + x_2^2}{(1 - x_3)^2} = \frac{1 + x_3}{1 - x_3},$$

and hence

$$x_3 = \frac{|z|^2 - 1}{|z|^2 + 1}. \tag{25}$$

Further computation yields

$$\begin{aligned} x_1 &= \frac{z + \bar{z}}{1 + |z|^2} \\ x_2 &= \frac{z - \bar{z}}{i(1 + |z|^2)}. \end{aligned} \tag{26}$$

The correspondence can be completed by letting the point at infinity correspond to $(0,0,1)$, and we can thus regard the sphere as a representation of the extended plane or of the extended number system. We note that the hemisphere $x_3 < 0$ corresponds to the disk $|z| < 1$ and the hemisphere $x_3 > 0$ to its outside $|z| > 1$. In function theory the sphere S is referred to as the *Riemann sphere.*

If the complex plane is identified with the (x_1,x_2)-plane with the x_1- and x_2-axis corresponding to the real and imaginary axis, respectively, the transformation (24) takes on a simple geometric meaning. Writing $z = x + iy$ we can verify that

$$x:y:-1 = x_1:x_2:x_3 - 1, \tag{27}$$

and this means that the points $(x,y,0)$ (x_1,x_2,x_3), and $(0,0,1)$ are in a straight line. Hence the correspondence is a central projection from the center $(0,0,1)$ as shown in Fig. 3. It is called a *stereographic projection.*

In the spherical representation there is no simple interpretation of addition and multiplication. Its advantage lies in the fact that the point at infinity is no longer distinguished.

It is geometrically evident that the stereographic projection transforms every straight line in the z-plane into a circle on S which passes through the pole $(0,0,1)$, and the converse is also true. More generally, any circle on the sphere corresponds to a circle or straight line in the z-plane. To prove this we observe that a circle on the sphere lies in a plane $\alpha_1x_1 + \alpha_2x_2 + \alpha_3x_3 = \alpha_0$, where we can assume that $\alpha_1^2 + \alpha_2^2 + \alpha_3^2 = 1$ and $0 \leqq \alpha_0 < 1$. In terms of z and $\bar{z}$ this equation takes the form

$$\alpha_1(z + \bar{z}) - \alpha_2 i(z - \bar{z}) + \alpha_3(|z|^2 - 1) = \alpha_0(|z|^2 + 1)$$

or

$$(\alpha_0 - \alpha_3)(x^2 + y^2) - 2\alpha_1 x - 2\alpha_2 y + \alpha_0 + \alpha_3 = 0.$$

For $\alpha_0 \neq \alpha_3$ this is the equation of a circle, and for $\alpha_0 = \alpha_3$ it represents a straight line. Conversely, the equation of any circle or straight line

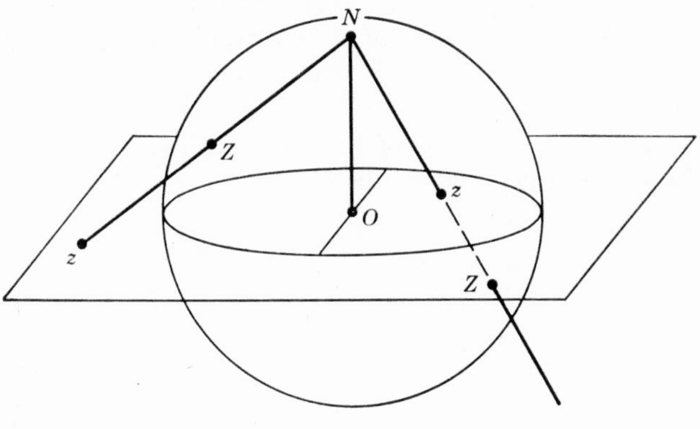

FIG. 3. Stereographic projection.

can be written in this form. The correspondence is consequently one to one.

It is easy to calculate the distance $d(z,z')$ between the stereographic projections of z and z'. If the points on the sphere are denoted by (x_1,x_2,x_3), (x_1',x_2',x_3'), we have first

$$(x_1 - x_1')^2 + (x_2 - x_2')^2 + (x_3 - x_3')^2 = 2 - 2(x_1x_1' + x_2x_2' + x_3x_3').$$

From (35) and (36) we obtain after a short computation

$$\begin{aligned} x_1x_1' + x_2x_2' + x_3x_3' \\ &= \frac{(z + \bar{z})(z' + \bar{z}') - (z - \bar{z})(z' - \bar{z}') + (|z|^2 - 1)(|z'|^2 - 1)}{(1 + |z|^2)(1 + |z'|^2)} \\ &= \frac{(1 + |z|^2)(1 + |z'|^2) - 2|z - z'|^2}{(1 + |z|^2)(1 + |z'|^2)}. \end{aligned}$$

As a result we find that

$$d(z,z') = \frac{2|z - z'|}{\sqrt{(1 + |z|^2)(1 + |z'|^2)}}. \tag{28}$$

For $z' = \infty$ the corresponding formula is

$$d(z, \infty) = \frac{2}{\sqrt{1 + |z|^2}}.$$

EXERCISES

1. Show that z and z' correspond to diametrically opposite points on the Riemann sphere if and only if $z\bar{z}' = -1$.

2. A cube has its vertices on the sphere S and its edges parallel to the coordinate axes. Find the stereographic projections of the vertices.

3. Same problem for a regular tetrahedron in general position.

4. Let Z, Z' denote the stereographic projections of z, z', and let N be the north pole. Show that the triangles NZZ' and Nzz' are similar, and use this to derive (28).

5. Find the radius of the spherical image of the circle in the plane whose center is a and radius R.

2 COMPLEX FUNCTIONS

1. INTRODUCTION TO THE CONCEPT OF ANALYTIC FUNCTION

The theory of functions of a complex variable aims at extending calculus to the complex domain. Both differentiation and integration acquire new depth and significance; at the same time the range of applicability becomes radically restricted. Indeed, only the *analytic* or *holomorphic* functions can be freely differentiated and integrated. They are the only true "functions" in the sense of the French "Théorie des fonctions" or the German "Funktionentheorie."

Nevertheless, we shall use the term "function" in its modern meaning. Therefore, when stepping up to complex numbers we have to consider four different kinds of functions: real functions of a real variable, real functions of a complex variable, complex functions of a real variable, and complex functions of a complex variable. As a practical matter we agree that the letters z and w shall always denote complex variables; thus, to indicate a complex function of a complex variable we use the notation $w = f(z)$.† The notation $y = f(x)$ will be used in a neutral manner with the understanding that x and y can be either real or complex. When we want to indicate that a variable is definitely restricted to real values, we shall usually denote it by t. By these agreements we

† Modern students are well aware that f stands for the function and $f(z)$ for a value of the function. However, analysts are traditionally minded and continue to speak of "the function $f(z)$."

do not wish to cancel the earlier convention whereby a notation $z = x + iy$ automatically implies that x and y are real.

It is essential that the law by which a function is defined be formulated in clear and unambiguous terms. In other words, all functions must be *well defined* and consequently, until further notice, *single-valued*.†

It is *not* necessary that a function be defined for all values of the independent variable. For the moment we shall deliberately underemphasize the role of point set theory. Therefore we make merely an informal agreement that every function be defined on an *open set*, by which we mean that if $f(a)$ is defined, then $f(x)$ is defined for all x sufficiently close to a. The formal treatment of point set topology is deferred until the next chapter.

1.1. Limits and Continuity. The following basic definition will be adopted:

Definition 1. *The function $f(x)$ is said to have the limit A as x tends to a,*

$$\lim_{x \to a} f(x) = A, \tag{1}$$

if and only if the following is true:

For every $\varepsilon > 0$ there exists a number $\delta > 0$ with the property that $|f(x) - A| < \varepsilon$ for all values of x such that $|x - a| < \delta$ and $x \neq a$.

This definition makes decisive use of the absolute value. Since the notion of absolute value has a meaning for complex as well as for real numbers, we can use the same definition regardless of whether the variable x and the function $f(x)$ are real or complex.

As an alternative simpler notation we sometimes write: $f(x) \to A$ for $x \to a$.

There are some familiar variants of the definition which correspond to the case where a or A is infinite. In the real case we can distinguish between the limits $+\infty$ and $-\infty$, but in the complex case there is only one infinite limit. We trust the reader to formulate correct definitions to cover all the possibilities.

The well-known results concerning the limit of a sum, a product, and a quotient continue to hold in the complex case. Indeed, the proofs depend only on the properties of the absolute value expressed by

$$|ab| = |a| \cdot |b| \qquad \text{and} \qquad |a + b| \leqq |a| + |b|.$$

† We shall sometimes use the pleonastic term *single-valued function* to underline that the function has only one value for each value of the variable.

Condition (1) is evidently equivalent to

$$\lim_{x \to a} \overline{f(x)} = \bar{A}. \tag{2}$$

From (1) and (2) we obtain

$$\begin{aligned} \lim_{x \to a} \operatorname{Re} f(x) &= \operatorname{Re} A \\ \lim_{x \to a} \operatorname{Im} f(x) &= \operatorname{Im} A. \end{aligned} \tag{3}$$

Conversely, (1) is a consequence of (3).

The function $f(x)$ is said to be *continuous at a* if and only if $\lim_{x \to a} f(x) = f(a)$. A *continuous function*, without further qualification, is one which is continuous at all points where it is defined.

The sum $f(x) + g(x)$ and the product $f(x)g(x)$ of two continuous functions are continuous; the quotient $f(x)/g(x)$ is defined and continuous at a if and only if $g(a) \neq 0$. If $f(x)$ is continuous, so are $\operatorname{Re} f(x)$, $\operatorname{Im} f(x)$, and $|f(x)|$.

The derivative of a function is defined as a particular limit and can be considered regardless of whether the variables are real or complex. The formal definition is

$$f'(a) = \lim_{x \to a} \frac{f(x) - f(a)}{x - a}. \tag{4}$$

The usual rules for forming the derivative of a sum, a product, or a quotient are all valid. The derivative of a composite function is determined by the chain rule.

There is nevertheless a fundamental difference between the cases of a real and a complex independent variable. To illustrate our point, let $f(z)$ be a *real* function of a *complex* variable whose derivative exists at $z = a$. Then $f'(a)$ is on one side real, for it is the limit of the quotients

$$\frac{f(a + h) - f(a)}{h}$$

as h tends to zero through real values. On the other side it is also the limit of the quotients

$$\frac{f(a + ih) - f(a)}{ih}$$

and as such purely imaginary. Therefore $f'(a)$ must be zero. Thus a real function of a complex variable either has the derivative zero, or else the derivative does not exist.

The case of a complex function of a real variable can be reduced to the real case. If we write $z(t) = x(t) + iy(t)$ we find indeed

$$z'(t) = x'(t) + iy'(t),$$

and the existence of $z'(t)$ is equivalent to the simultaneous existence of $x'(t)$ and $y'(t)$. The complex notation has nevertheless certain formal advantages which it would be unwise to give up.

In contrast, the existence of the derivative of a complex function of a complex variable has far-reaching consequences for the structural properties of the function. The investigation of these consequences is the central theme in complex-function theory.

1.2. Analytic Functions. The class of *analytic functions* is formed by the complex functions of a complex variable which possess a derivative wherever the function is defined. The term *holomorphic function* is used with identical meaning. For the purpose of this preliminary investigation the reader may think primarily of functions which are defined in the whole plane.

The sum and the product of two analytic functions are again analytic. The same is true of the quotient $f(z)/g(z)$ of two analytic functions, provided that $g(z)$ does not vanish. In the general case it is necessary to exclude the points at which $g(z) = 0$. Strictly speaking, this very typical case will thus not be included in our considerations, but it will be clear that the results remain valid except for obvious modifications.

The definition of the derivative can be rewritten in the form

$$f'(z) = \lim_{h \to 0} \frac{f(z+h) - f(z)}{h}.$$

As a first consequence $f(z)$ is necessarily continuous. Indeed, from $f(z + h) - f(z) = h \cdot (f(z + h) - f(z))/h$ we obtain

$$\lim_{h \to 0} (f(z+h) - f(z)) = 0 \cdot f'(z) = 0.$$

If we write $f(z) = u(z) + iv(z)$ it follows, moreover, that $u(z)$ and $v(z)$ are both continuous.

The limit of the difference quotient must be the same regardless of the way in which h approaches zero. If we choose real values for h, then the imaginary part y is kept constant, and the derivative becomes a partial derivative with respect to x. We have thus

$$f'(z) = \frac{\partial f}{\partial x} = \frac{\partial u}{\partial x} + i\frac{\partial v}{\partial x}.$$

Similarly, if we substitute purely imaginary values ik for h, we obtain

$$f'(z) = \lim_{k \to 0} \frac{f(z + ik) - f(z)}{ik} = -i \frac{\partial f}{\partial y} = -i \frac{\partial u}{\partial y} + \frac{\partial v}{\partial y}.$$

It follows that $f(z)$ must satisfy the partial differential equation

$$\frac{\partial f}{\partial x} = -i \frac{\partial f}{\partial y} \tag{5}$$

which resolves into the real equations

$$\frac{\partial u}{\partial x} = \frac{\partial v}{\partial y}, \qquad \frac{\partial u}{\partial y} = -\frac{\partial v}{\partial x}. \tag{6}$$

These are the *Cauchy-Riemann* differential equations which must be satisfied by the real and imaginary part of any analytic function.†

We remark that the existence of the four partial derivatives in (6) is implied by the existence of $f'(z)$. Using (6) we can write down four formally different expressions for $f'(z)$; the simplest is

$$f'(z) = \frac{\partial u}{\partial x} + i \frac{\partial v}{\partial x}.$$

For the quantity $|f'(z)|^2$ we have, for instance,

$$|f'(z)|^2 = \left(\frac{\partial u}{\partial x}\right)^2 + \left(\frac{\partial u}{\partial y}\right)^2 = \left(\frac{\partial u}{\partial x}\right)^2 + \left(\frac{\partial v}{\partial x}\right)^2 = \frac{\partial u}{\partial x}\frac{\partial v}{\partial y} - \frac{\partial u}{\partial y}\frac{\partial v}{\partial x}.$$

The last expression shows that $|f'(z)|^2$ is the Jacobian of u and v with respect to x and y.

We shall prove later that the derivative of an analytic function is itself analytic. By this fact u and v will have continuous partial derivatives of all orders, and in particular the mixed derivatives will be equal. Using this information we obtain from (6)

$$\Delta u = \frac{\partial^2 u}{\partial x^2} + \frac{\partial^2 u}{\partial y^2} = 0$$

$$\Delta v = \frac{\partial^2 v}{\partial x^2} + \frac{\partial^2 v}{\partial y^2} = 0.$$

A function u which satisfies *Laplace's equation* $\Delta u = 0$ is said to be *harmonic*. The real and imaginary part of an analytic function are thus harmonic. If two harmonic functions u and v satisfy the Cauchy-Riemann equations (6), then v is said to be the *conjugate harmonic func-*

† *Augustin Cauchy* (1789–1857) and *Bernhard Riemann* (1826–1866) are regarded as the founders of complex-function theory. Riemann's work emphasized the geometric aspects in contrast to the purely analytic approach of Cauchy.

tion of u. Under the same circumstances u is evidently the conjugate harmonic function of $-v$.

This is not the place to discuss the weakest conditions of regularity which can be imposed on harmonic functions. We wish to prove, however, that the function $u + iv$ determined by a pair of conjugate harmonic functions is always analytic, and for this purpose we make the explicit assumption that u and v have continuous first-order partial derivatives. It is proved in calculus, under exactly these regularity conditions, that we can write

$$u(x + h,y + k) - u(x,y) = \frac{\partial u}{\partial x} h + \frac{\partial u}{\partial y} k + \varepsilon_1$$
$$v(x + h,y + k) - v(x,y) = \frac{\partial v}{\partial x} h + \frac{\partial v}{\partial y} k + \varepsilon_2,$$

where the remainders ε_1, ε_2 tend to zero more rapidly than $h + ik$ in the sense that $\varepsilon_1/(h + ik) \to 0$ and $\varepsilon_2/(h + ik) \to 0$ for $h + ik \to 0$. With the notation $f(z) = u(x,y) + iv(x,y)$ we obtain by virtue of the relations (6)

$$f(z + h + ik) - f(z) = \left(\frac{\partial u}{\partial x} + i \frac{\partial v}{\partial x}\right)(h + ik) + \varepsilon_1 + i\varepsilon_2$$

and hence

$$\lim_{h+ik\to 0} \frac{f(z + h + ik) - f(z)}{h + ik} = \frac{\partial u}{\partial x} + i \frac{\partial v}{\partial x}.$$

We conclude that $f(z)$ is analytic.

The real and imaginary parts of an analytic function are harmonic functions which satisfy the Cauchy-Riemann differential equations.

Conversely, if the harmonic functions u and v satisfy these equations, then $u + iv$ is an analytic function.

The conjugate of a harmonic function can be found by integration, and in simple cases the computation can be made explicit. For instance, $u = x^2 - y^2$ is harmonic and $\partial u/\partial x = 2x$, $\partial u/\partial y = -2y$. The conjugate function must therefore satisfy

$$\frac{\partial v}{\partial x} = 2y, \qquad \frac{\partial v}{\partial y} = 2x.$$

From the first equation $v = 2xy + \varphi(y)$, where $\varphi(y)$ is a function of y alone. Substitution in the second equation yields $\varphi'(y) = 0$. Hence $\varphi(y)$ is a constant, and the most general conjugate function of $x^2 - y^2$ is $2xy + c$ where c is a constant. Observe that $x^2 - y^2 + 2ixy = z^2$. The analytic function with the real part $x^2 - y^2$ is hence $z^2 + ic$.

There is an interesting formal procedure which throws considerable light on the nature of analytic functions. We present this procedure with an explicit warning to the reader that it is purely formal and does not possess any power of proof.

Consider a complex function $f(x,y)$ of two real variables. Introducing the complex variable $z = x + iy$ and its conjugate $\bar{z} = x - iy$, we can write $x = \frac{1}{2}(z + \bar{z})$, $y = -\frac{1}{2}i(z - \bar{z})$. With this change of variable we can consider $f(x,y)$ as a function of z and $\bar{z}$ which we will treat as independent variables (forgetting that they are in fact conjugate to each other). If the rules of calculus were applicable, we would obtain

$$\frac{\partial f}{\partial z} = \frac{1}{2}\left(\frac{\partial f}{\partial x} - i\frac{\partial f}{\partial y}\right), \qquad \frac{\partial f}{\partial \bar{z}} = \frac{1}{2}\left(\frac{\partial f}{\partial x} + i\frac{\partial f}{\partial y}\right).$$

These expressions have no convenient definition as limits, but we can nevertheless introduce them as symbolic derivatives with respect to z and $\bar{z}$. By comparison with (5) we find that analytic functions are characterized by the condition $\partial f/\partial \bar{z} = 0$. We are thus tempted to say that an analytic function is independent of $\bar{z}$, and a function of z alone.

This formal reasoning supports the point of view that analytic functions are true functions of a complex variable as opposed to functions which are more adequately described as complex functions of two real variables.

By similar formal arguments we can derive a very simple method which allows us to compute, without use of integration, the analytic function $f(z)$ whose real part is a given harmonic function $u(x,y)$. We remark first that the conjugate function $\overline{f(z)}$ has the derivative zero with respect to z and may, therefore, be considered as a function of $\bar{z}$; we denote this function by $\bar{f}(\bar{z})$. With this notation we can write down the identity

$$u(x,y) = \tfrac{1}{2}[f(x + iy) + \bar{f}(x - iy)].$$

It is reasonable to expect that this is a formal identity, and then it holds even when x and y are complex. If we substitute $x = z/2$, $y = z/2i$, we obtain

$$u(z/2, z/2i) = \tfrac{1}{2}[f(z) + \bar{f}(0)].$$

Since $f(z)$ is only determined up to a purely imaginary constant, we may as well assume that $f(0)$ is real, which implies $\bar{f}(0) = u(0,0)$. The function $f(z)$ can thus be computed by means of the formula

$$f(z) = 2u(z/2, z/2i) - u(0,0).$$

A purely imaginary constant can be added at will.

In this form the method is definitely limited to functions $u(x,y)$ which are rational in x and y, for the function must have a meaning for complex values of the argument. Suffice it to say that the method can be extended to the general case and that a complete justification can be given.

EXERCISES

1. If $g(w)$ and $f(z)$ are analytic functions, show that $g(f(z))$ is also analytic.

2. Verify Cauchy-Riemann's equations for the functions z^2 and z^3.

3. Find the most general harmonic polynomial of the form $ax^3 + bx^2y + cxy^2 + dy^3$. Determine the conjugate harmonic function and the corresponding analytic function by integration and by the formal method.

4. Show that an analytic function cannot have a constant absolute value without reducing to a constant.

5. Prove rigorously that the functions $f(z)$ and $\overline{f(\bar{z})}$ are simultaneously analytic.

6. Prove that the functions $u(z)$ and $u(\bar{z})$ are simultaneously harmonic.

7. Show that a harmonic function satisfies the formal differential equation

$$\frac{\partial^2 u}{\partial z\, \partial \bar{z}} = 0.$$

1.3. Polynomials. Every constant is an analytic function with the derivative 0. The simplest nonconstant analytic function is z whose derivative is 1. Since the sum and product of two analytic functions are again analytic, it follows that every polynomial

$$P(z) = a_0 + a_1 z + \cdots + a_n z^n \tag{7}$$

is an analytic function. Its derivative is

$$P'(z) = a_1 + 2a_2 z + \cdots + n a_n z^{n-1}.$$

The notation (7) shall imply that $a_n \neq 0$, and the polynomial is then said to be of degree n. The constant 0, considered as a polynomial, is in many respects exceptional and will be excluded from our considerations.†

For $n > 0$ the equation $P(z) = 0$ has at least one root. This is the so-called fundamental theorem of algebra which we shall prove later. If $P(\alpha_1) = 0$, it is shown in elementary algebra that $P(z) = (z - \alpha_1)P_1(z)$ where $P_1(z)$ is a polynomial of degree $n - 1$. Repetition of this process finally leads to a complete factorization

$$P(z) = a_n(z - \alpha_1)(z - \alpha_2) \cdots (z - \alpha_n) \tag{8}$$

† For formal reasons, if the constant 0 is regarded as a polynomial, its degree is set equal to $-\infty$.

where the $\alpha_1, \alpha_2, \ldots, \alpha_n$ are not necessarily distinct. From the factorization we conclude that $P(z)$ does not vanish for any value of z different from $\alpha_1, \alpha_2, \ldots, \alpha_n$. Moreover, the factorization is uniquely determined except for the order of the factors.

If exactly h of the α_j coincide, their common value is called a *zero* of $P(z)$ of the *order* h. We find that the sum of the orders of the zeros of a polynomial is equal to its degree. More simply, if each zero is counted as many times as its order indicates, a polynomial of degree n has exactly n zeros.

The order of a zero α can also be determined by consideration of the successive derivatives of $P(z)$ for $z = \alpha$. Suppose that α is a zero of order h. Then we can write $P(z) = (z - \alpha)^h P_h(z)$ with $P_h(\alpha) \neq 0$. Successive derivation yields $P(\alpha) = P'(\alpha) = \cdots = P^{(h-1)}(\alpha) = 0$ while $P^{(h)}(\alpha) \neq 0$. In other words, the order of a zero equals the order of the first nonvanishing derivative. A zero of order 1 is called a simple zero and is characterized by the conditions $P(\alpha) = 0$, $P'(\alpha) \neq 0$.

As an application we shall prove the following theorem, known as *Lucas's theorem:*

Theorem 1. *If all zeros of a polynomial $P(z)$ lie in a half plane, then all zeros of the derivative $P'(z)$ lie in the same half plane.*

From (8) we obtain

$$\frac{P'(z)}{P(z)} = \frac{1}{z - \alpha_1} + \cdots + \frac{1}{z - \alpha_n}. \tag{9}$$

Suppose that the half plane H is defined as the part of the plane where $\operatorname{Im}(z - a)/b < 0$ (see Chap. 1, Sec. 2.3). If α_k is in H and z is not, we have then

$$\operatorname{Im} \frac{z - \alpha_k}{b} = \operatorname{Im} \frac{z - a}{b} - \operatorname{Im} \frac{\alpha_k - a}{b} > 0.$$

But the imaginary parts of reciprocal numbers have opposite sign. Therefore, under the same assumption, $\operatorname{Im} b(z - \alpha_k)^{-1} < 0$. If this is true for all k we conclude from (9) that

$$\operatorname{Im} \frac{bP'(z)}{P(z)} = \sum_{k=1}^{n} \operatorname{Im} \frac{b}{z - \alpha_k} < 0,$$

and consequently $P'(z) \neq 0$.

In a sharper formulation the theorem tells us that the smallest convex polygon that contains the zeros of $P(z)$ also contains the zeros of $P'(z)$.

1.4. Rational Functions. We turn to the case of a rational function

$$R(z) = \frac{P(z)}{Q(z)}, \tag{10}$$

given as the quotient of two polynomials. We assume, and this is essential, that $P(z)$ and $Q(z)$ have no common factors and hence no common zeros. $R(z)$ will be given the value ∞ at the zeros of $Q(z)$. It must therefore be considered as a function with values in the extended plane, and as such it is continuous. The zeros of $Q(z)$ are called *poles* of $R(z)$, and the order of a pole is by definition equal to the order of the corresponding zero of $Q(z)$.

The derivative

$$R'(z) = \frac{P'(z)Q(z) - Q'(z)P(z)}{Q(z)^2} \tag{11}$$

exists only when $Q(z) \neq 0$. However, as a rational function defined by the right-hand member of (11), $R'(z)$ has the same poles as $R(z)$, the order of each pole being increased by one. In case $Q(z)$ has multiple zeros, it should be noticed that the expression (11) does not appear in reduced form.

Greater unity is achieved if we let the variable z as well as the function $R(z)$ range over the extended plane. We may define $R(\infty)$ as the limit of $R(z)$ as $z \to \infty$, but this definition would not determine the order of a zero or pole at ∞. It is therefore preferable to consider the function $R(1/z)$, which we can rewrite as a rational function $R_1(z)$, and set

$$R(\infty) = R_1(0).$$

If $R_1(0) = 0$ or ∞, the order of the zero or pole at ∞ is defined as the order of the zero or pole of $R_1(z)$ at the origin.

With the notation

$$R(z) = \frac{a_0 + a_1z + \cdots + a_nz^n}{b_0 + b_1z + \cdots + b_mz^m}$$

we obtain

$$R_1(z) = z^{m-n}\frac{a_0z^n + a_1z^{n-1} + \cdots + a_n}{b_0z^m + b_1z^{m-1} + \cdots + b_m}$$

where the power z^{m-n} belongs either to the numerator or to the denominator. Accordingly, if $m > n$ $R(z)$ has a zero of order $m - n$ at ∞, if $m < n$ the point at ∞ is a pole of order $n - m$, and if $m = n$

$$R(\infty) = a_n/b_m \neq 0, \infty.$$

We can now count the total number of zeros and poles in the extended plane. The count shows that the number of zeros, including those at ∞, is equal to the greater of the numbers m and n. The number of poles is the same. This common number of zeros and poles is called the *order* of the rational function.

If a is any constant, the function $R(z) - a$ has the same poles as $R(z)$, and consequently the same order. The zeros of $R(z) - a$ are roots of the equation $R(z) = a$, and if the roots are counted as many times as the order of the zero indicates, we can state the following result:

A rational function $R(z)$ of order p has p zeros and p poles, and every equation $R(z) = a$ has exactly p roots.

A rational function of order 1 is a linear fraction

$$S(z) = \frac{\alpha z + \beta}{\gamma z + \delta}$$

with $\alpha\delta - \beta\gamma \neq 0$. Such fractions, or *linear transformations*, will be studied at length in Chap. 3, Sec. 3. For the moment we note merely that the equation $w = S(z)$ has exactly one root, and we find indeed

$$z = S^{-1}(w) = \frac{\delta w - \beta}{-\gamma w + \alpha}.$$

The transformations S and S^{-1} are inverse to each other.

The linear transformation $z + a$ is called a *parallel translation*, and $1/z$ is an *inversion*. The former has a fixpoint at ∞, the latter interchanges 0 and ∞.

Every rational function has a representation by *partial fractions*. In order to derive this representation we assume first that $R(z)$ has a pole at ∞. We carry out the division of $P(z)$ by $Q(z)$ until the degree of the remainder is at most equal to that of the denominator. The result can be written in the form

$$R(z) = G(z) + H(z) \tag{12}$$

where $G(z)$ is a polynomial without constant term, and $H(z)$ is finite at ∞. The degree of $G(z)$ is the order of the pole at ∞, and the polynomial $G(z)$ is called the *singular part* of $R(z)$ at ∞.

Let the distinct finite poles of $R(z)$ be denoted by $\beta_1, \beta_2, \ldots, \beta_q$. The function $R\left(\beta_j + \frac{1}{\zeta}\right)$ is a rational function of ζ with a pole at $\zeta = \infty$. By use of the decomposition (12) we can write

$$R\left(\beta_j + \frac{1}{\zeta}\right) = G_j(\zeta) + H_j(\zeta),$$

or with a change of variable

$$R(z) = G_j\left(\frac{1}{z - \beta_j}\right) + H_j\left(\frac{1}{z - \beta_j}\right).$$

Here $G_j\left(\frac{1}{z - \beta_j}\right)$ is a polynomial in $\frac{1}{z - \beta_j}$ without constant term, called the singular part of $R(z)$ at β_j. The function $H_j\left(\frac{1}{z - \beta_j}\right)$ is finite for $z = \beta_j$.

Consider now the expression

$$R(z) - G(z) - \sum_{j=1}^{q} G_j\left(\frac{1}{z - \beta_j}\right). \tag{13}$$

This is a rational function which cannot have other poles than $\beta_1, \beta_2, \ldots, \beta_q$ and ∞. At $z = \beta_j$ we find that the two terms which become infinite have a difference $H_j\left(\frac{1}{z - \beta_j}\right)$ with a finite limit, and the same is true at ∞. Therefore (11) has neither any finite poles nor a pole at ∞. A rational function without poles must reduce to a constant, and if this constant is absorbed in $G(z)$ we obtain

$$R(z) = G(z) + \sum_{j=1}^{q} G_j\left(\frac{1}{z - \beta_j}\right). \tag{14}$$

This representation is well known from the calculus where it is used as a technical device in integration theory. However, it is only with the introduction of complex numbers that it becomes completely successful.

We shall make a minor application of (14) to the determination of all rational functions of order 2. More precisely, we shall determine the simplest forms which can be achieved by linear transformations of the dependent and independent variable.

A rational function of order 2 has either one double or two simple poles. In the first case we can throw the pole to ∞ by a preliminary linear transformation of z. The function will then have the form

$$w = az^2 + bz + c = a\left(z + \frac{b}{2a}\right)^2 + c - \frac{b^2}{4a}.$$

and by further linear transformations it can be reduced to the normal form $w = z^2$. In the case of two simple poles we may choose the poles at $z = 0$ and $z = \infty$. The representation (14) will then have the form

$$w = Az + B + \frac{C}{z} \tag{15}$$

If we replace z by $z' = z\sqrt{A/C}$ the coefficients of z' and $1/z'$ become equal, and a further linear change of w will reduce (15) to the form

$$w = \frac{1}{2}\left(z + \frac{1}{z}\right)$$

which we choose as the normal form for a rational function of order 2 with distinct poles.

EXERCISES

1. Use the method of the text to develop

$$\frac{z^4}{z^3 - 1} \quad \text{and} \quad \frac{1}{z(z+1)^2(z+2)^3}$$

in partial fractions.

2. If Q is a polynomial with distinct roots $\alpha_1, \ldots, \alpha_n$, and if P is a polynomial of degree $< n$, show that

$$\frac{P(z)}{Q(z)} = \sum_{k=1}^{n} \frac{P(\alpha_k)}{Q'(\alpha_k)(z - \alpha_k)}.$$

3. Use the formula in the preceding exercise to prove that there exists a unique polynomial P of degree $< n$ with given values c_k at the points α_k (Lagrange's interpolation polynomial).

4. What is the general form of a rational function which has absolute value 1 on the circle $|z| = 1$? In particular, how are the zeros and poles related to each other?

5. If a rational function is real on $|z| = 1$, how are the zeros and poles situated?

2. ELEMENTARY THEORY OF POWER SERIES

Polynomials and rational functions are very special analytic functions. The easiest way to achieve greater variety is to form limits. For instance, the sum of a convergent series is such a limit. If the terms are functions of a variable, so is the sum, and if the terms are analytic functions, chances are good that the sum will also be analytic.

Of all series with analytic terms the power series with complex coefficients are the simplest. In this section we study only the most elementary properties of power series. A strong motivation for taking up this study when we are not yet equipped to prove the most general properties (those that depend on integration) is that we need power series to construct the exponential function (Sec. 3).

2.1. Sequences. The sequence $\{a_n\}_1^\infty$ has the limit A if to every $\varepsilon > 0$ there exists an n_0 such that $|a_n - A| < \varepsilon$ for $n \geqq n_0$. A sequence with a finite limit is said to be *convergent*, and any sequence which does not converge is *divergent*. If $\lim_{n\to\infty} a_n = \infty$, the sequence may be said to *diverge to infinity*.

Only in rare cases can the convergence be proved by exhibiting the limit, so it is extremely important to make use of a method that permits proof of the existence of a limit even when it cannot be determined explicitly. The test that serves this purpose bears the name of Cauchy. A sequence will be called *fundamental*, or a *Cauchy sequence*, if it satisfies the following condition: given any $\varepsilon > 0$ there exists an n_0 such that $|a_n - a_m| < \varepsilon$ whenever $n \geqq n_0$ and $m \geqq n_0$. The test reads:

A sequence is convergent if and only if it is a Cauchy sequence.

The necessity is immediate. If $a_n \to A$ we can find n_0 such that $|a_n - A| < \varepsilon/2$ for $n \geqq n_0$. For $m,n \geqq n_0$ it follows by the triangle inequality that $|a_n - a_m| \leqq |a_n - A| + |a_m - A| < \varepsilon$.

The sufficiency is closely connected with the definition of real numbers, and one way in which real numbers can be introduced is indeed to postulate the sufficiency of Cauchy's condition. However, we wish to use only the property that every bounded monotone sequence of real numbers has a limit.

The real and imaginary parts of a Cauchy sequence are again Cauchy sequences, and if they converge, so does the original sequence. For this reason we need to prove the sufficiency only for real sequences. We use the opportunity to recall the notions of *limes superior* and *limes inferior*. Given a real sequence $\{\alpha_n\}_1^\infty$ we shall set $a_n = \max\{\alpha_1, \ldots, \alpha_n\}$, that is, a_n is the greatest of the numbers $\alpha_1, \ldots, \alpha_n$. The sequence $\{a_n\}_1^\infty$ is nondecreasing; hence it has a limit A_1 which is finite or equal to $+\infty$. The number A_1 is known as the *least upper bound* or *supremum* (*l.u.b.* or *sup*) of the numbers α_n; indeed, it is the least number which is $\geqq$ all α_n. Construct in the same way the least upper bound A_k of the sequence $\{\alpha_n\}_k^\infty$ obtained from the original sequence by deleting $\alpha_1, \ldots, \alpha_{k-1}$. It is clear that $\{A_k\}$ is a nonincreasing sequence, and we denote its limit by A. It may be finite, $+\infty$, or $-\infty$. In any case we write

$$A = \limsup_{n\to\infty} \alpha_n.$$

It is easy to characterize the limes superior by its properties. If A is finite and $\varepsilon > 0$ there exists an n_0 such that $A_{n_0} < A + \varepsilon$, and it follows that $\alpha_n \leqq A_{n_0} < A + \varepsilon$ for $n \geqq n_0$. In the opposite direction, if $\alpha_n \leqq A - \varepsilon$ for $n \geqq n_0$, then $A_{n_0} \leqq A - \varepsilon$, which is impossible. In other words, there are arbitrarily large n for which $\alpha_n > A - \varepsilon$. If

$A = +\infty$ there are arbitrarily large α_n, and $A = -\infty$ if and only if α_n tends to $-\infty$. In all cases there cannot be more than one number A with these properties.

The limes inferior can be defined in the same manner with inequalities reversed. It is quite clear that the limes inferior and limes superior will be equal if and only if the sequence converges to a finite limit or diverges to $+\infty$ or to $-\infty$. The notations are frequently simplified to $\overline{\lim}$ and $\underline{\lim}$. The reader should prove the following relations:

$$\underline{\lim}\ \alpha_n + \underline{\lim}\ \beta_n \leqq \underline{\lim}\ (\alpha_n + \beta_n) \leqq \underline{\lim}\ \alpha_n + \overline{\lim}\ \beta_n$$
$$\underline{\lim}\ \alpha_n + \overline{\lim}\ \beta_n \leqq \overline{\lim}\ (\alpha_n + \beta_n) \leqq \overline{\lim}\ \alpha_n + \overline{\lim}\ \beta_n.$$

Now we return to the sufficiency of Cauchy's condition. From $|\alpha_n - \alpha_{n_0}| < \varepsilon$ we obtain $|\alpha_n| < |\alpha_{n_0}| + \varepsilon$ for $n \geqq n_0$, and it follows that $A = \overline{\lim}\ \alpha_n$ and $a = \underline{\lim}\ \alpha_n$ are both finite. If $a \neq A$ choose

$$\varepsilon = \frac{(A - a)}{3}$$

and determine a corresponding n_0. By definition of a and A there exists an $\alpha_n < a + \varepsilon$ and an $\alpha_m > A - \varepsilon$ with $m,n \geqq n_0$. It follows that $A - a = (A - \alpha_m) + (\alpha_m - \alpha_n) + (\alpha_n - a) < 3\varepsilon$, contrary to the choice of ε. Hence $a = A$, and the sequence converges.

2.2. Series. A very simple application of Cauchy's condition permits us to deduce the convergence of one sequence from that of another. If it is true that $|b_m - b_n| \leqq |a_m - a_n|$ for all pairs of subscripts, the sequence $\{b_n\}$ may be termed a *contraction* of the sequence $\{a_n\}$ (this is not a standard term). Under this condition, if $\{b_n\}$ is a Cauchy sequence, so is $\{a_n\}$. Hence convergence of $\{b_n\}$ implies convergence of $\{a_n\}$.

An infinite series is a formal infinite sum

$$a_1 + a_2 + \cdots + a_n + \cdots. \tag{16}$$

Associated with this series is the sequence of its partial sums

$$s_n = a_1 + a_2 + \cdots + a_n.$$

The series is said to converge if and only if the corresponding sequence is convergent, and if this is the case the limit of the sequence is the *sum* of the series.

Applied to a series Cauchy's convergence test yields the following condition: The series (16) converges if and only if to every $\varepsilon > 0$ there exists an n_0 such that $|a_n + a_{n+1} + \cdots + a_{n+p}| < \varepsilon$ for all $n > n_0$ and $p \geqq 0$. For $p = 0$ we find in particular that $|a_n| < \varepsilon$. Hence the general term of a convergent series tends to zero. This condition is necessary, but of course not sufficient.

If a finite number of the terms of the series (16) are omitted, the new series converges or diverges together with (16). In the case of convergence, let R_n be the sum of the series which begins with the term a_{n+1}. Then the sum of the whole series is $S = s_n + R_n$.

The series (16) can be compared with the series

$$(17) \qquad |a_1| + |a_2| + \cdots + |a_n| + \cdots$$

formed by the absolute values of the terms. The sequence of partial sums of (16) is a contraction of the sequence corresponding to (17), for $|a_n + a_{n+1} + \cdots + a_{n+p}| \leqq |a_n| + |a_{n+1}| + \cdots + |a_{n+p}|$. Therefore, convergence of (17) implies that the original series (16) is convergent. A series with the property that the series formed by the absolute values of the terms converges is said to be *absolutely convergent.*

2.3. Uniform Convergence. Consider a sequence of functions $f_n(x)$, all defined on the same set E. If the sequence of values $\{f_n(x)\}$ converges for every x that belongs to E, then the limit $f(x)$ is again a function on E. By definition, if $\varepsilon > 0$ and x belongs to E there exists an n_0 such that $|f_n(x) - f(x)| < \varepsilon$ for $n \geqq n_0$, but n_0 is allowed to depend on x. For instance, it is true that

$$\lim_{n\to\infty} \left(1 + \frac{1}{n}\right) x = x$$

for all x, but in order to have $|(1 + 1/n)x - x| = |x|/n < \varepsilon$ for $n \geqq n_0$ it is necessary that $n_0 > |x|/\varepsilon$. Such an n_0 exists for every fixed x, but the requirement cannot be met simultaneously for all x.

We say in this situation that the sequence converges pointwise, but not uniformly. In positive formulation: *The sequence $\{f_n(x)\}$ converges uniformly to $f(x)$ on the set E if to every $\varepsilon > 0$ there exists an n_0 such that $|f_n(x) - f(x)| < \varepsilon$ for all $n \geqq n_0$ and all x in E.*

The most important consequence of uniform convergence is the following:

The limit function of a uniformly convergent sequence of continuous functions is itself continuous.

Suppose that the functions $f_n(x)$ are continuous and tend uniformly to $f(x)$ on the set E. For any $\varepsilon > 0$ we are able to find an n such that $|f_n(x) - f(x)| < \varepsilon/3$ for all x in E. Let x_0 be a point in E. Because $f_n(x)$ is continuous at x_0 we can find $\delta > 0$ such that $|f_n(x) - f_n(x_0)| < \varepsilon/3$ for all x in E with $|x - x_0| < \delta$. Under the same condition on x it follows that

$$|f(x) - f(x_0)| \leqq |f(x) - f_n(x)| + |f_n(x) - f_n(x_0)| + |f_n(x_0) - f(x_0)| < \varepsilon,$$

and we have proved that $f(x)$ is continuous at x_0.

In the theory of analytic functions we shall find uniform convergence much more important than pointwise convergence. However, in most cases it will be found that the convergence is uniform only on a part of the set on which the functions are originally defined.

Cauchy's necessary and sufficient condition has a counterpart for uniform convergence. We assert:

The sequence $\{f_n(x)\}$ *converges uniformly on* E *if and only if to every* $\varepsilon > 0$ *there exists an* n_0 *such that* $|f_m(x) - f_n(x)| < \varepsilon$ *for all* $m,n \geqq n_0$ *and all* x *in* E.

The necessity is again trivial. For the sufficiency we remark that the limit function $f(x)$ exists by the ordinary form of Cauchy's test. In the inequality $|f_m(x) - f_n(x)| < \varepsilon$ we can keep n fixed and let m tend to ∞. It follows that $|f(x) - f_n(x)| \leqq \varepsilon$ for $n \geqq n_0$ and all x in E. Hence the convergence is uniform.

For practical use the following test is the most applicable: If a sequence of functions $\{f_n(x)\}$ is a contraction of a convergent sequence of constants $\{a_n\}$, then the sequence $\{f_n(x)\}$ is uniformly convergent. The hypothesis means that $|f_m(x) - f_n(x)| \leqq |a_m - a_n|$ on E, and the conclusion follows immediately by Cauchy's condition.

In the case of series this criterion, in a somewhat weaker form, becomes particularly simple. We say that a series with variable terms

$$f_1(x) + f_2(x) + \cdots + f_n(x) + \cdots$$

has the series with positive terms

$$a_1 + a_2 + \cdots + a_n + \cdots$$

for a *majorant* if it is true that $|f_n(x)| \leqq Ma_n$ for some constant M and for all sufficiently large n; conversely, the first series is a *minorant* of the second. In these circumstances we have

$$|f_n(x) + f_{n+1}(x) + \cdots + f_{n+p}(x)| \leqq M(a_n + a_{n+1} + \cdots + a_{n+p}).$$

Therefore, if the majorant converges, the minorant converges uniformly. This condition is frequently referred to as the *Weierstrass M test.* It has the slight weakness that it applies only to series which are also absolutely convergent. The general principle of contraction is more complicated, but has a wider range of applicability.

EXERCISES

1. Prove that a convergent sequence is bounded.

2. If $\lim\limits_{n\to\infty} z_n = A$, prove that

$$\lim_{n\to\infty} \frac{1}{n}(z_1 + z_2 + \cdots + z_n) = A.$$

3. Show that the sum of an absolutely convergent series does not change if the terms are rearranged.

4. Discuss completely the convergence and uniform convergence of the sequence $\{nz^n\}_1^\infty$.

5. Discuss the uniform convergence of the series

$$\sum_{n=1}^{\infty} \frac{x}{n(1 + nx^2)}$$

for real values of x.

6. If $U = u_1 + u_2 + \cdots$, $V = v_1 + v_2 + \cdots$ are convergent series, prove that $UV = u_1v_1 + (u_1v_2 + u_2v_1) + (u_1v_3 + u_2v_2 + u_3v_1) + \cdots$ provided that at least one of the series is absolutely convergent. (It is easy if both series are absolutely convergent. Try to arrange the proof so economically that the absolute convergence of the second series is not needed.)

2.4. Power Series.

A *power series* is of the form

$$a_0 + a_1z + a_2z^2 + \cdots + a_nz^n + \cdots \tag{18}$$

where the coefficients a_n and the variable z are complex. A little more generally we may consider series

$$\sum_{n=0}^{\infty} a_n(z - z_0)^n$$

which are power series with respect to the center z_0, but the difference is so slight that we need not do so in a formal manner.

As an almost trivial example we consider the *geometric series*

$$1 + z + z^2 + \cdots + z^n + \cdots$$

whose partial sums can be written in the form

$$1 + z + \cdots + z^{n-1} = \frac{1 - z^n}{1 - z}.$$

Since $z^n \to 0$ for $|z| < 1$ and $|z^n| \geqq 1$ for $|z| \geqq 1$ we conclude that the geometric series converges to $1/(1 - z)$ for $|z| < 1$, diverges for $|z| \geqq 1$.

It turns out that the behavior of the geometric series is typical. Indeed, we shall find that every power series converges inside a circle and diverges outside the same circle, except that it may happen that the series converges only for $z = 0$, or that it converges for all values of z.

More precisely, we shall prove the following theorem due to *Abel:*

Theorem 2. *For every power series* (18) *there exists a number* R, $0 \leqq R \leqq \infty$, *called the radius of convergence, with the following properties:*

(i) *The series converges absolutely for every* z *with* $|z| < R$. *If* $0 \leqq \rho < R$ *the convergence is uniform for* $|z| \leqq \rho$.

(ii) *If* $|z| > R$ *the terms of the series are unbounded, and the series is consequently divergent.*

(iii) *In* $|z| < R$ *the sum of the series is an analytic function. The derivative can be obtained by termwise differentiation, and the derived series has the same radius of convergence.*

The circle $|z| = R$ is called the *circle of convergence;* nothing is claimed about the convergence on the circle. We shall show that the assertions in the theorem are true if R is chosen according to the formula

$$1/R = \limsup_{n \to \infty} \sqrt[n]{|a_n|}. \tag{19}$$

This is known as *Hadamard's formula* for the radius of convergence.

If $|z| < R$ we can find ρ so that $|z| < \rho < R$. Then $1/\rho > 1/R$, and by the definition of limes superior there exists an n_0 such that $|a_n|^{1/n} < 1/\rho$, $|a_n| < 1/\rho^n$ for $n \geqq n_0$. It follows that $|a_nz^n| < (|z|/\rho)^n$ for large n, so that the power series (18) has a convergent geometric series as a majorant, and is consequently convergent. To prove the uniform convergence for $|z| \leqq \rho < R$ we choose a ρ' with $\rho < \rho' < \infty$ and find $|a_nz^n| \leqq (\rho'/\rho)_n$ for $n \geqq n_0$. Since the majorant is convergent and has constant terms we conclude by Weierstrass's M test that the power series is uniformly convergent.

If $|z| > R$ we choose ρ so that $R < \rho < |z|$. Since $1/\rho < 1/R$ there are arbitrarily large n such that $|a_n|^{1/n} > 1/\rho$, $|a_n| > 1/\rho^n$. Thus $|a_nz^n| > (|z|/\rho)^n$ for infinitely many n, and the terms are unbounded.

The derived series $\sum_1^\infty na_nz^{n-1}$ has the same radius of convergence, because $\sqrt[n]{n} \to 1$. *Proof:* Set $\sqrt[n]{n} = 1 + \delta_n$. Then $\delta_n > 0$, and by use of the binomial theorem $n = (1 + \delta_n)^n > 1 + \frac{1}{2}\,n(n-1)\delta_n^2$. This gives $\delta_n^2 < 2/n$, and hence $\delta_n \to 0$.

For $|z| < R$ we shall write

$$f(z) = \sum_0^\infty a_nz^n = s_n(z) + R_n(z)$$

where

$$s_n(z) = a_0 + a_1z + \cdots + a_{n-1}z^{n-1},\ R_n(z) = \sum_{k=n}^{\infty} a_kz^k,$$

and also

$$f_1(z) = \sum_1^{\infty} na_nz^{n-1} = \lim_{n\to\infty} s_n'(z).$$

We have to show that $f'(z) = f_1(z)$.

Consider the identity

$$(20)\quad \frac{f(z) - f(z_0)}{z - z_0} - f_1(z_0) = \left(\frac{s_n(z) - s_n(z_0)}{z - z_0} - s_n'(z_0)\right) + (s_n'(z_0) - f_1(z_0)) + \left(\frac{R_n(z) - R_n(z_0)}{z - z_0}\right),$$

where we assume that $z \neq z_0$ and $|z|, |z_0| < \rho < R$. The last term can be rewritten as

$$\sum_{k=n}^{\infty} a_k(z^{k-1} + z^{k-2}z_0 + \cdots + zz_0^{k-2} + z_0^{k-1}),$$

and we conclude that

$$\left|\frac{R_n(z) - R_n(z_0)}{z - z_0}\right| \leqq \sum_{k=n}^{\infty} k|a_k|\rho^{k-1}.$$

The expression on the right is the remainder term in a convergent series. Hence we can find n_0 such that

$$\left|\frac{R_n(z) - R_n(z_0)}{z - z_0}\right| < \frac{\varepsilon}{3}$$

for $n \geqq n_0$.

There is also an n_1 such that $|s_n'(z_0) - f_1(z_0)| < \varepsilon/3$ for $n \geqq n_1$. Choose a fixed $n \geqq n_0, n_1$. By the definition of derivative we can find $\delta > 0$ such that $0 < |z - z_0| < \delta$ implies

$$\left|\frac{s_n(z) - s_n(z_0)}{z - z_0} - s_n'(z_0)\right| < \frac{\varepsilon}{3}.$$

When all these inequalities are combined it follows by (20) that

$$\left|\frac{f(z) - f(z_0)}{z - z_0} - f_1(z_0)\right| < \varepsilon$$

when $0 < |z - z_0| < \delta$. We have proved that $f'(z_0)$ exists and equals $f_1(z_0)$.

Since the reasoning can be repeated we have in reality proved much more: A power series with positive radius of convergence has derivatives of all orders, and they are given explicitly by

$$\begin{aligned} f(z) &= a_0 + a_1 z + a_2 z^2 + \cdots \\ f'(z) &= a_1 + 2a_2 z + 3a_3 z^2 + \cdots \\ f''(z) &= 2a_2 + 6a_3 z + 12a_4 z^2 + \cdots \\ &\cdots\cdots\cdots\cdots\cdots\cdots \\ f^{(k)}(z) &= k!a_k + \frac{(k+1)!}{1!} a_{k+1} z + \frac{(k+2)!}{2!} a_{k+2} z^2 + \cdots \end{aligned}$$

In particular, if we look at the last line we see that $a_k = f^{(k)}(0)/k!$, and the power series becomes

$$f(z) = f(0) + f'(0)z + \frac{f''(0)}{2\,!} z^2 + \cdots + \frac{f^{(n)}(0)}{n!} z^n + \cdots$$

This is the familiar Taylor-Maclaurin development, but we have proved it only under the assumption that $f(z)$ *has* a power series development. We do know that the development is uniquely determined, if it exists, but the main part is still missing, namely that every analytic function has a Taylor development.

EXERCISES

1. Expand $(1 - z)^{-m}$, m a positive integer, in powers of z.

2. Expand $\dfrac{2z+3}{z+1}$ in powers of $z - 1$. What is the radius of convergence?

3. Find the radius of convergence of the following power series:

$$\sum n^p z^n, \sum \frac{z^n}{n!}, \sum n! z^n, \sum q^{n^2} z^n \; (|q| < 1), \sum z^{n!}$$

4. If $\Sigma a_n z^n$ has radius of convergence R, what is the radius of convergence of $\Sigma a_n z^{2n}$? of $\Sigma a_n^2 z^n$?

5. If $f(z) = \Sigma a_n z^n$, what is $\Sigma n^3 a_n z^n$?

6. If $\Sigma a_n z^n$ and $\Sigma b_n z^n$ have radii of convergence R_1 and R_2, show that the radius of convergence of $\Sigma a_n b_n z^n$ is at least $R_1 R_2$.

7. If $\lim_{n\to\infty} |a_n|/|a_{n+1}| = R$, prove that $\Sigma a_n z^n$ has radius of convergence R.

8. For what values of z is

$$\sum_0^\infty \left(\frac{z}{1+z}\right)^n$$

convergent?

9. Same question for

$$\sum_0^\infty \frac{z^n}{1+z^{2n}}.$$

2.5. Abel's Limit Theorem. There is a second theorem of Abel's which refers to the case where a power series converges at a point of the circle of convergence. We lose no generality by assuming that $R = 1$ and that the convergence takes place at $z = 1$.

Theorem 3. *If $\sum_0^\infty a_n$ converges, then $f(z) = \sum_0^\infty a_n z^n$ tends to $f(1)$ as z approaches 1 in such a way that $|1 - z|/(1 - |z|)$ remains bounded.*

Remark. Geometrically, the condition means that z stays in an angle $<180°$ with vertex 1, symmetrically to the part $(-\infty, 1)$ of the real axis. It is customary to say that the approach takes place in a *Stolz angle.*

Proof. We may assume that $\sum_0^\infty a_n = 0$, for this can be attained by adding a constant to a_0. We write $s_n = a_0 + a_1 + \cdots + a_n$ and make use of the identity (summation by parts)

$$\begin{aligned} s_n(z) &= a_0 + a_1 z + \cdots + a_n z^n = s_0 + (s_1 - s_0)z + \cdots + (s_n - s_{n-1})z^n \\ &= s_0(1 - z) + s_1(z - z^2) + \cdots + s_{n-1}(z^{n-1} - z^n) + s_n z^n \\ &= (1 - z)(s_0 + s_1 z + \cdots + s_{n-1}z^{n-1}) + s_n z^n. \end{aligned}$$

But $s_n z^n \to 0$, so we obtain the representation

$$f(z) = (1 - z)\sum_0^\infty s_n z^n.$$

We are assuming that $|1 - z| \leqq K(1 - |z|)$, say, and that $s_n \to 0$. Choose m so large that $|s_n| < \varepsilon$ for $n \geqq m$. The remainder of the series $\Sigma s_n z^n$, from $n = m$ on, is then dominated by the geometric series $\varepsilon \sum_m^\infty |z|^n = \varepsilon |z|^m/(1 - |z|) < \varepsilon/(1 - |z|)$. It follows that

$$|f(z)| \leqq |1 - z| \left| \sum_0^{m-1} s_k z^k \right| + K\varepsilon.$$

The first term on the right can be made arbitrarily small by choosing z sufficiently close to 1, and we conclude that $f(z) \to 0$ when $z \to 1$ subject to the stated restriction.

3. THE EXPONENTIAL AND TRIGONOMETRIC FUNCTIONS

The person who approaches calculus exclusively from the point of view of real numbers will not expect any relationship between the exponential function e^x and the trigonometric functions $\cos x$ and $\sin x$. Indeed, these functions seem to be derived from completely different sources and with different purposes in mind. He will notice, no doubt, a similarity between the Taylor developments of these functions, and if willing to use imaginary arguments he will be able to derive *Euler's formula* $e^{ix} = \cos x + i \sin x$ as a formal identity. But it took the genius of a Gauss to analyze its full depth.

With the preparation given in the preceding section it will be easy to define e^z, $\cos z$ and $\sin z$ for complex z, and to derive the relations between these functions. At the same time we can define the logarithm as the inverse function of the exponential, and the logarithm leads in turn to the correct definition of the argument of a complex number, and hence to the nongeometric definition of angle.

3.1. The Exponential. We may begin by defining the *exponential function* as the solution of the differential equation

$$f'(z) = f(z) \tag{21}$$

with the initial value $f(0) = 1$. We solve it by setting

$$\begin{aligned} f(z) &= a_0 + a_1 z + \cdots + a_n z^n + \cdots \\ f'(z) &= a_1 + 2a_2 z + \cdots + na_n z^{n-1} + \cdots \end{aligned}$$

If (21) is to be satisfied, we must have $a_{n-1} = na_n$, and the initial condition gives $a_0 = 1$. It follows by induction that $a_n = 1/n!$.

The solution is denoted by e^z or $\exp z$, depending on purely typographical considerations. We must show of course that the series

$$e^z = 1 + \frac{z}{1!} + \frac{z^2}{2!} + \cdots + \frac{z^n}{n!} + \cdots \tag{22}$$

converges. It does so in the whole plane, for $\sqrt[n]{n!} \to \infty$ (proof by the reader).

It is a consequence of the differential equation that e^z satisfies the *addition theorem*

$$e^{a+b} = e^a \cdot e^b. \tag{23}$$

Indeed, we find that $D(e^z \cdot e^{c-z}) = e^z \cdot e^{c-z} + e^z \cdot (-e^{c-z}) = 0$. Hence $e^z \cdot e^{c-z}$ is a constant. The value of the constant is found by setting $z = 0$. We conclude that $e^z \cdot e^{c-z} = e^c$, and (23) follows for $z = a$, $c = a + b$.

Remark: We have used that $f(z)$ is constant if $f'(z)$ is identically zero. This is certainly so if f is defined in the whole plane. For if $f = u + iv$ we obtain $\frac{\partial u}{\partial x} = \frac{\partial u}{\partial y} = \frac{\partial v}{\partial x} = \frac{\partial v}{\partial y} = 0$, and the real version of the theorem shows that f is constant on every horizontal and every vertical line.

As a particular case of the addition theorem $e^z \cdot e^{-z} = 1$. This shows that e^z *is never zero.* For real x the series development (22) shows that $e^x > 1$ for $x > 0$, and since e^x and e^{-x} are reciprocals, $0 < e^x < 1$ for $x < 0$. The fact that the series has real coefficients shows that $\exp \bar{z}$ is the complex conjugate of $\exp z$. Hence $|e^{iy}|^2 = e^{iy} \cdot e^{-iy} = 1$, and $|e^{x+iy}| = e^x$.

3.2. The Trigonometric Functions. The trigonometric functions are defined by

$$\cos z = \frac{e^{iz} + e^{-iz}}{2}, \quad \sin z = \frac{e^{iz} - e^{-iz}}{2i}. \tag{24}$$

Substitution in (22) shows that they have the series developments

$$\begin{aligned} \cos z &= 1 - \frac{z^2}{2!} + \frac{z^4}{4!} - \cdots \\ \sin z &= z - \frac{z^3}{3!} + \frac{z^5}{5!} - \cdots \end{aligned} \tag{25}$$

For real z they reduce to the familiar Taylor developments of $\cos x$ and $\sin x$, with the significant difference that we have now redefined these functions without use of geometry.

From (24) we obtain further Euler's formula

$$e^{iz} = \cos z + i \sin z \tag{26}$$

as well as the identity

$$\cos^2 z + \sin^2 z = 1. \tag{27}$$

It follows likewise that

$$D \cos z = -\sin z, \qquad D \sin z = \cos z. \tag{28}$$

The addition formulas

$$\begin{aligned} \cos (a + b) &= \cos a \cos b - \sin a \sin b \\ \sin (a + b) &= \cos a \sin b + \sin a \cos b \end{aligned}$$

are direct consequences of (24) and the addition theorem for the exponential function.

The other trigonometric functions $\tan z$, $\cot z$, $\sec z$, $\operatorname{cosec} z$ are of secondary importance. They are defined in terms of $\cos z$ and $\sin z$ in the customary manner. We find for instance

$$\tan z = -i\frac{e^{iz} - e^{-iz}}{e^{iz} + e^{-iz}}.$$

Observe that all the trigonometric functions are rational functions of e^{iz}.

EXERCISES

1. Find the values of $\sin i$, $\cos i$, $\tan (1 + i)$.

2. The hyperbolic cosine and sine are defined by $\cosh z = (e^z + e^{-z})/2$, $\sinh z = (e^z - e^{-z})/2$. Express them through $\cos iz$, $\sin iz$. Derive the addition formulas, and formulas for $\cosh 2z$, $\sinh 2z$.

3. Use the addition formulas to separate $\cos (x + iy)$, $\sin (x + iy)$ in real and imaginary parts.

4. Show that

$$|\cos z|^2 = \sinh^2 y + \cos^2 x = \cosh^2 y - \sin^2 x = \frac{1}{2}(\cosh 2y + \cos 2x)$$

and

$$|\sin z|^2 = \sinh^2 y + \sin^2 x = \cosh^2 y - \cos^2 x = \frac{1}{2}(\cosh 2y - \cos 2x).$$

3.3. The Periodicity. We say that $f(z)$ has the *period* c if $f(z + c) = f(z)$ for all z. Thus a period of e^z satisfies $e^{z+c} = e^z$, or $e^c = 1$. It follows that $c = i\omega$ with real ω; we prefer to say that ω is a period of e^{iz}. We shall show that there are periods, and that they are all integral multiples of a positive period ω_0.

Of the many ways to prove the existence of a period we choose the following: From $D \sin y = \cos y \leqq 1$ and $\sin 0 = 0$ we obtain $\sin y < y$ for $y > 0$, either by integration or by use of the mean-value theorem. In the same way $D \cos y = -\sin y > -y$ and $\cos 0 = 1$ gives $\cos y > 1 - y^2/2$, which in turn leads to $\sin y > y - y^3/6$ and finally to $\cos y < 1 - y^2/2 + y^4/24$. This inequality shows that $\cos \sqrt{3} < 0$, and therefore there is a y_0 between 0 and $\sqrt{3}$ with $\cos y_0 = 0$. Because

$$\cos^2 y_0 + \sin^2 y_0 = 1$$

we have $\sin y_0 = \pm 1$, that is, $e^{iy_0} = \pm i$, and hence $e^{4iy_0} = 1$. We have shown that $4y_0$ is a period.

Actually, it is the smallest positive period. To see this, take $0 < y < y_0$. Then $\sin y > y(1 - y^2/6) > y/2 > 0$, which shows that $\cos y$ is strictly decreasing. Because $\sin y$ is positive and $\cos^2 y + \sin^2 y = 1$ it follows that $\sin y$ is strictly increasing, and hence $\sin y < \sin y_0 = 1$.

The double inequality $0 < \sin y < 1$ guarantees that e^{iy} is neither ± 1 nor $\pm i$. Therefore $e^{4iy} \neq 1$, and $4y_0$ is indeed the smallest positive period. We denote it by ω_0.

Consider now an arbitrary period ω. There exists an integer n such that $n\omega_0 \leqq \omega < (n + 1)\omega_0$. If ω were not equal to $n\omega_0$, then $\omega - n\omega_0$ would be a positive period $< \omega_0$. Since this is not possible, every period must be an integral multiple of ω_0.

The smallest positive period of e^{iz} is denoted by 2π.

In the course of the proof we have shown that

$$e^{\pi i/2} = i, \qquad e^{\pi i} = -1, \qquad e^{2\pi i} = 1.$$

These equations demonstrate the intimate relationship between the numbers e and π.

When y increases from 0 to 2π, the point $w = e^{iy}$ describes the unit circle $|w| = 1$ in the positive sense, namely from 1 over i to -1 and back over $-i$ to 1. For every w with $|w| = 1$ there is one and only one y from the half-open interval $0 \leqq y < 2\pi$ such that $w = e^{iy}$. All this follows readily from the established fact that $\cos y$ is strictly decreasing in the "first quadrant," that is, between 0 and $\pi/2$.

From an algebraic point of view the mapping $w = e^{iy}$ establishes a *homomorphism* between the additive group of real numbers and the multiplicative group of complex numbers with absolute value 1. The *kernel* of the homomorphism is the subgroup formed by all integral multiples $2\pi n$.

3.4. The Logarithm. Together with the exponential function we must also study its inverse function, the *logarithm*. By definition, $z = \log w$ is a root of the equation $e^z = w$. First of all, since e^z is always $\neq 0$, *the number 0 has no logarithm.* For $w \neq 0$ the equation $e^{x+iy} = w$ is equivalent to

$$e^x = |w|, \qquad e^{iy} = w/|w|. \tag{29}$$

The first equation has a unique solution $x = \log |w|$, the *real logarithm* of the positive number $|w|$. The right-hand member of the second equation (29) is a complex number of absolute value 1. Therefore, as we have just seen, it has one and only one solution in the interval $0 \leqq y < 2\pi$. In addition, it is also satisfied by all y that differ from this solution by an integral multiple of 2π. We see that *every complex number other than 0 has infinitely many logarithms which differ from each other by multiples of $2\pi i$.*

The imaginary part of $\log w$ is also called the *argument* of w, $\arg w$, and it is interpreted geometrically as the *angle*, measured in radians, between the positive real axis and the half line from 0 through the point w. According to this definition the argument has infinitely many values which differ by multiples of 2π, and

$$\log w = \log |w| + i \arg w.$$

With a change of notation, if $|z| = r$ and $\arg z = \theta$, then $z = re^{i\theta}$. This notation is so convenient that it is used constantly, even when the exponential function is not otherwise involved.

By convention the logarithm of a positive number shall always mean the real logarithm, unless the contrary is stated. The symbol a^b, where a and b are arbitrary complex numbers except for the condition $a \neq 0$, is always interpreted as an equivalent of $\exp(b \log a)$. If a is restricted to positive numbers, $\log a$ shall be real, and a^b has a single value. Otherwise $\log a$ is the complex logarithm, and a^b has in general infinitely many values which differ by factors $e^{2\pi inb}$. There will be a single value if and only if b is an integer n, and then a^b can be interpreted as a power of a or a^{-1}. If b is a rational number with the reduced form p/q, then a^b has exactly q values and can be represented as $\sqrt[q]{a^p}$.

The addition theorem of the exponential function clearly implies

$$\begin{aligned}\log (z_1z_2) &= \log z_1 + \log z_2\\ \arg (z_1z_2) &= \arg z_1 + \arg z_2,\end{aligned}$$

but only in the sense that both sides represent the same infinite set of complex numbers. If we want to compare a value on the left with a value on the right, then we can merely assert that they differ by a multiple of $2\pi i$ (or 2π). (Compare with the remarks in Chap. 1, Sec. 2.1.)

Finally we discuss the inverse cosine which is obtained by solution of the equation

$$\cos z = \frac{1}{2}(e^{iz} + e^{-iz}) = w.$$

This is a quadratic equation in e^{iz} with the roots

$$e^{iz} = w \pm \sqrt{w^2 - 1},$$

and consequently

$$z = \text{arc} \cos w = -i \log (w \pm \sqrt{w^2 - 1}).$$

We can also write these values in the form

$$\text{arc} \cos w = \pm i \log (w + \sqrt{w_2 - 1}),$$

for $w + \sqrt{w^2 - 1}$ and $w - \sqrt{w^2 - 1}$ are reciprocal numbers. The infinitely many values of arc cos w reflect the evenness and periodicity of cos z. The inverse sine is most easily defined by

$$\text{arc sin } w = \frac{\pi}{2} - \text{arc cos } w.$$

It is worth emphasizing that in the theory of complex analytic functions all elementary transcendental functions can thus be expressed through e^z and its inverse $\log z$. In other words, there is essentially only one elementary transcendental function.

EXERCISES

1. For real y, show that every remainder in the series for cos y and sin y has the same sign as the leading term (this generalizes the inequalities used in the periodicity proof, Sec. 3.3).

2. Prove, for instance, that $3 < \pi < 2\sqrt{3}$.

3. Find the value of e^z for $z = -\frac{\pi i}{2}, \frac{3}{4}\pi i, \frac{2}{3}\pi i$.

4. For what values of z is e^z equal to $2, -1, i, -i/2, -1 - i, 1 + 2i$?

5. Find the real and imaginary parts of $\exp(e^z)$.

6. Determine all values of $2^i, i^i, (-1)^{2i}$.

7. Determine the real and imaginary parts of z^z.

8. Express arc tan w in terms of the logarithm.

9. Show how to define the "angles" in a triangle, bearing in mind that they should lie between 0 and π. With this definition, prove that the sum of the angles is π.

10. Show that the roots of the binomial equation $z^n = a$ are the vertices of a regular polygon (equal sides and angles).

3 ANALYTIC FUNCTIONS AS MAPPINGS

A function $w = f(z)$ may be viewed as a mapping which represents a point z by its image w. The purpose of this chapter is to study, in a preliminary way, the special properties of a mapping that is defined by an analytic function.

In order to carry out this program it is desirable to develop the underlying concepts with sufficient generality, for otherwise we would soon be forced to introduce a great number of ad hoc definitions whose mutual relationship would be far from clear. Since present-day students are exposed to abstraction and generality at quite an early stage, no apologies are needed. It is perhaps more appropriate to sound a warning that greatest possible generality should not become a purpose.

In the first section we develop the fundamentals of point set topology and metric spaces. There is no need to go very far, for our main concern is with the properties that are essential for the study of analytic functions. If the student feels that he is already thoroughly familiar with this material, he should read it only for terminology.

The author believes that proficiency in the study of analytic functions requires a mixture of geometric feeling and computational skill. The second and third sections, only loosely connected with the first, are expressly designed to develop geometric feeling by way of detailed study of elementary mappings. At the same time we try to stress rigor in geometric thinking, to the point where the geometric image becomes the guide but not the foundation of reasoning.

1. ELEMENTARY POINT SET TOPOLOGY

The branch of mathematics which goes under the name of *topology* is concerned with all questions directly or indirectly related to continuity. The term is traditionally used in a very wide sense and without strict limits. Topological considerations are extremely important for the foundation of the study of analytic functions, and the first systematic study of topology was motivated by this need.

The logical foundations of set theory belong to another discipline. Our approach will be quite naive, in keeping with the fact that all our applications will be to very familiar objects. In this limited framework no logical paradoxes can occur.

1.1. Sets and Elements. In our language a *set* will be a collection of identifiable objects, its *elements*. The reader is familiar with the notation $x \in X$ which expresses that x is an element of X (as a rule we denote sets by capital letters and elements by small letters). Two sets are equal if and only if they have the same elements. X is a subset of Y if every element of X is also an element of Y, and this relationship is indicated by $X \subset Y$ or $Y \supset X$ (we do not exclude the possibility that $X = Y$). The empty set is denoted by 0 (the possibility of confusion with the number 0 is very remote).

A set can also be referred to as a *space*, and an element as a *point*. Subsets of a given space are usually called point sets. This lends a geometric flavor to the language, but should not be taken too literally. For instance, we shall have occasion to consider spaces whose elements are functions; in that case a "point" is a function.

The *intersection* of two sets X and Y, denoted by $X \cap Y$, is formed by all points which are elements of both X and Y. The *union* $X \cup Y$ consists of all points which are elements of either X or Y, including those which are elements of both.† One can of course form the intersection and union of arbitrary collections of sets, whether finite or infinite in number.

The *complement* of a set X consists of all points which are not in X; it will be denoted by $\sim X$. We note that the complement depends on the totality of points under consideration. For instance, a set of real numbers has one complement with respect to the real line and another with respect to the complex plane. More generally, if $X \subset Y$ we can consider the relative complement $Y \sim X$ which consists of all points that are in Y but not in X (we find it clearer to use this notation only when $X \subset Y$).

† The notations XY for intersection and $X + Y$ for union are obsolete.

It is helpful to keep in mind the *distributive laws*

$$X \cup (Y \cap Z) = (X \cup Y) \cap (X \cup Z)$$
$$X \cap (Y \cup Z) = (X \cap Y) \cup (X \cap Z)$$

and the *De Morgan laws*

$$\sim(X \cup Y) = \sim X \cap \sim Y$$
$$\sim(X \cap Y) = \sim X \cup \sim Y.$$

These are purely logical identities, and they have obvious generalizations to arbitrary collections of sets.

1.2. Metric Spaces. For all considerations of limits and continuity it is essential to give a precise meaning to the terms "sufficiently near" and "arbitrarily near." In the spaces **R** and **C** of real and complex numbers, respectively, such nearness can be expressed by a quantitative condition $|x - y| < \varepsilon$. For instance, to say that a set X *contains all* x *sufficiently near to* y means that there exists an $\varepsilon < 0$ such that $x \in X$ whenever $|x - y| < \varepsilon$. Similarly, X *contains points arbitrarily near to* y if to every $\varepsilon > 0$ there exists an $x \in X$ such that $|x - y| < \varepsilon$.

What we need to describe nearness in quantitative terms is obviously a *distance* $d(x,y)$ between any two points. We say that a set S is a *metric space* if there is defined, for every pair $x \in S$, $y \in S$, a nonnegative real number $d(x,y)$ in such a way that the following conditions are fulfilled:

1. $d(x,y) = 0$ if and only if $x = y$.
2. $d(y,x) = d(x,y)$.
3. $d(x,z) \leqq d(x,y) + d(y,z)$.

The last condition is the *triangle inequality*.

For instance, **R** and **C** are metric spaces with $d(x,y) = |x - y|$. The n-dimensional euclidean space $\mathbf{R}^n$ is the set of real n-tuples

$$x = (x_1, \ldots, x_n)$$

with a distance defined by $d(x,y)^2 = \sum_1^n (x_i - y_i)^2$. We recall that we have defined a distance in the extended complex plane by

$$d(z,z') = \frac{2|z - z'|}{\sqrt{(1 + |z|^2)(1 + |z'|^2)}}$$

(see Chap. 1, Sec. 2.4); since this represents the euclidean distance between the stereographic images on the Riemann sphere, the triangle inequality is obviously fulfilled. An example of a function space is given by $C[a,b]$.

the set of all continuous functions defined on the interval $a \leqq x \leqq b$. It becomes a metric space if we define distance by $d(f,g) = \max |f(x) - g(x)|$.

In terms of distance we introduce the following terminology: The set $N_\delta(y)$ of all points $x \in S$ with $d(x,y) < \delta$ is called the δ-neighborhood of y. More essential still is the definition of an arbitrary neighborhood:

Definition 1. *A set $N \subset S$ is called a neighborhood of y if it contains a δ-neighborhood $N_\delta(y)$.*

In other words, a neighborhood of y is a set which contains all points sufficiently near to y. We use the notion of neighborhood to define *open set:*

Definition 2. *A set is an open set if it is a neighborhood of each of its elements.*

The definition is interpreted to mean that the empty set is open (the condition is fulfilled because the set has no elements). The following is an immediate consequence of the triangle inequality:

Every δ-neighborhood is an open set.

Indeed, if $z \in N_\delta(y)$, then $\delta' = \delta - d(y,z) > 0$. The triangle inequality shows that $N_{\delta'}(z) \subset N_\delta(y)$, for $d(x,z) < \delta'$ gives

$$d(x,y) < \delta' + d(y,z) = \delta.$$

Hence $N_\delta(y)$ is a neighborhood of z, and since z was any point in $N_\delta(y)$, we conclude that $N_\delta(y)$ is an open set.

For instance, in the complex plane a δ-neighborhood $N_\delta(z_0)$ is an *open disk* with center z_0 and radius δ; it consists of all complex numbers z which satisfy the inequality $|z - z_0| < \delta$.† We have just proved that it is an open set, and the reader is urged to interpret the proof in geometric terms.

It is convenient to consider not only open sets, but also *closed* sets. From a logical point of view this contributes nothing new, for by definition a set is closed if its complement is open. In positive formulation, X *is closed if it contains all points x with the property that every $N_\delta(x)$ intersects X.*

The reader should beware of a false impression that the terminology could easily convey: the terms "open" and "closed" are *not* contradictory.

† The standard notation is to write $N_\delta(z_0) = \{z; |z - z_0| < \delta\}$. We shall use this notation very sparingly. Even if the practice is slightly objectionable, we shall not hesitate to speak of "the disk $|z - z_0| < \delta$." It is to be clearly distinguished from "the circle $|z - z_0| = \delta$."

The empty set 0 and the whole space S are at the same time open and closed, and there may be other sets with the same property.

The following properties of open and closed sets are fundamental:

The intersection of a finite number of open sets is open.

The union of any collection of open sets is open.

The union of a finite number of closed sets is closed.

The intersection of any collection of closed sets is closed.

The proofs are so obvious that they can be left to the reader. It should be noted that the last two statements follow from the first two by use of the De Morgan laws.

There are many terms in common usage which are directly related to the idea of open sets. A complete list would be more confusing than helpful, and we shall limit ourselves to the following: *interior, closure, boundary, exterior.*

(i) The interior of a set X is the largest open set contained in X. It exists, for it may be characterized as the union of all open sets $\subset X$. It can also be described as the set of all points of which X is a neighborhood. We denote it by Int X.

(ii) The closure of X is the smallest closed set which contains X, or the intersection of all closed sets $\supset X$. A point belongs to the closure of X if and only if all its neighborhoods intersect X. The closure is usually denoted by X^-, infrequently by Cl X.

(iii) The boundary of X is the closure minus the interior. A point belongs to the boundary if and only if all its neighborhoods intersect both X and $\sim X$. Notation: Bd X or ∂X.

(iv) The exterior of X is the interior of $\sim X$. It is also the complement of the closure. As such it can be denoted by $\sim X^-$.

Observe that $\text{Int } X \subset X \subset X^-$ and that X is open if $\text{Int } X = X$, closed if $X^- = X$. Also, $X \subset Y$ implies $\text{Int } X \subset \text{Int } Y$, $X^- \subset Y^-$. For added convenience we shall also introduce the notions of *isolated point* and *accumulation point.* We say that $x \in X$ is an isolated point of X if x has a neighborhood whose intersection with X reduces to the point x. An accumulation point is a point of X^- which is not an isolated point. It is clear that x is an accumulation point of X if and only if every neighborhood of x contains infinitely many points from X.

EXERCISES

1. If S is a metric space with distance function $d(x,y)$, show that S with the distance function $\delta(x,y) = d(x,y)/[1 + d(x,y)]$ is also a metric space. The latter space is bounded in the sense that all distances lie under a fixed bound.

2. Suppose that there are given two distance functions $d(x,y)$ and

$d_1(x,y)$ on the same space S. They are said to be equivalent if they determine the same open sets. Show that d and d_1 are equivalent if to every $\varepsilon > 0$ there exists a $\delta < 0$ such that $d(x,y) < \delta$ implies $d_1(x,y) < \varepsilon$, and vice versa. Verify that this condition is fulfilled in the preceding exercise.

3. Show by strict application of the definition that the closure of $|z - z_0| < \delta$ is $|z - z_0| \leqq \delta$.

4. If X is the set of complex numbers whose real and imaginary parts are rational, what is Int X, X^-, ∂X?

5. It is sometimes typographically simpler to write X' for $\sim X$. With this notation, how is $X'^{-\prime}$ related to X? Show that $X^{-\prime-\prime-\prime-\prime} = X^{-\prime-\prime}$.

6. A set is said to be discrete if all its points are isolated. Show that a discrete set in **R** or **C** is countable.

7. Show that the accumulation points of any set form a closed set.

1.3. Connectedness. If E is any nonempty subset of a metric space S we may consider E as a metric space in its own right with the same distance function $d(x,y)$ as on all of S. Neighborhoods and open sets on E are defined as on any metric space, but an open set on E need not be open when regarded as a subset of S. To avoid confusion neighborhoods and open sets are often referred to as relative neighborhoods and relatively open sets. As an example, if we regard the closed interval $0 \leqq x \leqq 1$ as a subspace of R, then the semiclosed interval $0 \leqq x < 1$ is relatively open, but not open in R. Henceforth, when we say that a subset E has some specific topological property, we shall always mean that it has this property as a subspace, and its subspace topology is called the relative topology.

Intuitively speaking, a space is *connected* if it consists of a single piece. This is meaningness unless we define the statement in terms of nearness. The easiest way is to give a negative characterization: *S is not connected if there exists a partition $S = A \cup B$ into open subsets A and B.* It is understood that A and B are *disjoint* and *nonempty*. The connectedness of a space is often used in the following manner: Suppose that we are able to construct two complementary open subsets A and B of S; if S is connected, we may conclude that either A or B is empty.

A subset $E \subset S$ is said to be connected if it is connected in the relative topology. At the risk of being pedantic we repeat:

Definition 3. *A subset of a metric space is connected if it cannot be represented as the union of two disjoint relatively open sets none of which is empty.*

If E is open, a subset of E is relatively open if and only if it is open. Similarly, if E is closed, relatively closed means the same as closed. We can therefore state: *An open set is connected if it cannot be decomposed into two open sets, and a closed set is connected if it cannot be decomposed into two closed sets.* Again, none of the sets is allowed to be empty.

Trivial examples of connected sets are the empty set and any set that consists of a single point.

In the case of the real line it is possible to name all connected sets. The most important result is that the whole line is connected, and this is indeed one of the fundamental properties of the real-number system.

An *interval* is defined by an inequality of one of the four types: $a < x < b$, $a \leqq x < b$, $a < x \leqq b$, $a \leqq x \leqq b$.† For $a = -\infty$ or $b = +\infty$ this includes the semi-infinite intervals and the whole line.

Theorem 1. *The nonempty connected subsets of the real line are the intervals.*

We reproduce one of the classical proofs, based on the fact that any monotone sequence has a finite or infinite limit.

Suppose that the real line $\mathbf{R}$ is represented as the union $\mathbf{R} = A \cup B$ of two disjoint closed sets. If neither is empty we can find $a_1 \in A$ and $b_1 \in B$; we may assume that $a_1 < b_1$. We bisect the interval (a_1,b_1) and note that one of the two halves has its left end point in A and its right end point in B. We denote this interval by (a_2,b_2) and continue the process indefinitely. In this way we obtain a sequence of nested intervals (a_n,b_n) with $a_n \in A$, $b_n \in B$. The sequences $\{a_n\}$ and $\{b_n\}$ have a common limit c. Since A and B are closed c would have to be a common point of A and B. This contradiction shows that either A or B is empty, and hence $\mathbf{R}$ is connected.

With minor modifications the same proof applies to any interval.

Before proving the converse we make an important remark. Let E be an arbitrary subset of $\mathbf{R}$ and call α a *lower bound* of E if $\alpha \leqq x$ for all $x \in E$. Consider the set A of all lower bounds. It is evident that the complement of A is open. As to A itself it is easily seen that A is open whenever it does not contain any largest number. Because the line is connected, A and its complement cannot both be open unless one of them is empty. There are thus three possibilities: either A is empty, A contains a largest number, or A is the whole line. The largest number a of A, if it exists, is called the *greatest lower bound* of E; it is commonly denoted as g.l.b. x or inf x for $x \in E$. If A is empty, we agree to set $a = -\infty$, and if A is the whole line we set $a = +\infty$. With this convention every set of real numbers has a uniquely determined greatest lower bound; it is clear that $a = +\infty$ if and only if the set E is empty.

† It is common usage to denote the open interval by (a,b) and the closed interval by $[a,b]$.

The *least upper bound*, denoted as l.u.b. x or sup x for $x \in E$, is defined in a corresponding manner.†

Returning to the proof we assume that E is a connected set with the greatest lower bound a and the least upper bound b. All points of E lie between a and b, limits included. Suppose that a point ξ from the interval $a < \xi < b$ did not belong to E. Then the open sets $x < \xi$ and $x > \xi$ would cover E, and because E is connected one of them must fail to intersect E. Suppose, for instance, that no point of E lies to the left of ξ. In this case ξ would be a lower bound in contradiction with the fact that a was the greatest lower bound. The opposite assumption would lead to a similar contradiction, and we conclude that ξ must belong to E. Hence E is identical with one of the four intervals (a,b), and the proof is completed.

In the course of the proof we have introduced the notions of greatest lower bound and least upper bound. If the set is closed and if the bounds are finite, they must belong to the set, in which case they are called the minimum and the maximum. In order to be sure that the bounds are finite we must know that the set is not empty and that there is some finite lower bound and some finite upper bound. In other words, the set must lie in a finite interval; such a set is said to be *bounded*. We have proved:

Theorem 2. *Any closed and bounded nonempty set of real numbers has a minimum and a maximum.*

The structure of connected sets in the plane is not nearly so simple as in the case of the line, but the following characterization of open connected sets contains essentially all the information we shall need.

Theorem 3. *A nonempty open set in the plane is connected if and only if any two of its points can be joined by a polygon which lies in the set.*

The notion of a joining polygon is so simple that we need not give a formal definition.

We prove first that the condition is necessary. Let A be an open connected set, and choose a point $a \in A$. We denote by A_1 the subset of A whose points can be joined to a by polygons in A, and by A_2 the subset whose points cannot be so joined. Let us prove that A_1 and A_2 are both open. First, if $a_1 \in A_1$ there exists a neighborhood $|z - a_1| < \varepsilon$ contained in A. All points in this neighborhood can be joined to a_1 by a line segment, and from there to a by a polygon. Hence the whole neighborhood

† The supremum of a sequence was introduced already in Chap. 2, Sec. 2.1.

is contained in A_1, and A_1 is open. Secondly, if $a_2 \in A_2$, let $|z - a_2| < \varepsilon$ be a neighborhood contained in A. If a point in this neighborhood could be joined to a by a polygon, then a_2 could be joined to this point by a line segment, and from there to a. This is contrary to the definition of A_2, and we conclude that A_2 is open. Since A was connected either A_1 or A_2 must be empty. But A_1 contains the point a; hence A_2 is empty, and all points can be joined to a. Finally, any two points in A can be joined by way of a, and we have proved that the condition is necessary.

For future use we remark that it is even possible to join any two points by a polygon whose sides are parallel to the coordinate axes. The proof is the same.

In order to prove the sufficiency we assume that A has a representation $A = A_1 \cup A_2$ as the union of two disjoint open sets. Choose $a_1 \in A_1$, $a_2 \in A_2$ and suppose that these points can be joined by a polygon in A. One of the sides of the polygon must then join a point in A_1 to a point in A_2, and for this reason it is sufficient to consider the case where a_1 and a_2 are joined by a line segment. This segment has a parametric representation $z = a_1 + t(a_2 - a_1)$ where t runs through the interval $0 \leqq t \leqq 1$. The subsets of the interval $0 < t < 1$ which correspond to points in A_1 and A_2, respectively, are evidently open, disjoint, and nonvoid. This contradicts the connectedness of the interval, and we have proved that the condition of the theorem is sufficient.

The theorem generalizes easily to $\mathbf{R}^n$ and $\mathbf{C}^n$.

Definition 4. *A nonempty connected open set is called a region.*

By Theorem 3 the whole plane, an open disk $|z - a| < \rho$, and a half plane are regions. The same is true of any δ-neighborhood in $\mathbf{R}^n$. A region is the more-dimensional analogue of an open interval. The closure of a region is called a *closed region*. It should be observed that different regions may have the same closure.

It happens frequently that we have to analyze the structure of sets which are defined very implicitly, for instance in the course of a proof. In such cases the first step is to decompose the set into its maximal connected *components*. As the name indicates, a component of a set is a connected subset which is not contained in any larger connected subset.

Theorem 4. *Every set has a unique decomposition into components.*

If E is the given set, consider a point $a \in E$ and let $C(a)$ denote the union of all connected subsets of E that contain a. Then $C(a)$ is sure to contain a, for the set consisting of the single point a is connected. If we can show that $C(a)$ is connected, then it is a maximal connected set, in other words a component. It would follow, moreover, that any two components are either disjoint or identical, which is precisely what we want to prove. Indeed, if $c \in C(a) \cap C(b)$, then $C(a) \subset C(c)$ by the definition of $C(c)$ and the connectedness of $C(a)$. Hence $a \in C(c)$, and by the same reasoning $C(c) \subset C(a)$, so that in fact $C(a) = C(c)$. Similarly $C(b) = C(c)$, and consequently $C(a) = C(b)$. We call $C(a)$ the component of a.

Suppose that $C(a)$ were not connected. Then we could find relatively open sets $A, B \neq 0$ such that $C(a) = A \cup B$, $A \cap B = 0$. We may assume that $a \in A$ while B contains a point b. Since $b \in C(a)$ there is a connected set $E_0 \subset E$ which contains a and b. The representation $E_0 = (E_0 \cap A) \cup (E_0 \cap B)$ would be a decomposition into relatively open subsets, and since $a \in E_0 \cap A$, $b \in E_0 \cap B$ neither part would be empty. This is a contradiction, and we conclude that $C(a)$ is connected.

Theorem 5. *In $\mathbf{R}^n$ the components of any open set are open.*

This is a consequence of the fact that the δ-neighborhoods in $\mathbf{R}^n$ are connected. Consider $a \in C(a) \subset E$. If E is open it contains an $N_\delta(a)$, and because $N_\delta(a)$ is connected $N_\delta(a) \subset C(a)$. Hence $C(a)$ is open. A little more generally the assertion is true for any space S which is *locally connected.* By this we mean that any neighborhood of a point a contains a connected neighborhood of a. The proof is left to the reader.

In the case of $\mathbf{R}^n$ we can conclude, furthermore, that the number of components is countable. To see this we observe that every open set must contain a point with rational coordinates. The set of points with rational coordinates is countable, and may thus be expressed as a sequence $\{p_k\}$. For each component $C(a)$, determine the smallest k such that $p_k \in C(a)$. To different components correspond different k. We conclude that the components are in one-to-one correspondence with a subset of the natural numbers, and consequently the set of components is countable.

For instance, *every open subset of $\mathbf{R}$ is a countable union of disjoint open intervals.*

Again, it is possible to analyze the proof and thereby arrive at a more general result. We shall say that a set E is *dense* in S if $E^- = S$, and we shall say that a metric space is *separable* if there exists a countable subset which is dense in S. We are led to the following result:

In a locally connected separable space every open set is a countable union of disjoint regions.

EXERCISES

1. If $X \subset S$, show that the relatively open (closed) subsets of X are precisely those sets that can be expressed as the intersection of X with an open (closed) subset of S.

2. Show that the union of two regions is a region if and only if they have a common point.

3. Prove that the closure of a connected set is connected.

4. Let A be the set of points $(x,y) \in \mathbf{R}^2$ with $x = 0$, $|y| \leqq 1$, and let B be the set with $x > 0$, $y = \sin 1/x$. Is $A \cup B$ connected?

5. Let E be the set of points $(x,y) \in \mathbf{R}^2$ such that $0 \leqq x \leqq 1$ and either $y = 0$ or $y = 1/n$ for some positive integer n. What are the components of E? Are they all closed? Are they relatively open? Verify that E is not locally connected.

6. Prove that the components of a closed set are closed (use Ex. 3).

7. A set is said to be *discrete* if all its points are isolated. Show that a discrete set in a separable metric space is countable.

1.4. Compactness. The notions of convergent sequences and Cauchy sequences are obviously meaningful in any metric space. Indeed, we would say that $x_n \to x$ if $d(x_n,x) \to 0$, and we would say that $\{x_n\}$ is a Cauchy sequence if $d(x_n,x_m) \to 0$ as n and m tend to ∞. It is clear that every convergent sequence is a Cauchy sequence. For $\mathbf{R}$ and $\mathbf{C}$ we have proved the converse, namely that every Cauchy sequence is convergent (Chap. 2, Sec. 2.1), and it is not hard to see that this property carries over to any $\mathbf{R}^n$. In view of its importance the property deserves a special name.

Definit'on 5. *A metric space is said to be complete if every Cauchy sequence is convergent.*

A subset is complete if it is complete when regarded as a subspace. The reader will find no difficulty in proving that *a complete subset of a metric space is closed*, and that *a closed subset of a complete space is complete.*

We shall now introduce the stronger concept of *compactness.* It is stronger than completeness in the sense that every compact space or set is complete, but not conversely. As a matter of fact it will turn out that the compact subsets of $\mathbf{R}$ and $\mathbf{C}$ are the closed bounded sets. In view of this result it would be possible to dispense with the notion of compactness, at least for the purposes of this book, but this would be unwise, for it would mean shutting our eyes to the most striking property of bounded and closed sets of real or complex numbers. The outcome would be that we would have to repeat essentially the same proof in many different connections.

There are several equivalent characterizations of compactness, and it is a matter of taste which one to choose as definition. Whatever we do the uninitiated reader will feel somewhat bewildered, for he will not be able to discern the purpose of the definition. This is not surprising, for it took a whole generation of mathematicians to agree on the best approach. The consensus of present opinion is that it is best to focus the attention on the different ways in which a given set can be covered by open sets.

Let us say that a collection of open sets is an *open covering* of a set X if X is contained in the union of the open sets. A *subcovering* is a subcollection with the same property, and a *finite covering* is one that consists of a finite number of sets. The definition of compactness reads:

Definition 6. *A set X is compact if and only if every open covering of X contains a finite subcovering.*

In this context we are thinking of X as a subset of a metric space S, and the covering is by open sets of S. But if U is an open set in S, then $U \cap X$ is an open subset of X (a relatively open set), and conversely every open subset of X can be expressed in this form (Sec. 1.3, Ex. 1). For this reason it makes no difference whether we formulate the definition for a full space or for a subset.

The property in the definition is frequently referred to as the *Heine-Borel property*. Its importance lies in the fact that many proofs become particularly simple when formulated in terms of open coverings.

We prove first that every compact space is complete. Suppose that X is compact, and let $\{x_n\}$ be a Cauchy sequence in X. If y is not the limit of $\{x_n\}$ there exists an $\varepsilon > 0$ such that $d(x_n,y) > 2\varepsilon$ for infinitely many n. Determine n_0 such that $d(x_m,x_n) < \varepsilon$ for $m, n \geqq n_0$. We choose a fixed $n \geqq n_0$ for which $d(x_n,y) > 2\varepsilon$. Then $d(x_m,y) \geqq d(x_n,y) - d(x_m,x_n) > \varepsilon$ for all $m \geqq n_0$. It follows that the ε-neighborhood $N_\varepsilon(y)$ contains only finitely many x_n (better: contains x_n only for finitely many n).

Consider now the collection of all open sets U which contain only finitely many x_n. If $\{x_n\}$ is not convergent, it follows by the preceding reasoning that this collection is an open covering of X. Therefore it must contain a finite subcovering, formed by $U_1, \ldots, U_N$. But that is clearly impossible, for since each U_i contains only finitely many x_n it would follow that the given sequence is finite.

Secondly, a compact set is necessarily *bounded* (a metric space is bounded if all distances lie under a finite bound). To see this, choose a point x_0 and consider all neighborhoods $N_\rho(x_0)$†. This is an open covering, and if X is compact it contains a finite subcovering; in other words, $X \subset N_{\rho_1}(x_0) \cup \cdots \cup N_{\rho_m}(x_0)$ which means the same as $X \subset N_\rho(x_0)$ with $\rho = \max(\rho_1, \ldots, \rho_m)$. For any $x, y \in X$ it follows that $d(x,y) \leqq d(x,x_0) + d(y,x_0) < 2\rho$, and we have proved that X is bounded.

But boundedness is not all we can prove. It is convenient to define a stronger property, called *total boundedness:*

Definition 7. *A set X is totally bounded if, for every $\varepsilon > 0$, X can be covered by finitely many ε-neighborhoods.*

This is certainly true of any compact set. For the collection of all ε-neighborhoods is an open covering, and the compactness implies that we can select finitely many that cover X. We observe that a totally bounded set is necessarily bounded, for if $X \subset N_\varepsilon(x_1) \cup \cdots \cup N_\varepsilon(x_m)$ then any two points of X have a distance $< 2\varepsilon + \max d(x_i,x_j)$. (The preceding proof that any compact set is bounded becomes redundant; it was included because of its elementary nature.)

We have now proved one part of the following theorem:

Theorem 6. *A set is compact if and only if it is complete and totally bounded.*

To prove the other part, assume that the metric space S is complete and totally bounded. Suppose that there exists an open covering which does not contain any finite subcovering. Set $\varepsilon_n = 2^{-n}$. We know that S can be covered by finitely many ε_1-neighborhoods. If each had a finite subcovering the same would be true of S; hence there exists an $N_{\varepsilon_1}(x_1)$ which does not admit a finite subcovering. Because $N_{\varepsilon_1}(x_1)$ is itself totally bounded we can find an $x_2 \in N_{\varepsilon_1}(x_1)$ such that $N_{\varepsilon_2}(x_2)$ has no finite subcovering.‡ It is clear how to continue the construction: we obtain a sequence $\{x_n\}$ with the property that $N_{\varepsilon_n}(x_n)$ has no finite subcovering and $x_{n+1} \in N_{\varepsilon_n}(x_n)$. The second property means that $d(x_n,x_{n+1}) < \varepsilon_n$, and hence $d(x_n,x_{n+p}) < \varepsilon_n + \varepsilon_{n+1} + \cdots + \varepsilon_{n+p-1} < 2^{-n+1}$. It follows that $\{x_n\}$ is a Cauchy sequence. It converges to a limit y, and this y belongs to one of the open sets U in the given covering. Because U is open it contains

† We are used to consider only small neighborhoods, but here we must include the neighborhoods with large ρ. From this point of view the name "ρ-spheroid" would be preferable.

‡ Here we are using the fact that any subset of a totally bounded set is totally bounded. The reader should prove this.

an $N_\delta(y)$. Choose n so large that $d(x_n,y) < \delta/2$ and $\varepsilon_n < \delta/2$. Then $N_{\varepsilon_n}(x_n) \subset N_\delta(y)$, for $d(x,x_n) < \varepsilon_n$ implies $d(x,y) \leqq d(x,x_n) + d(x_n,y) < \delta$. Therefore $N_{\varepsilon_n}(x_n)$ admits a finite subcovering, namely by the set U. This is a contradiction, and we conclude that S has the Heine-Borel property.

Corollary. *A subset of* **R** *or* **C** *is compact if and only if it is closed and bounded.*

We have already mentioned this particular consequence. In one direction the conclusion is immediate: We know that a compact set is bounded and complete; but **R** and **C** are complete, and complete subsets of a complete space are closed. For the opposite conclusion we need to show that every bounded set in **R** or **C** is totally bounded. Let us take the case of **C**. If X is bounded it is contained in a disk, and hence in a square. The square can be subdivided into a finite number of squares with arbitrarily small side, and the squares can in turn be covered by disks with arbitrarily small radius. This proves that X is totally bounded, except for a small point that should not be glossed over. When Definition 7 is applied to a subset $X \subset S$ it is slightly ambiguous, for it is not clear whether the ε-neighborhoods should be with respect to X or with respect to S; that is, it is not clear whether we require their centers to lie on X. It happens that this is of no avail. In fact, suppose that we have covered X by ε-neighborhoods whose centers do not necessarily lie on X. If such a neighborhood does not meet X it is superfluous, and can be dropped. If it does contain a point from X, then we can replace it by a 2ε-neighborhood around that point, and we obtain a finite covering by 2ε-neighborhoods with centers on X. For this reason the ambiguity is only apparent, and our proof that bounded subsets of C are totally bounded is valid.

There is a third characterization of compact sets. It deals with the notion of *limit point* (sometimes called *cluster value*): We say that y is a limit point of the sequence $\{x_n\}$ if there exists a subsequence $\{x_{n_k}\}$ that converges to y. A limit point is almost the same as an accumulation point of the set formed by the points x_n, except that a sequence permits repetitions of the same point. If y is a limit point, every neighborhood of y contains infinitely many x_n. The converse is also true. Indeed, suppose that $\varepsilon_k \to 0$. If every $N_{\varepsilon_k}(y)$ contains infinitely many x_n we can choose subscripts n_k, by induction, in such a way that $x_{n_k} \in N_{\varepsilon_k}(y)$ and $n_{k+1} > n_k$. It is clear that $\{x_{n_k}\}$ converges to y.

Theorem 7. *A metric space is compact if and only if every infinite sequence has a limit point.*

This theorem is usually referred to as the *Bolzano-Weierstrass theorem.* The original formulation was that every bounded sequence of complex numbers has a convergent subsequence. It came to be recognized as an important theorem precisely because of the role it plays in the theory of analytic functions.

The first part of the proof is a repetition of an earlier argument. If y is not a limit point of $\{x_n\}$ it has a neighborhood which contains only finitely many x_n (abbreviated version of the correct phrase). If there were no limit points the open sets containing only finitely many x_n would form an open covering. In the compact case we could select a finite subcovering, and it would follow that the sequence is finite. The previous time we used this reasoning was to prove that a compact space is complete. We showed in essence that every sequence has a limit point, and then we observed that a Cauchy sequence with a limit point is necessarily convergent. For strict economy of thought it would thus have been better to prove Theorem 7 before Theorem 6, but we preferred to emphasize the importance of total boundedness as early as possible.

It remains to prove the converse. In the first place it is clear that the Bolzano-Weierstrass property implies completeness. Indeed, we just pointed out that a Cauchy sequence with a limit point must be convergent. Suppose now that the space is not totally bounded. Then there exists an $\varepsilon > 0$ such that the space cannot be covered by finitely many ε-neighborhoods. We construct a sequence $\{x_n\}$ as follows: x_1 is arbitrary, and when $x_1, \ldots, x_n$ have been selected we choose x_{n+1} so that it does not lie in $N_\varepsilon(x_1) \cup \cdots \cup N_\varepsilon(x_n)$. This is always possible because these neighborhoods do not cover the whole space. But it is clear that $\{x_n\}$ has no convergent subsequence, for $d(x_m,x_n) > \varepsilon$ for all m and n. We conclude that the Bolzano-Weierstrass property implies total boundedness. In view of Theorem 6 that is what we had to prove.

The reader should reflect on the fact that we have exhibited three characterizations of compactness whose logical equivalence is not at all trivial. It should be clear that results of this kind are particularly valuable for the purpose of presenting proofs as concisely as possible.

EXERCISES

1. Give an alternate proof of the fact that every bounded sequence of complex numbers has a convergent subsequence (for instance by use of the limes inferior).

2. Show that the Heine-Borel property can also be expressed in the following manner: Every collection of closed sets with an empty intersection contains a finite subcollection with empty intersection.

3. Use compactness to prove that a closed bounded set of real numbers has a maximum.

4. If $E_1 \supset E_2 \supset E_3 \supset \cdots$ is a decreasing sequence of nonempty compact sets, then the intersection $\bigcap_1^\infty E_n$ is not empty (Cantor's lemma). Show by example that this need not be true if the sets are merely closed.

5. Let S be the set of all sequences $x = \{x_n\}$ of real numbers such that only a finite number of the x_n are $\neq 0$. Define $d(x,y) = \max |x_n - y_n|$. Is the space complete? Show that the δ-neighborhoods are not totally bounded.

1.5. Continuous Functions. We shall consider functions f which are defined on a metric space S and have values in another metric space S'. Functions are also referred to as *mappings:* we say that f maps S into S', and we write $f:S \to S'$. Naturally, we shall be mainly concerned with real- or complex-valued functions; occasionally the latter are allowed to take values in the extended complex plane, ordinary distance being replaced by distance on the Riemann sphere.

The space S is the *domain* of the function. We are of course free to consider functions f whose domain is only a subset of S, in which case the domain is regarded as a subspace. In most cases it is safe to slur over the distinction: a function on S and its restriction to a subset are usually denoted by the same symbol. If $X \subset S$ the set of all values $f(x)$ for $x \in S$ is called the *image* of X under f, and it is denoted by $f(X)$. The *inverse image* $f^{-1}(X')$ of $X' \subset S'$ consists of all $x \in S$ such that $f(x) \in X'$. Observe that $f(f^{-1}(X')) \subset X'$, and $f^{-1}(f(X)) \supset X$.

The definition of a continuous function needs practically no modification: f is continuous at a if to every $\varepsilon > 0$ there exists $\delta > 0$ such that $d(x,a) < \delta$ implies $d'(f(x),f(a)) < \varepsilon$. We are mainly concerned with functions that are continuous at all points in the domain of definition. The following characterizations are immediate consequences of the definition:

A function is continuous if and only if the inverse image of every open set is open.

A function is continuous if and only if the inverse image of every closed set is closed.

If f is not defined on all of S, the words "open" and "closed," when referring to the inverse image, should of course be interpreted relatively to the domain of f. It is very important to observe that these properties hold only for the inverse image, not for the direct image. For instance the mapping $f(x) = x^2/(1 + x^2)$ of $\mathbf{R}$ into $\mathbf{R}$ has the image $f(\mathbf{R}) = \{y; 0 \leq y < 1\}$ which is neither open nor closed. In this example $f(\mathbf{R})$

fails to be closed because $\mathbf{R}$ is not compact. In fact, the following is true:

Theorem 8. *Under a continuous mapping the image of every compact set is compact, and consequently closed.*

Suppose that f is defined and continuous on the compact set X. Consider a covering of $f(X)$ by open sets U. The inverse images $f^{-1}(U)$ are open and form a covering of X. Because X is compact we can select a finite subcovering: $X \subset f^{-1}(U_1) \cup \cdots \cup f^{-1}(U_m)$. It follows that $f(X) \subset U_1 \cup \cdots \cup U_m$, and we have proved that $f(X)$ is compact.

Corollary. *A continuous real-valued function on a compact set has a maximum and a minimum.*

The image is a closed bounded subset of $\mathbf{R}$. The existence of a maximum and a minimum follows by Theorem 2.

Theorem 9. *Under a continuous mapping the image of any connected set is connected.*

We may assume that f is defined and continuous on the whole space S, and that $f(S)$ is all of S'. Suppose that $S' = A \cup B$ where A and B are open and disjoint. Then $S = f^{-1}(A) \cup f^{-1}(B)$ is a representation of S as a union of disjoint open sets. If S is connected either $f^{-1}(A) = 0$ or $f^{-1}(B) = 0$, and hence $A = 0$ or $B = 0$. We conclude that S' is connected.

A typical application is the assertion that a real-valued function which is continuous and never zero on a connected set is either always positive or always negative. In fact, the image is connected, and hence an interval. But an interval which contains positive and negative numbers also contains zero.

A mapping $f: S \to S'$ is said to be *one to one* if $f(x) = f(y)$ only for $x = y$; it is said to be *onto* if $f(S) = S'$.† A mapping with both these properties has an inverse f^{-1}, defined on S'; it satisfies $f^{-1}(f(x)) = x$ and $f(f^{-1}(x')) = x'$. In this situation, if f and f^{-1} are both continuous we say that f is a *topological mapping* or a *homeomorphism*. A property of a set which is shared by all topological images is called a *topological property*. For instance, we have proved that compactness and connectedness are topological properties (Theorems 8 and 9). In this connection it is per-

† These linguistically clumsy terms can be replaced by *injective* (for one to one) and *surjective* (for onto). A mapping with both properties is called *bijective*.

haps useful to point out that the property of being an open subset is not topological. If $X \subset S$ and $Y \subset S'$ and if X is homeomorphic to Y there is no reason why X and Y should be simultaneously open. It happens to be true if $S = S' = \mathbf{R}^n$ (*invariance of the region*), but this is a deep theorem that we shall not need.

The notion of *uniform continuity* will be in constant use. Quite generally, a condition is said to hold uniformly with respect to a parameter if it can be expressed by inequalities which do not involve the parameter. Accordingly, a function f is said to be *uniformly continuous* on X if, to every $\varepsilon > 0$, there exists a $\delta > 0$ such that $d'(f(x_1),f(x_2)) < \varepsilon$ for all pairs (x_1,x_2) with $d(x_1,x_2) < \delta$. The emphasis is on the fact that δ is not allowed to depend on x_1.

Theorem 10. *On a compact set every continuous function is uniformly continuous.*

The proof is typical of the way the Heine-Borel property can be used. Suppose that f is continuous on a compact set X. Every $y \in X$ has a neighborhood $N_\rho(y)$ such that $d'(f(x),f(y)) < \varepsilon/2$ for $x \in N_\rho(y)$; here ρ may depend on y. Consider the open covering of X by the smaller neighborhoods $N_{\rho/2}(y)$. We can find a finite subcovering: $X \subset N_{\rho_1/2}(y_1) \cup \cdots \cup N_{\rho_m/2}(y_m)$. Let δ be the smallest of the numbers $\rho_1/2, \ldots, \rho_m/2$. Consider a pair (x_1,x_2) with $d(x_1,x_2) < \delta$. There exists a y_k with $d(x_1,y_k) < \rho_k/2$, and we obtain $d(x_2,y_k) < \rho_k/2 + \delta \leqq \rho_k$. Hence $d'(f(x_1),f(y_k)) < \varepsilon/2$ and $d'(f(x_2),f(y_k)) < \varepsilon/2$ so that $d'(f(x_1),f(x_2)) < \varepsilon$ as desired.

On sets which are not compact some continuous functions are uniformly continuous and others are not. For instance, the function z is uniformly continuous on the whole complex plane, but the function z^2 is not.

EXERCISES

1. Construct a topological mapping of the open disk $|z| < 1$ onto the whole plane.

2. Prove that a subset of the real line which is topologically equivalent to an open interval is an open interval. (Consider the effect of removing a point.)

3. Prove that every continuous one-to-one mapping of a compact space is topological. (Show that closed sets are mapped on closed sets.)

4. Let X and Y be closed sets in a complete metric space, at least one of them compact. Prove that there exist $x \in X$, $y \in Y$ such that $d(x,y)$ is a minimum.

5. Which of the following functions are uniformly continuous on the whole real line: $\sin x$, $x \sin x$, $x \sin (x^2)$, $|x|^{\frac{1}{2}} \sin x$?

1.6. Topological Spaces. It is not necessary, and not always convenient, to express nearness in terms of distance. The observant reader will have noticed that most results in the preceding sections were formulated in terms of open sets. True enough, we used distances to define open sets, but there is really no strong reason to do this. If we decide to consider the open sets as the primary objects we must postulate axioms that they have to satisfy. The following axioms lead to the commonly accepted definition of a *topological space:*

Definition 8. *A topological space is a set T together with a collection of its subsets, called open sets. The following conditions have to be fulfilled:*

(i) *The empty set* 0 *and the whole space T are open sets.*
(ii) *The intersection of any two open sets is an open set.*
(iii) *The union of an arbitrary collection of open sets is an open set.*

We recognize at once that this terminology is consistent with our earlier definition of an open subset of a metric space. Indeed, properties (ii) and (iii) were strongly emphasized, and (i) is trivial.

Closed sets are the complements of open sets, and it is immediately clear how to define interior, closure, boundary, and so on. Neighborhoods could be avoided, but they are rather convenient: N is a neighborhood of x if there exists an open set U such that $x \in U$ and $U \subset N$.

Connectedness was defined purely by means of open sets. Hence the definition carries over to topological spaces, and the theorems remain true. The Heine-Borel property is also one that deals only with open sets. Therefore it makes perfect sense to speak of a compact topological space. However, Theorem 6 becomes meaningless, and Theorem 7 becomes false.

As a matter of fact, the first serious difficulty we encounter is with convergent sequences. The definition is clear: we say that $x_n \to x$ if every neighborhood of x contains all but a finite number of the x_n. But if $x_n \to x$ and $x_n \to y$ we are not able to prove that $x = y$. This awkward situation is remedied by introducing a new axiom which characterizes the topological space as a *Hausdorff space:*

Definition 9. *A topological space is called a Hausdorff space if any two distinct points are contained in disjoint open sets.*

In other words, if $x \neq y$ we require the existence of open sets U, V such that $x \in U$, $y \in V$ and $U \cap V = 0$. In the presence of this condition it is obvious that the limit of a convergent sequence is unique. We shall never in this book have occasion to consider a space that is not a Hausdorff space.

This is not the place to give examples of topologies that cannot be derived from a distance function. Such examples would necessarily be very complicated and would not further the purposes of this book. The point is that it may be unnatural to introduce a distance in situations when one is not really needed. The reason for including this section has been to alert the reader that distances are dispensable.

2. CONFORMALITY

We now return to our original setting where all functions and variables are restricted to real or complex numbers. The role of metric spaces will seem disproportionately small: all we actually need are some simple applications of connectedness and compactness.

The whole section is mainly descriptive. It centers on the geometric consequences of the existence of a derivative.

2.1. Arcs and Closed Curves. The equation of an *arc* γ in the plane is most conveniently given in parametric form $x = x(t)$, $y = y(t)$ where t runs through an interval $\alpha \leqq t \leqq \beta$ and $x(t)$, $y(t)$ are continuous functions. We can also use the complex notation $z = z(t) = x(t) + iy(t)$ which has several advantages.

Considered as a point set an arc is thus the image of a closed finite interval under a continuous mapping. As such it is compact and connected. However, an arc is not merely a set of points, but very essentially also a succession of points, ordered by increasing values of the parameter. If a nondecreasing function $t = \varphi(\tau)$ maps an interval $\alpha' \leqq \tau \leqq \beta'$ onto $\alpha \leqq t \leqq \beta$, then $z = z(\varphi(\tau))$ defines the same succession of points as $z = z(t)$. We say that the first equation arises from the second by a *change of parameter*. The change is *reversible* if and only if $\varphi(\tau)$ is strictly increasing. For instance, the equation $z = t^2 + it^4$, $0 \leqq t \leqq 1$ arises by a reversible change of parameter from the equation $z = t + it^2$, $0 \leqq t \leqq 1$. A change of the parametric interval (α,β) can always be brought about by a *linear* change of parameter, which is one of the form $t = a\tau + b$, $a > 0$.

Logically, the simplest course is to consider two arcs as different as soon as they are given by different equations, regardless of whether one equation may arise from the other by a change of parameter. In following this course, as we will, it is important to show that certain properties of arcs are invariant under a change of parameter. For instance, the *initial* and *terminal point* of an arc remain the same after a change of parameter.

If the derivative $z'(t) = x'(t) + iy'(t)$ exists and is $\neq 0$, the arc γ has a *tangent* whose direction is determined by $\arg z'(t)$. We shall say that the arc is *differentiable* if $z'(t)$ exists and is continuous (the term continuously differentiable is too unwieldy); if, in addition, $z'(t) \neq 0$ the arc is said to be *regular*. An arc is *piecewise differentiable* or *piecewise regular* if the same conditions hold except for a finite number of values t; at these points $z(t)$ shall still be continuous with left and right derivatives which are equal to the left and right limits of $z'(t)$ and, in the case of a piecewise regular arc, $\neq 0$.

The differentiable or regular character of an arc is invariant under the change of parameter $t = \varphi(\tau)$ provided that $\varphi'(\tau)$ is continuous and, for regularity, $\neq 0$. When this is the case, we speak of a differentiable or regular change of parameter.

An arc is *simple*, or a *Jordan arc*, if $z(t_1) = z(t_2)$ only for $t_1 = t_2$. An arc is a *closed curve* if the end points coincide: $z(\alpha) = z(\beta)$. For closed curves a *shift* of the parameter is defined as follows: If the original equation is $z = z(t)$, $\alpha \leqq t \leqq \beta$, we choose a point t_0 from the interval (α,β) and define a new closed curve whose equation is $z = z(t)$ for $t_0 \leqq t \leqq \beta$ and $z = z(t - \beta + \alpha)$ for $\beta \leqq t \leqq t_0 + \beta - \alpha$. The purpose of the shift is to get rid of the distinguished position of the initial point. The correct definitions of a differentiable or regular closed curve and of a *simple closed curve* (or *Jordan curve*) are obvious.

The *opposite arc* of $z = z(t)$, $\alpha \leqq t \leqq \beta$, is the arc $z = z(-t)$, $-\beta \leqq t \leqq -\alpha$. Opposite arcs are sometimes denoted by γ and $-\gamma$, sometimes by γ and γ^{-1}, depending on the connection. A constant function $z(t)$ defines a *point curve*.

A circle C, originally defined as a locus $|z - a| = r$, can be considered as a closed curve with the equation $z = a + re^{it}$, $0 \leqq t \leqq 2\pi$. We will use this standard parametrization whenever a finite circle is introduced. This convention saves us from writing down the equation each time it is needed; also, and this is its most important purpose, it serves as a definite rule to distinguish between C and $-C$.

2.2. Analytic Functions in Regions. When we consider the derivative

$$f'(z) = \lim_{h \to 0} \frac{f(z + h) - f(z)}{h}$$

of a complex-valued function, defined on a set A in the complex plane, it is of course understood that $z \in A$ and that the limit is with respect to values

h such that $z + h \in A$. The existence of the derivative will therefore have different meaning depending on whether z is an interior point or a boundary point of A. The only simple way to avoid this is to insist that all analytic functions be defined on open sets. We shall find that further advantages ensue if every analytic function is defined in a region.

We give a formal statement of the definition:

Definition 10. *A complex-valued function $f(z)$ is said to be analytic in the region Ω if it is defined and has a derivative at each point of Ω.*

According to this definition an analytic function in Ω is always single-valued. It is very important that the definition is localized to a fixed region Ω, and it is not permissible to speak of an analytic function without specifying the region in which it is considered. Sometimes the region is clearly implied by the context, and in such cases the explicit reference may be omitted.

For greater flexibility of the language it is desirable to introduce the following complement to Definition 11:

Definition 11. *A function $f(z)$ is analytic on an arbitrary point set A if it is analytic in some region which contains A.*

It is clear that the last definition is merely an agreement to use a convenient terminology. This is a case in which the region Ω need not be explicitly mentioned, for it will be found that the specific choice of Ω is immaterial as long as it contains A. A typical application is the use of the phrase: "Let $f(z)$ be analytic at z_0." It means that a function $f(z)$ is defined and has a derivative in some neighborhood of z_0 which need not be specified.

Although our definition requires all analytic functions to be single-valued, it is possible to consider such multiple-valued functions as $\sqrt{z}$, $\log z$, or $\arccos z$, provided that they are restricted to a definite region in which it is possible to select a single-valued and analytic branch of the function.

For instance, we may choose for Ω the complement of the negative real axis $z \leqq 0$; this set is indeed open and connected. In Ω one and only one of the values of $\sqrt{z}$ has a positive real part. With this choice $w = \sqrt{z}$ becomes a single-valued function in Ω; let us prove that it is continuous. Choose two points $z_1, z_2 \in \Omega$ and denote the corresponding values of w by $w_1 = u_1 + iv_1$, $w_2 = u_2 + iv_2$ with $u_1, u_2 > 0$. Then

$$|z_1 - z_2| = |w_1^2 - w_2^2| = |w_1 - w_2| \cdot |w_1 + w_2|$$

and $|w_1 + w_2| \geqq u_1 + u_2 > u_1$. Hence

$$|w_1 - w_2| < \frac{|z_1 - z_2|}{u_1}$$

and it follows that $w = \sqrt{z}$ is continuous at z_1. Once the continuity is established the analyticity follows by derivation of the inverse function $z = w^2$. Indeed, with the notations used in calculus $\Delta z \to 0$ implies $\Delta w \to 0$. Therefore,

$$\lim_{\Delta z \to 0} \frac{\Delta w}{\Delta z} = \lim_{\Delta w \to 0} \frac{\Delta w}{\Delta z}$$

and we obtain

$$\frac{dw}{dz} = \frac{1}{\dfrac{dz}{dw}} = \frac{1}{2w} = \frac{1}{2\sqrt{z}}$$

with the same branch of $\sqrt{z}$.

In the case of $\log z$ we can use the same region Ω, obtained by excluding the negative real axis, and define the *principal branch* of the logarithm by the condition $|\text{Im} \log z| < \pi$. Again, the continuity must be proved, but this time we have no algebraic identity at our disposal, and we are forced to use a more general reasoning. Denote the principal branch by $w = u + iv = \log z$. For a given point $w_1 = u_1 + iv_1$, $|v_1| < \pi$, and a given $\varepsilon > 0$, consider the set A in the w-plane which is defined by the inequalities $|w - w_1| \geqq \varepsilon$, $|v| \leqq \pi$, $|u - u_1| \leqq \log 2$. This set is closed and bounded, and for sufficiently small ε it is not empty. The continuous function $|e^w - e^{w_1}|$ has consequently a minimum ρ on A (Theorem 8, Corollary). This minimum is positive, for A does not contain any point $w_1 + n \cdot 2\pi i$. Choose $\delta = \min(\rho, \frac{1}{2}e^{u_1})$, and assume that

$$|z_1 - z_2| = |e^{w_1} - e^{w_2}| < \delta.$$

Then w_2 cannot lie in A, for this would make $|e^{w_1} - e^{w_2}| \geqq \rho \geqq \delta$. Neither is it possible that $u_2 < u_1 - \log 2$ or $u_2 > u_1 + \log 2$; in the former case we would obtain $|e^{w_1} - e^{w_2}| \geqq e^{u_1} - e^{u_2} > \frac{1}{2}e^{u_1} \geqq \delta$, and in the latter case $|e^{w_1} - e^{w_2}| \geqq e^{u_2} - e^{u_1} > e^{u_1} > \delta$. Hence w_2 must lie in the disk $|w - w_1| < \varepsilon$, and we have proved that w is a continuous function of z. From the continuity we conclude as above that the derivative exists and equals $1/z$.

The infinitely many values of $\text{arc} \cos z$ are the same as the values of $i \log (z + \sqrt{z^2 - 1})$. In this case we restrict z to the complement Ω' of the half-lines $x \leqq 0$, $y = 0$ and $x \geqq 1$, $y = 0$. Since $1 - z^2$ is never real and $\leqq 0$ in Ω', we can define $\sqrt{1 - z^2}$ as in the first example and then set $\sqrt{z^2 - 1} = i\sqrt{1 - z^2}$. Moreover, $z + \sqrt{z^2 - 1}$ cannot be negative or zero in Ω'; indeed, since $z + \sqrt{z^2 - 1}$ and $z - \sqrt{z^2 - 1}$ are reciprocal. $z + \sqrt{z^2 - 1} < 0$ would imply $z - \sqrt{z^2 - 1} < 0$ and hence, $2z < 0$. We can thus define an analytic branch of $\log (z + \sqrt{z^2 - 1})$ whose imaginary part lies between $-\pi$ and π. In this way we obtain a single-valued analytic function

$$\arccos z = i \log (z + \sqrt{z^2 - 1})$$

in Ω' whose derivative is

$$D \arccos z = i \frac{1}{z + \sqrt{z^2 - 1}} \left(1 + \frac{z}{\sqrt{z^2 - 1}}\right) = \frac{1}{\sqrt{1 - z^2}}$$

where $\sqrt{1 - z^2}$ has a positive real part.

There is nothing unique about the way in which the region and the single-valued branches have been chosen in these examples. Therefore, each time we consider a function such as $\log z$ the choice of the branch has to be specified. It is a fundamental fact that it is *impossible* to define a single-valued and analytic branch of $\log z$ in certain regions. This will be proved in the chapter on integration.

All the results of Chap. II, Sec. 1.2 remain valid for functions which are analytic in a region. In particular, the real and imaginary parts of an analytic function in Ω satisfy the Cauchy-Riemann equations

$$\frac{\partial u}{\partial x} = \frac{\partial v}{\partial y}, \qquad \frac{\partial u}{\partial y} = -\frac{\partial v}{\partial x}.$$

Conversely, if u and v satisfy these equations in Ω, and if the partial derivatives are continuous, then $u + iv$ is an analytic function in Ω.

An analytic function in Ω *degenerates* if it reduces to a constant. In the following theorem we shall list some simple conditions which have this consequence:

Theorem 11. *An analytic function in a region Ω whose derivative vanishes identically must reduce to a constant. The same is true if either the real part, the imaginary part, the modulus, or the argument is constant.*

The vanishing of the derivative implies that $\partial u/\partial x$, $\partial u/\partial y$, $\partial v/\partial x$, $\partial v/\partial y$ are all zero. It follows that u and v are constant on any line segment in Ω which is parallel to one of the coordinate axes. In Sec. 1.3 we remarked, in connection with Theorem 3, that any two points in a region can be joined within the region by a polygon whose sides are parallel to the axes. We conclude that $u + iv$ is constant.

If u or v is constant,

$$f'(z) = \frac{\partial u}{\partial x} - i\frac{\partial u}{\partial y} = \frac{\partial v}{\partial y} + i\frac{\partial v}{\partial x} = 0,$$

and hence $f(z)$ must be constant. If $u^2 + v^2$ is constant, we obtain

$$u\frac{\partial u}{\partial x} + v\frac{\partial v}{\partial x} = 0$$

and

$$u\frac{\partial u}{\partial y} + v\frac{\partial v}{\partial y} = -u\frac{\partial v}{\partial x} + v\frac{\partial u}{\partial x} = 0.$$

These equations permit the conclusion $\partial u/\partial x = \partial v/\partial x = 0$ unless the determinant $u^2 + v^2$ vanishes. But if $u^2 + v^2 = 0$ at a single point it is constantly zero and $f(z)$ vanishes identically. Hence $f(z)$ is in any case a constant.

Finally, if $\arg f(z)$ is constant, we can set $u = kv$ with constant k (unless v is identically zero). But $u - kv$ is the real part of $(1 + ik)f$, and we conclude again that f must reduce to a constant.

EXERCISES

1. Give a precise definition of a single-valued branch of $\sqrt{1+z} + \sqrt{1-z}$ in a suitable region, and prove that it is analytic.

2. Same problem for $\log \log z$.

3. Suppose that $f(z) = u + iv$ is analytic in a region Ω and that $F(u,v) = 0$ where F is a real-valued function with continuous first derivatives. Under what condition can one conclude that $f(z)$ is constant?

4. Suppose that $f(z)$ is analytic and satisfies the condition $|f(z)^2 - 1| < 1$ in a region Ω. Show that either $\operatorname{Re} f(z) > 0$ or $\operatorname{Re} f(z) < 0$ throughout Ω.

2.3. Conformal Mapping. Suppose that an arc γ with the equation $z = z(t)$, $\alpha \leqq t \leqq \beta$, is contained in a region Ω, and let $f(z)$ be defined and continuous in Ω. Then the equation $w = w(t) = f(z(t))$ defines an arc γ' in the w-plane which may be called the *image* of γ.

Consider the case of an $f(z)$ which is analytic in Ω. If $z'(t)$ exists, we find that $w'(t)$ also exists and is determined by

$$w'(t) = f'(z(t))z'(t). \tag{1}$$

We will investigate the meaning of this equation at a point $z_0 = z(t_0)$ with $z'(t_0) \neq 0$ and $f'(z_0) \neq 0$.

The first conclusion is that $w'(t_0) \neq 0$. Hence γ' has a tangent at

$w_0 = f(z_0)$, and its direction is determined by

$$\arg w'(t_0) = \arg f'(z_0) + \arg z'(t_0). \tag{2}$$

This relation asserts that the angle between the directed tangents to γ at z_0 and to γ' at w_0 is equal to $\arg f'(z_0)$. It is hence independent of the curve γ. For this reason curves through z_0 which are tangent to each other are mapped onto curves with a common tangent at w_0. Moreover, two curves which form an angle at z_0 are mapped upon curves forming the same angle, in sense as well as in size. In view of this property the mapping by $w = f(z)$ is said to be *conformal* at all points with $f'(z) \neq 0$.

A related property of the mapping is derived by consideration of the modulus $|f'(z_0)|$. We have

$$\lim_{z \to z_0} \frac{|f(z) - f(z_0)|}{|z - z_0|} = |f'(z_0)|,$$

and this means that any small line segment with one end point at z_0 is, in the limit, contracted or expanded in the ratio $|f'(z_0)|$. In other words, the linear change of scale at z_0, effected by the transformation $w = f(z)$, is independent of the direction. In general this change of scale will vary from point to point.

Conversely, it is clear that both kinds of conformality together imply the existence of $f'(z_0)$. It is less obvious that each kind will separately imply the same result, at least under additional regularity assumptions.

To be more precise, let us assume that the partial derivatives $\partial f/\partial x$ and $\partial f/\partial y$ are continuous. Under this condition the derivative of $w(t) = f(z(t))$ can be expressed in the form

$$w'(t_0) = \frac{\partial f}{\partial x} x'(t_0) + \frac{\partial f}{\partial y} y'(t_0)$$

where the partial derivatives are taken at z_0. In terms of $z'(t_0)$ this can be rewritten as

$$w'(t_0) = \frac{1}{2}\left(\frac{\partial f}{\partial x} - i\frac{\partial f}{\partial y}\right) z'(t_0) + \frac{1}{2}\left(\frac{\partial f}{\partial x} + i\frac{\partial f}{\partial y}\right) \overline{z'(t_0)}.$$

If angles are preserved, $\arg [w'(t_0)/z'(t_0)]$ must be independent of $\arg z'(t_0)$. The expression

$$\frac{1}{2}\left(\frac{\partial f}{\partial x} - i\frac{\partial f}{\partial y}\right) + \frac{1}{2}\left(\frac{\partial f}{\partial x} + i\frac{\partial f}{\partial y}\right) \frac{\overline{z'(t_0)}}{z'(t_0)} \tag{3}$$

must therefore have a constant argument. As $\arg z'(t_0)$ is allowed to vary, the point represented by (3) describes a circle having the radius

$\frac{1}{2}|(\partial f/\partial x) + i(\partial f/\partial y)|$. The argument cannot be constant on this circle unless its radius vanishes, and hence we must have

$$\frac{\partial f}{\partial x} = -i\frac{\partial f}{\partial y} \tag{4}$$

which is the complex form of the Cauchy-Riemann equations.

Quite similarly, the condition that the change of scale shall be the same in all directions implies that the expression (3) has a constant modulus. On a circle the modulus is constant only if the radius vanishes or if the center lies at the origin. In the first case we obtain (4), and in the second case

$$\frac{\partial f}{\partial x} = i\frac{\partial f}{\partial y}.$$

The last equation expresses the fact that $\overline{f(z)}$ is analytic. A mapping by the conjugate of an analytic function with a nonvanishing derivative is said to be *indirectly conformal.* It evidently preserves the size but reverses the sense of angles.

If the mapping of Ω by $w = f(z)$ is topological, then the inverse function $z = f^{-1}(w)$ is also analytic. This follows easily if $f'(z) \neq 0$, for then the derivative of the inverse function must be equal to $1/f'(z)$ at the point $z = f^{-1}(w)$. We shall prove later that $f'(z)$ can never vanish in the case of a topological mapping by an analytic function.

The knowledge that $f'(z_0) \neq 0$ is sufficient to conclude that the mapping is topological if it is restricted to a sufficiently small neighborhood of z_0. This follows by the theorem on implicit functions known from the calculus, for the Jacobian of the functions $u = u(x,y)$, $v = v(x,y)$ at the point z_0 is $|f'(z_0)|^2$ and hence $\neq 0$. Later we shall present a simpler proof of this important theorem.

But even if $f'(z) \neq 0$ throughout the region Ω, we cannot assert that the mapping of the whole region is necessarily topological. To illustrate what may happen we refer to Fig. 4. Here the mappings of the sub-

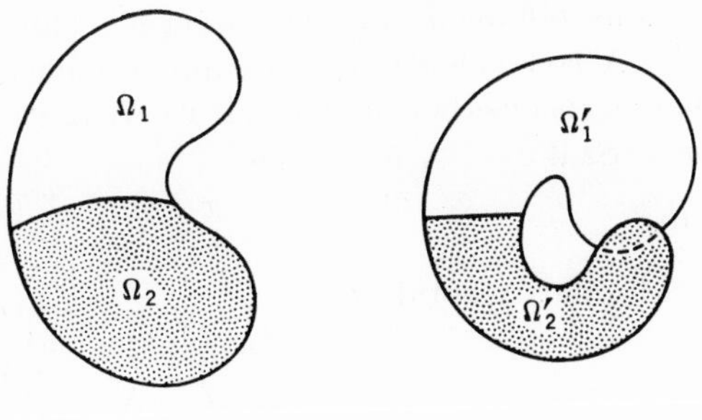

FIG. 4. Doubly covered region.

regions Ω_1 and Ω_2 are one to one, but the images overlap. It is helpful to think of the image of the whole region as a transparent film which partly covers itself. This is the simple and fruitful idea used by Riemann when he introduced the generalized regions now known as *Riemann surfaces.*

3. LINEAR TRANSFORMATIONS

Of all analytic functions the first-order rational functions have the simplest mapping properties, for they define mappings of the extended plane onto itself which are at the same time conformal and topological. The linear transformations have also very remarkable geometric properties, and for that reason their importance goes far beyond serving as simple examples of conformal mappings. The reader will do well to pay particular attention to this geometric aspect, for it will equip him with simple but very valuable techniques.

3.1. The Linear Group. We have already remarked in Chap. 2, Sec. 1.4 that a *linear fractional transformation*

$$w = S(z) = \frac{az + b}{cz + d} \tag{5}$$

with $ad - bc \neq 0$ has an inverse

$$z = S^{-1}(w) = \frac{dw - b}{-cw + a}.$$

The special values $S(\infty) = a/c$ and $S(-d/c) = \infty$ can be introduced either by convention or as limits for $z \to \infty$ and $z \to -d/c$. With the latter interpretation it becomes obvious that S is a topological mapping of the extended plane onto itself, the topology being defined by distances on the Riemann sphere.

For linear transformations we shall usually replace the notation $S(z)$ by Sz. The representation (5) is said to be normalized if $ad - bc = 1$. It is clear that every linear transformation has two normalized representations, obtained from each other by changing the signs of the coefficients.

A convenient way to express a linear transformation is by use of homogeneous coordinates. If we write $z = z_1/z_2$, $w = w_1/w_2$ we find that $w = Sz$ if

$$\begin{aligned} w_1 &= az_1 + bz_2 \\ w_2 &= cz_1 + dz_2 \end{aligned} \tag{6}$$

or, in matrix notation,

$$\begin{pmatrix} w_1 \\ w_2 \end{pmatrix} = \begin{pmatrix} a & b \\ c & d \end{pmatrix} \begin{pmatrix} z_1 \\ z_2 \end{pmatrix}.$$

The main advantage of this notation is that it leads to a simple determination of a composite transformation $w = S_1S_2z$. If we use subscripts to distinguish between the matrices that correspond to S_1, S_2 it is immediate that S_1S_2 belongs to the matrix product

$$\begin{pmatrix} a_1 & b_1 \\ c_1 & d_1 \end{pmatrix}\begin{pmatrix} a_2 & b_2 \\ c_2 & d_2 \end{pmatrix} = \begin{pmatrix} a_1a_2 + b_1c_2 & a_1b_2 + b_1d_2 \\ c_1a_2 + d_1c_2 & c_1b_2 + d_1d_2 \end{pmatrix}.$$

All linear transformations form a group. Indeed, the associative law $(S_1S_2)S_3 = S_1(S_2S_3)$ holds for arbitrary transformations, the identity $w = z$ is a linear transformation, and the inverse of a linear transformation is linear. The ratios $z_1{:}z_2 \neq 0{:}0$ are the points of the complex projective line, and (6) identifies the group of linear transformations with the one-dimensional projective group over the complex numbers, usually denoted by $P(1,\mathbf{C})$. If we use only normalized representations, we can also identify it with the group of two-by-two matrices with determinant 1 (denoted $SL(2,\mathbf{C})$), except that there are two opposite matrices corresponding to the same linear transformation.

We shall make no further use of the matrix notation, except for remarking that the simplest linear transformations belong to matrices of the form

$$\begin{pmatrix} 1 & \alpha \\ 0 & 1 \end{pmatrix}, \begin{pmatrix} k & 0 \\ 0 & 1 \end{pmatrix}, \begin{pmatrix} 0 & 1 \\ 1 & 0 \end{pmatrix}.$$

The first of these, $w = z + \alpha$, is called a *parallel translation.* The second, $w = kz$, is a *rotation* if $|k| = 1$ and a *homothetic transformation* if $k > 0$. For arbitrary complex $k \neq 0$ we can set $k = |k| \cdot k/|k|$, and hence $w = kz$ can be represented as the result of a homothetic transformation followed by a rotation. The third transformation, $w = 1/z$, is called an *inversion.*

If $c \neq 0$ we can write

$$\frac{az + b}{cz + d} = \frac{bc - ad}{c^2(z + d/c)} + \frac{a}{c},$$

and this decomposition shows that the most general linear transforma-ion is composed by a translation, an inversion, a rotation, and a homothetic transformation followed by another translation. If $c = 0$, the inversion falls out and the last translation is not needed.

EXERCISES

1. Prove that the reflection $z \to \bar{z}$ is not a linear transformation.

2. If

$$T_1z = \frac{z + 2}{z + 3}, \qquad T_2z = \frac{z}{z + 1},$$

find T_1T_2z, T_2T_1z and $T_1^{-1}T_2z$.

3. Prove that the most general transformation which leaves the origin fixed and preserves all distances is either a rotation or a rotation followed by reflexion in the real axis.

4. Show that any linear transformation which transforms the real axis into itself can be written with real coefficients.

3.2. The Cross Ratio. Given three distinct points z_2, z_3, z_4 in the extended plane, there exists a linear transformation S which carries them into 1, 0, ∞ in this order. If none of the points is ∞, S will be given by

$$Sz = \frac{z - z_3}{z - z_4} : \frac{z_2 - z_3}{z_2 - z_4}. \tag{7}$$

If z_2, z_3 or $z_4 = \infty$ the transformation reduces to

$$\frac{z - z_3}{z - z_4}, \qquad \frac{z_2 - z_4}{z - z_4}, \qquad \frac{z - z_3}{z_2 - z_3}$$

respectively.

If T were another linear transformation with the same property, then ST^{-1} would leave 1, 0, ∞ invariant. Direct calculation shows that this is true only for the identity transformation, and we would have $S = T$. We conclude that S is uniquely determined.

Definition 12. *The cross ratio* (z_1,z_2,z_3,z_4) *is the image of* z_1 *under the linear transformation which carries* z_2,z_3,z_4 *into* 1, 0, ∞.

The definition is meaningful only if z_2,z_3,z_4 are distinct. A conventional value can be introduced as soon as any three of the points are distinct, but this is unimportant.

The cross ratio is invariant under linear transformations. In more precise formulation:

Theorem 12. *If* z_1, z_2, z_3, z_4 *are distinct points in the extended plane and* T *any linear transformation, then* $(Tz_1,Tz_2,Tz_3,Tz_4) = (z_1,z_2,z_3,z_4)$.

The proof is immediate, for if $Sz = (z,z_2,z_3,z_4)$, then ST^{-1} carries Tz_2, Tz_3, Tz_4 into 1, 0, ∞. By definition we have hence

$$(Tz_1,Tz_2,Tz_3,Tz_4) = ST^{-1}(Tz_1) = Sz_1 = (z_1,z_2,z_3,z_4).$$

With the help of this property we can immediately write down the linear transformation which carries three given points z_1, z_2, z_3 to prescribed positions w_1, w_2, w_3. The correspondence must indeed be given by

$$(w,w_1,w_2,w_3) = (z,z_1,z_2,z_3). \tag{8}$$

In general it is of course necessary to solve this equation with respect to w.

Theorem 13. *The cross ratio* (z_1,z_2,z_3,z_4) *is real if and only if the four points lie on a circle or on a straight line.*

This is evident by elementary geometry, for we obtain

$$\arg (z_1,z_2,z_3,z_4) = \arg \frac{z_1 - z_3}{z_1 - z_4} - \arg \frac{z_2 - z_3}{z_2 - z_4},$$

and if the points lie on a circle this difference of angles is either 0 or $\pm\pi$, depending on the relative location.

For an analytic proof we need only show that the image of the real axis under any linear transformation is either a circle or a straight line. Indeed, $Tz = (z,z_2,z_3,z_4)$ is real on the image of the real axis under the transformation T^{-1} and nowhere else.

The values of $w = T^{-1}z$ for real z satisfy the equation $Tw = \overline{Tw}$. Explicitly, this condition is of the form

$$\frac{aw + b}{cw + d} = \frac{\bar{a}\bar{w} + \bar{b}}{\bar{c}\bar{w} + \bar{d}}.$$

By cross multiplication we obtain

$$(a\bar{c} - c\bar{a})|w^2| + (a\bar{d} - c\bar{b})w + (b\bar{c} - d\bar{a})\bar{w} + b\bar{d} - d\bar{b} = 0.$$

If $a\bar{c} - c\bar{a} = 0$ this is the equation of a straight line, for under this condition the coefficient $a\bar{d} - c\bar{b}$ cannot also vanish. If $a\bar{c} - c\bar{a} \neq 0$ we can divide by this coefficient and complete the square. After a simple computation we obtain

$$\left| w - \frac{\bar{a}d - \bar{c}b}{\bar{a}c - \bar{c}a} \right| = \left| \frac{ad - bc}{\bar{a}c - \bar{c}a} \right|$$

which is the equation of a circle.

The last result makes it clear that we should not, in the theory of linear transformations, distinguish between circles and straight lines. A further justification was found in the fact that both correspond to circles on the Riemann sphere. Accordingly we shall agree to use the word circle in this wider sense.†

† This agreement will be in force only when dealing with linear transformations.

The following is an immediate corollary of Theorems 12 and 13:

Theorem 14. *A linear transformation carries circles into circles.*

EXERCISES

1. Find the linear transformation which carries $0, i, -i$ into $1, -1, 0$.

2. Express the cross ratios corresponding to the 24 permutations of four points in terms of $\lambda = (z_1,z_2,z_3,z_4)$.

3. If the consecutive vertices z_1, z_2, z_3, z_4 of a quadrilateral lie on a circle, prove that

$$|z_1 - z_3| \cdot |z_2 - z_4| = |z_1 - z_2| \cdot |z_3 - z_4| + |z_2 - z_3| \cdot |z_1 - z_4|$$

and interpret the result geometrically.

4. Show that any four distinct points can be carried by a linear transformation to positions $1, -1, k, -k$, where the value of k depends on the points. How many solutions are there, and how are they related?

3.3. Symmetry. The points z and $\bar{z}$ are symmetric with respect to the real axis. A linear transformation with real coefficients carries the real axis into itself and z, $\bar{z}$ into points which are again symmetric. More generally, if a linear transformation T carries the real axis into a circle C, we shall say that the points $w = Tz$ and $w^* = T\bar{z}$ are *symmetric with respect to* C. This is a relation between w, w^* and C which does not depend on T. For if S is another transformation which carries the real axis into C, then $S^{-1}T$ is a real transformation, and hence $S^{-1}w = S^{-1}Tz$ and $S^{-1}w^* = S^{-1}T\bar{z}$ are also conjugate. Symmetry can thus be defined in the following terms:

Definition 13. *The points z and z^* are said to be symmetric with respect to the circle C through z_1, z_2, z_3 if and only if $(z^*,z_1,z_2,z_3) = \overline{(z,z_1,z_2,z_3)}$.*

The points on C, and only those, are symmetric to themselves. The mapping which carries z into z^* is a one-to-one correspondence and is called *reflection* with respect to C. Two reflections will evidently result in a linear transformation.

We wish to investigate the geometric significance of symmetry. Suppose first that C is a straight line. Then we can choose $z_3 = \infty$ and the condition for symmetry becomes

$$\frac{z^* - z_2}{z_1 - z_2} = \frac{\bar{z} - \bar{z}_2}{\bar{z}_1 - \bar{z}_2} \tag{9}$$

Taking absolute values we obtain $|z^* - z_2| = |z - z_2|$. Here z_2 can be any finite point on C, and we conclude that z and z^* are equidistant from all points on C. By (9) we have further

$$\operatorname{Im} \frac{z^* - z_2}{z_1 - z_2} = -\operatorname{Im} \frac{z - z_2}{z_1 - z_2},$$

and hence z and z^* are in different half planes determined by C.† We leave to the reader to prove that C is the bisecting normal of the segment between z and z^*.

Consider now the case of a finite circle C of center a and radius R. Systematic use of the invariance of the cross ratio allows us to conclude as follows:

$$\begin{aligned}\overline{(z,z_1,z_2,z_3)} &= \overline{(z - a, z_1 - a, z_2 - a, z_3 - a)} \\ &= \left(\bar{z} - \bar{a}, \frac{R^2}{z_1 - a}, \frac{R^2}{z_2 - a}, \frac{R^2}{z_3 - a}\right) = \left(\frac{R^2}{\bar{z} - \bar{a}}, z_1 - a, z_2 - a, z_3 - a\right) \\ &= \left(\frac{R^2}{\bar{z} - \bar{a}} + a, z_1, z_2, z_3\right).\end{aligned}$$

This equation shows that the symmetric point of z is $z^* = R^2/(\bar{z} - \bar{a}) + a$ or that z and z^* satisfy the relation

$$(z^* - a)(\bar{z} - \bar{a}) = R^2. \tag{10}$$

The product $|z^* - a| \cdot |z - a|$ of the distances to the center is hence R^2. Further, the ratio $(z^* - a)/(z - a)$ is positive, which means that z and z^* are situated on the same half line from a. There is a simple geometric construction for the symmetric point of z (Fig. 5). We note that the symmetric point of a is ∞.

† Unless they coincide and lie on C.

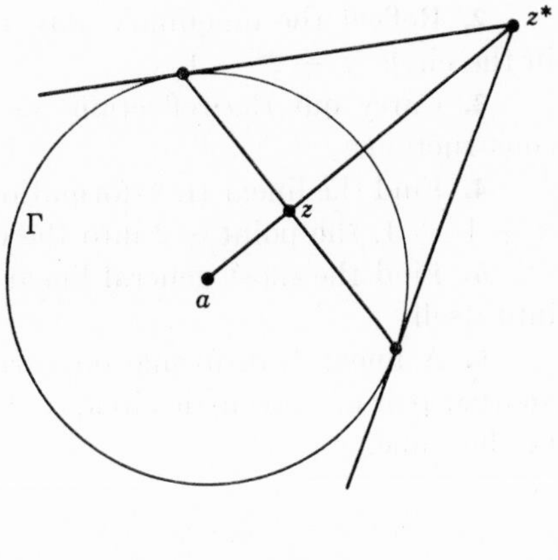

FIG. 5. Reflection in a circle.

Theorem 15. (*The symmetry principle.*) *If a linear transformation carries a circle C_1 into a circle C_2, then it transforms any pair of symmetric points with respect to C_1 into a pair of symmetric points with respect to C_2.*

Briefly, linear transformations preserve symmetry. If C_1 or C_2 is the real axis, the principle follows from the definition of symmetry. In the general case the assertion follows by use of an intermediate transformation which carries C_1 into the real axis.

There are two ways in which the principle of symmetry can be used. If the images of z and C under a certain linear transformation are known, then the principle allows us to find the image of z^*. On the other hand, if the images of z and z^* are known, we conclude that the image of C must be a line of symmetry of these images. While this is not enough to determine the image of C, the information we gain is nevertheless valuable.

The principle of symmetry is put to practical use in the problem of finding the linear transformations which carry a circle C into a circle C'. We can always determine the transformation by requiring that three points z_1, z_2, z_3 on C go over into three points w_1, w_2, w_3 on C'; the transformation is then $(w,w_1,w_2,w_3) = (z,z_1,z_2,z_3)$. But the transformation is also determined if we prescribe that a point z_1 on C shall correspond to a point w_1 on C' and that a point z_2 *not* on C shall be carried into a point w_2 *not* on C'. We know then that z_2^* (the symmetric point of z_2 with respect to C) must correspond to w_2^* (the symmetric point of w_2 with respect to C'). Hence the transformation will be obtained from the relation $(w,w_1,w_2,w_2^*) = (z,z_1,z_2,z_2^*)$.

EXERCISES

1. Prove that every reflection carries circles into circles.

2. Reflect the imaginary axis, the line $x = y$, and the circle $|z| = 1$ in the circle $|z - 2| = 1$.

3. Carry out the reflections in the preceding exercise by geometric construction.

4. Find the linear transformation which carries the circle $|z| = 2$ into $|z + 1| = 1$, the point -2 into the origin, and the origin into i.

5. Find the most general linear transformation of the circle $|z| = R$ into itself.

6. A linear transformation carries a pair of concentric circles into another pair of concentric circles. Prove that the ratios of the radii must be the same.

7. Find a linear transformation which carries $|z| = 1$ and $|z - \frac{1}{4}| = \frac{1}{4}$ into concentric circles. What is the ratio of the radii?

8. Same problem for $|z| = 1$ and $x = 2$.

3.4. Oriented Circles. Because $S(z)$ is analytic and

$$S'(z) = \frac{ad - bc}{(cz + d)^2} \neq 0$$

the mapping $w = S(z)$ is conformal for $z \neq -d/c$ and ∞. It follows that a pair of intersecting circles are mapped on circles that include the same angle. In addition, the sense of an angle is preserved. From an intuitive point of view this means that right and left are preserved, but a more precise formulation is desirable.

An orientation of a circle C is determined by an ordered triple of points z_1,z_2,z_3 on C. With respect to this orientation a point z not on C is said to lie to the *right* of C if $\text{Im}\,(z,z_1,z_2,z_3) > 0$ and to the *left* of C is $\text{Im}\,(z,z_1,z_2,z_3) < 0$ (this checks with everyday use because $(i,1,0,\infty) = i$). It is essential to show that there are only two different orientations. By this we mean that the distinction between left and right is the same for all triples, while the meaning may be reversed. Since the cross ratio is invariant, it is sufficient to consider the case where C is the real axis. Then

$$(z,z_1,z_2,z_3) = \frac{az + b}{cz + d}$$

can be written with real coefficients, and a simple calculation gives

$$\text{Im}\,(z,z_1,z_2,z_3) = \frac{ad - bc}{|cz + d|^2}\,\text{Im}\, z.$$

We recognize that the distinction between right and left is the same as the distinction between the upper and lower half plane. Which is which depends on the sign of the determinant $ad - bc$.

A linear transformation S carries the oriented circle C into a circle which we orient through the triple Sz_1, Sz_2, Sz_3. From the invariance of the cross ratio it follows that the left and right of C will be mapped on the left and right of the image circle.

If two circles are tangent to each other, their orientations can be compared. Indeed, we can use a linear transformation which throws their common point to ∞. The circles become parallel straight lines, and we know how to compare the directions of parallel lines.

In the geometric representation the orientation z_1, z_2, z_3 can be indicated by an arrow which points from z_1 over z_2 to z_3. With the usual choice of the coordinate system left and right will have their customary meaning with respect to this arrow.

When the finite plane is considered as part of the extended plane, the point at infinity is distinguished. We can therefore define an absolute positive orientation of all finite circles by the requirement that ∞ should lie to the right of the oriented circles. The points to the left are said to form the *inside* of the circle and the points to the right form its *outside.*

EXERCISES

1. If z_1, z_2, z_3, z_4 are points on a circle, show that z_1, z_3, z_4 and z_2, z_3, z_4 determine the same orientation if and only if $(z_1,z_2,z_3,z_4) > 0$.

2. Prove that a tangent to a circle is perpendicular to the radius through the point of contact (in this connection a tangent should be defined as a straight line with only one point in common with the circle).

3. Verify that the inside of the circle $|z - a| = R$ is formed by all points z with $|z - a| < R$.

4. The angle between two oriented circles at a point of intersection is defined as the angle between the tangents at that point, equipped with the same orientation. Prove by analytic reasoning, rather than geometric inspection, that the angles at the two points of intersection are opposite to each other.

3.5. Families of Circles.

A great deal can be done toward the visualization of linear transformations by the introduction of certain families of circles which may be thought of as coordinate lines in a circular coordinate system.

Consider a linear transformation of the form

$$w = k \cdot \frac{z - a}{z - b}.$$

Here $z = a$ corresponds to $w = 0$ and $z = b$ to $w = \infty$. It follows that the straight lines through the origin of the w-plane are images of the circles through a and b. On the other hand, the concentric circles about the origin, $|w| = \rho$, correspond to circles with the equation

$$\left|\frac{z - a}{z - b}\right| = \rho/|k|.$$

These are the *circles of Apollonius* with limit points a and b. By their equation they are the loci of points whose distances from a and b have a constant ratio.

Denote by C_1 the circles through a, b and by C_2 the circles of Apol-

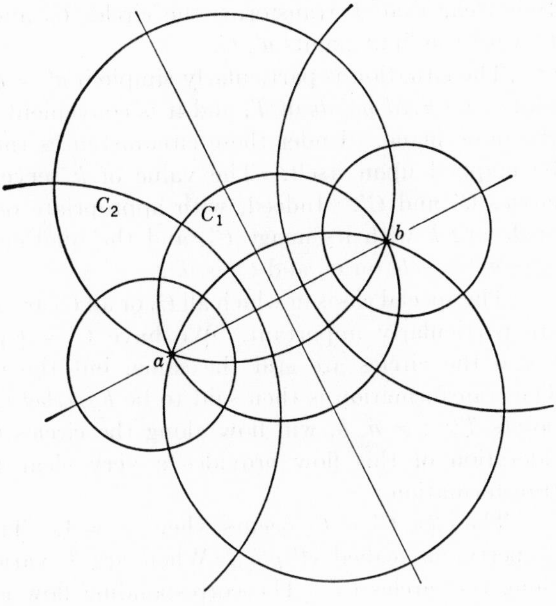

FIG. 6. Steiner circles.

lonius with these limit points. The configuration (Fig. 6) formed by all the circles C_1 and C_2 will be referred to as the *circular net* or the *Steiner circles* determined by a and b. It has many interesting properties of which we shall list a few:

1. There is exactly one C_1 and one C_2 through each point in the plane with the exception of the limit points.
2. Every C_1 meets every C_2 under right angles.
3. Reflection in a C_1 transforms every C_2 into itself and every C_1 into another C_1. Reflection in a C_2 transforms every C_1 into itself and every C_2 into another C_2.
4. The limit points are symmetric with respect to each C_2, but not with respect to any other circle.

These properties are all trivial when the limit points are 0 and ∞, *i.e.*, when the C_1 are lines through the origin and the C_2 concentric circles. Since the properties are invariant under linear transformations, they must continue to hold in the general case.

If a transformation $w = Tz$ carries a, b into a', b' it can be written in the form

$$\frac{w - a'}{w - b'} = k \cdot \frac{z - a}{z - b}. \tag{11}$$

It is clear that T transforms the circles C_1 and C_2 into circles C_1' and C_2' with the limit points a', b'.

The situation is particularly simple if $a' = a$, $b' = b$. Then a, b are said to be *fixed points* of T, and it is convenient to represent z and Tz in the same plane. Under these circumstances the whole circular net will be mapped upon itself. The value of k serves to identify the image circles C_1' and C_2'. Indeed, with appropriate orientations C_1 forms the angle arg k with its image C_1', and the quotient of the constant ratios $|z - a|/|z - b|$ on C_2' and C_2 is $|k|$.

The special cases in which all C_1 or all C_2 are mapped upon themselves are particularly important. We have $C_1' = C_1$ for all C_1 if $k > 0$ (if $k < 0$ the circles are still the same, but the orientation is reversed). The transformation is then said to be *hyperbolic*. When k increases the points Tz, $z \neq a, b$, will flow along the circles C_1 toward b. The consideration of this flow provides a very clear picture of a hyperbolic transformation.

The case $C_2' = C_2$ occurs when $|k| = 1$. Transformations with this property are called *elliptic*. When arg k varies, the points Tz move along the circles C_2. The corresponding flow circulates about a and b in different directions.

The general linear transformation with two fixed points is the product of a hyperbolic and an elliptic transformation with the same fixed points.

The fixed points of a linear transformation are found by solving the equation

$$z = \frac{\alpha z + \beta}{\gamma z + \delta}. \tag{12}$$

In general this is a quadratic equation with two roots; if $\gamma = 0$ one of the fixed points is ∞. It may happen, however, that the roots coincide. A linear transformation with coinciding fixed points is said to be *parabolic*. The condition for this is $(\alpha - \delta)^2 = 4\beta\gamma$.

If the equation (12) is found to have two distinct roots a and b, the transformation can be written in the form

$$\frac{w - a}{w - b} = k\,\frac{z - a}{z - b}.$$

We can then use the Steiner circles determined by a, b to discuss the nature of the transformation. It is important to note, however, that the method is by no means restricted to this case. We can write any linear transformation in the form (11) with arbitrary a, b and use the two circular nets to great advantage.

For the discussion of parabolic transformations it is desirable to introduce still another type of circular net. Consider the transformation

$$w = \frac{\omega}{z - a} + c.$$

It is evident that straight lines in the w-plane correspond to circles through a; moreover, parallel lines correspond to mutually tangent circles. In particular, if $w = u + iv$ the lines $u =$ constant and $v =$ constant correspond to two families of mutually tangent circles which intersect at right angles (Fig. 7). This configuration can be considered as a degenerate set of Steiner circles. It is determined by the point a and the tangent to one of the families of circles. We shall denote the images of the lines $v =$ constant by C_1, the circles of the other family by C_2. Clearly, the line $v = \text{Im}\, c$ corresponds to the tangent of the circles C_1; its direction is given by $\arg \omega$.

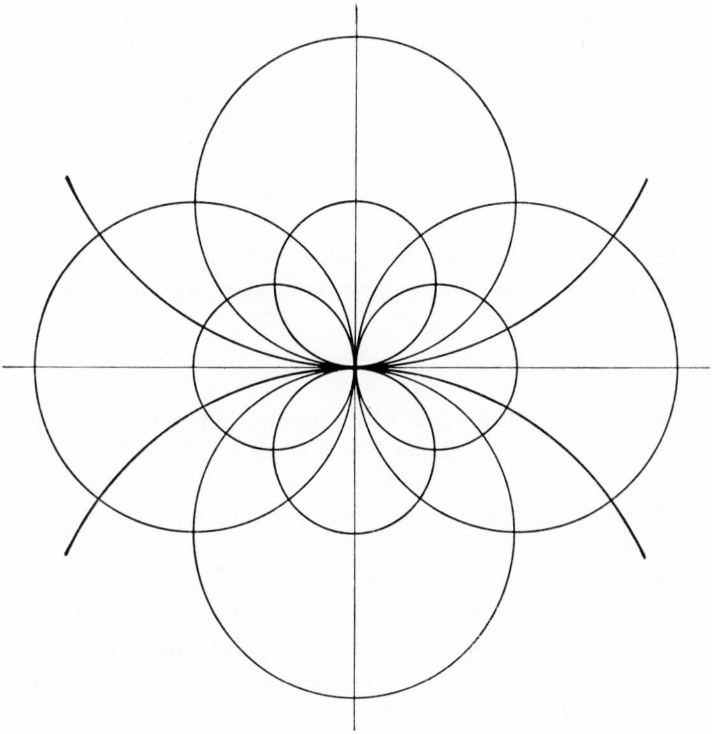

FIG. 7. Degenerate Steiner circles.

Any transformation which carries a into a' can be written in the form

$$\frac{\omega'}{w - a'} = \frac{\omega}{z - a} + c.$$

It is clear that the circles C_1 and C_2 are carried into the circles C_1' and C_2' determined by a' and ω'. We suppose now that $a = a'$ is the only fixed point. Then $\omega = \omega'$ and we can write

$$\frac{\omega}{w - a} = \frac{\omega}{z - a} + c. \tag{13}$$

By this transformation the configuration consisting of the circles C_1 and C_2 is mapped upon itself. In (13) a multiplicative factor is arbitrary, and we can hence suppose that c is real. Then every C_1 is mapped upon itself and the parabolic transformation can be considered as a flow along the circles C_2.

A linear transformation that is neither hyperbolic, elliptic, nor parabolic is said to be *loxodromic.*

EXERCISES

1. Find the fixed points of the linear transformations

$$w = \frac{z}{2z - 1}, \qquad w = \frac{2z}{3z - 1}, \qquad w = \frac{3z - 4}{z - 1}, \qquad w = \frac{z}{2 - z}.$$

Is any of these transformations elliptic, hyperbolic, or parabolic?

2. Suppose that the coefficients of the transformation

$$Sz = \frac{az + b}{cz + d}$$

are normalized by $ad - bc = 1$. Show that S is elliptic if and only if $-2 < a + d < 2$, parabolic if $a + d = \pm 2$, hyperbolic if $a + d < -2$ or >2.

3. Show that a linear transformation which satisfies $S^n z = z$ for some integer n is necessarily elliptic.

4. If S is hyperbolic or loxodromic, show that $S^n z$ converges to a fixpoint as $n \to \infty$, the same for all z, except when z coincides with the other fixpoint. (The limit is the *attractive* fixpoint, the other, if there is one, is the *repellent* fixpoint. What happens when $n \to -\infty$? What happens in the parabolic case?)

5. Find all linear transformations which represent rotations of the Riemann sphere.

6. Find all circles which are orthogonal to $|z| = 1$ and $|z - 1| = 4$.

7. In an obvious way, which we shall not try to make precise, a family of transformations depends on a certain number of real parameters. How many real parameters are there in the family of all linear transformations? How many in the families of hyperbolic, elliptic, parabolic transformations? How many linear transformations leave a given circle C invariant?

4. ELEMENTARY CONFORMAL MAPPINGS

The conformal mapping associated with an analytic function affords an excellent visualization of the properties of the latter; it can well be compared with the visualization of a real function by its graph. It is therefore natural that all questions connected with conformal mapping have received a great deal of attention; progress in this direction has increased our knowledge of analytic functions considerably. In addition, conformal mapping enters naturally in many branches of mathematical physics and in this way accounts for the immediate usefulness of complex-function theory.

One of the most important problems is to determine the conformal mappings of one region onto another. In this section we shall consider those mappings which can be defined by elementary functions.

4.1. The Use of Level Curves. When a conformal mapping is defined by an explicit analytic function $w = f(z)$, we naturally wish to gain information about the specific geometric properties of the mapping. One of the most fruitful ways is to study the correspondence of curves induced by the point transformation. The special properties of the function $f(z)$ may express themselves in the fact that certain simple curves are transformed into curves of a family of well-known character. Any such information will strengthen our visual conception of the mapping.

Such was the case for mappings by linear transformations. We have proved in Sec. 3 that a linear transformation carries circles into circles, provided that straight lines are included as a special case. By consideration of the Steiner circles it was possible to obtain a complete picture of the correspondence.

In more general cases it is advisable to begin with a study of the image curves of the lines $x = x_0$ and $y = y_0$. If we write $f(z) = u(x,y) + iv(x,y)$, the image of $x = x_0$ is given by the parametric equations $u = u(x_0,y)$, $v = v(x_0,y)$; y acts as a parameter and can be eliminated or retained according to convenience. The image of $y = y_0$ is determined in the same way. Together, the curves form an orthogonal net in the w-plane. Similarly, we may consider the curves $u(x,y) = u_0$ and $v(x,y) = v_0$ in the z-plane. They are also orthogonal and are called the *level curves* of u and v.

In other cases it may be more convenient to use polar coordinates and study the images of concentric circles and straight lines through the origin.

Among the simplest mappings are those by a power $w = z^\alpha$. We consider only the case of real α, and then we may as well suppose that α is positive. Since

$$|w| = |z|^\alpha$$
$$\arg w = \alpha \arg z$$

concentric circles about the origin are transformed into circles of the same family, and half lines from the origin correspond to other half lines. The mapping is conformal at all points $z \neq 0$, but an angle θ at the origin is transformed into an angle $\alpha\theta$. For $\alpha \neq 1$ the transformation of the whole plane is not one to one, and if α is fractional z^α is not even single-valued. In general we can therefore only consider the mapping of an angular sector onto another.

The sector $S(\varphi_1,\varphi_2)$, where $0 < \varphi_2 - \varphi_1 \leqq 2\pi$, shall be formed by all points $z \neq 0$ such that one value of $\arg z$ satisfies the inequality

$$\varphi_1 < \arg z < \varphi_2. \tag{14}$$

It is easy to show that $S_0(\varphi_1,\varphi_2)$ is a region. In this region a unique value of $w = z^\alpha$ is defined by the condition

$$\arg w = \alpha \arg z$$

where $\arg z$ stands for the value of the argument singled out by the condition (14). This function is analytic with the nonvanishing derivative

$$De^{\alpha \log z} = \alpha \frac{w}{z}.$$

The mapping is one to one only if $\alpha(\varphi_2 - \varphi_1) \leqq 2\pi$, and in this case $S_0(\varphi_1,\varphi_2)$ is mapped onto the sector $S_0(\alpha\varphi_1,\alpha\varphi_2)$ in the w-plane. It should be observed that $S_0(\varphi_1 + n \cdot 2\pi, \varphi_2 + n \cdot 2\pi)$ is geometrically identical with $S_0(\varphi_1,\varphi_2)$ but may determine a different branch of z^α.

Let us consider the mapping $w = z^2$ in detail. Since $u = x^2 - y^2$ and $v = 2xy$, we recognize that the level curves $u = u_0$ and $v = v_0$ are equilateral hyperbolas with the diagonals and the coordinate axes for asymptotes. They are of course orthogonal to each other. On the other hand, the image of $x = x_0$ is $v^2 = 4x_0^2(x_0^2 - u)$ and the image of $y = y_0$ is $v^2 = 4y_0^2(y_0^2 + u)$. Both families represent parabolas with the focus at the origin whose axes are pointed in the negative and positive direction of the u-axis. Their orthogonality is well-known from analytic geometry. The families of level curves are shown in Figs. 8 and 9.

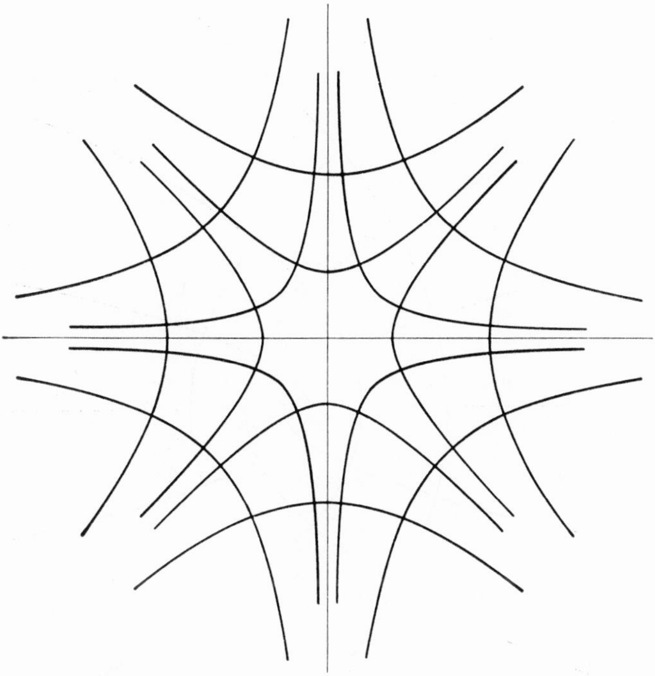

FIG. 8. z-plane.

For a different family of image curves consider the circles $|w - 1| = k$ in the w-plane. The equation of the inverse image can be written in the form

$$(x^2 + y^2)^2 = 2(x^2 - y^2) + k^2 - 1$$

and represents a family of lemniscates with the focal points ± 1. The orthogonal family is represented by

$$x^2 - y^2 = 2hxy + 1$$

and consists of all equilateral hyperbolas with center at the origin which pass through the points ± 1.

In the case of the third power $w = z^3$ the level curves in both planes are cubic curves. There is no point in deriving their equations, for their general shape is clear without calculation. For instance, the curves $u = u_0 > 0$ must have the form indicated in Fig. 10. Similarly, if we follow the change of arg w when z traces the line $x = x_0 > 0$, we find that the image curve must have a loop (Fig. 11). It is therefore a folium of Descartes.

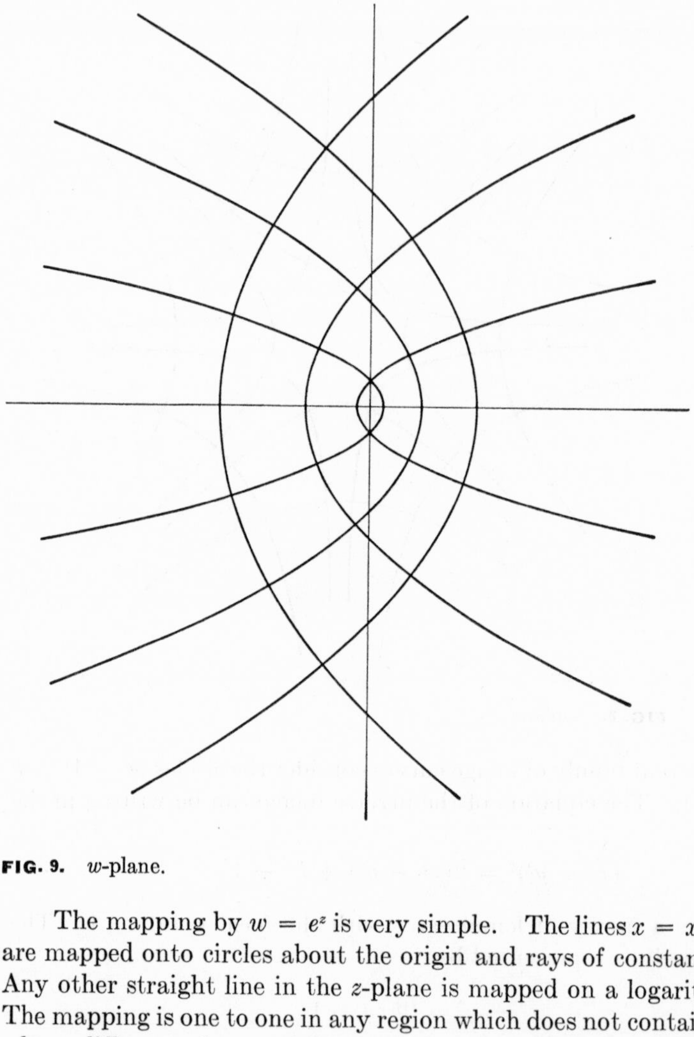

FIG. 9. w-plane.

The mapping by $w = e^z$ is very simple. The lines $x = x_0$ and $y = y_0$ are mapped onto circles about the origin and rays of constant argument. Any other straight line in the z-plane is mapped on a logarithmic spiral. The mapping is one to one in any region which does not contain two points whose difference is a multiple of $2\pi i$. In particular, a horizontal strip $y_1 < y < y_2$, $y_2 - y_1 \leqq 2\pi$ is mapped onto an angular sector, and if $y_2 - y_1 = \pi$ the image is a half plane. We are thus able to map a parallel strip onto a half plane, and hence onto any circular region. The left half of the strip, cut off by the imaginary axis, corresponds to a half circle.

It is useful to write down some explicit formulas for the mapping. The function $\zeta = \xi + i\eta = e^z$ maps the strip $-\pi/2 < y < \pi/2$ onto the half plane $\xi > 0$. On the other hand,

$$w = \frac{\zeta - 1}{\zeta + 1}$$

maps $\xi > 0$ onto $|w| < 1$. Hence

$$w = \frac{e^z - 1}{e^z + 1} = \tanh \frac{z}{2}.$$

4.2. A Survey of Elementary Mappings. When faced with the problem of mapping a region Ω_1 conformally onto another region Ω_2, it is usually advisable to proceed in two steps. First, we map Ω_1 onto a circular region, and then we map the circular region onto Ω_2. In other words, the general problem of conformal mapping can be reduced to the problem of mapping a region onto a disk or a half plane. We shall prove, in Chap. 6, that this mapping problem has a solution for every region whose boundary consists of a simple closed curve.

The main tools at our disposal are linear transformations and transformations by a power, by the exponential function, and by the logarithm. All these transformations have the characteristic property that they map a family of straight lines or circles on a similar family. For this reason, their use is essentially limited to regions whose boundary is made up of circular arcs and line segments. The power serves the particular purpose of straightening angles, and with the aid of the exponential function we can even transform zero angles into straight angles.

By these means we can first find a standard mapping of any region

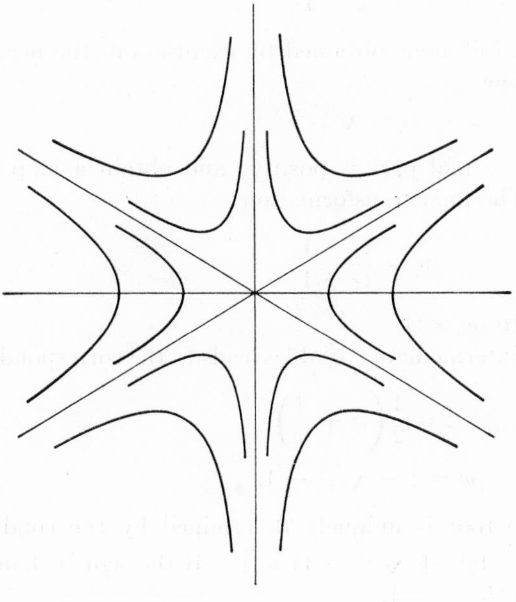

FIG. 10

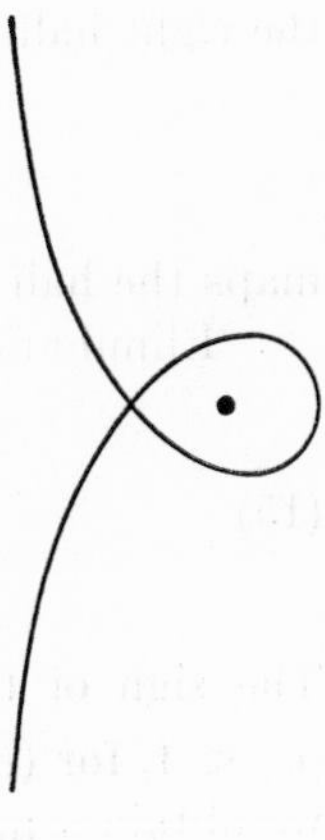

FIG. 11

whose boundary consists of two circular arcs with common end points. Such a region is either a circular wedge, whose angle may be greater than π, or its complement. If the end points of the arcs are a and b, we begin with the preliminary mapping $z_1 = (z - a)/(z - b)$ which transforms the given region into an angular sector. By an appropriate power $w = z_1^\alpha$ this sector can be mapped onto a half plane.

If the circles are tangent to each other at the point a, the transformation $z_1 = 1/(z - a)$ will map the region between them onto a parallel strip, and a suitable exponential transformation maps the strip onto a half plane.

A little more generally, the same method applies to a circular triangle with two right angles. In fact, if the third angle has the vertex a, and if the sides from a meet again at b, the linear transformation $z_1 = (z - a)/(z - b)$ maps the triangle onto a circular sector. By means of a power this sector can be transformed into a half circle; the half circle is a wedge-shaped region which in turn can be mapped onto a half plane.

In this connection we shall treat explicitly a special case which occurs frequently. Let it be required to map the complement of a line segment onto the inside or outside of a circle. The region is a wedge with the angle 2π; without loss of generality we may assume that the end points of the segment are ± 1. The preliminary transformation

$$z_1 = \frac{z + 1}{z - 1}$$

maps the wedge on the full angle obtained by exclusion of the negative real axis. Next we define

$$z_2 = \sqrt{z_1}$$

as the square root whose real part is positive and obtain a map onto the right half plane. The final transformation

$$w = \frac{z_2 - 1}{z_2 + 1}$$

maps the half plane onto $|w| < 1$.

Elimination of the intermediate variables leads to the correspondence

$$(15) \qquad \begin{aligned} z &= \frac{1}{2}\left(w + \frac{1}{w}\right) \\ w &= z - \sqrt{z^2 - 1}. \end{aligned}$$

The sign of the square root is uniquely determined by the condition $|w| < 1$, for $(z - \sqrt{z^2 - 1})(z + \sqrt{z^2 - 1}) = 1$. If the sign is changed, we obtain a mapping onto $|w| > 1$.

For a more detailed study of the mapping (15) we set $w = \rho e^{i\theta}$ and obtain

$$x = \frac{1}{2}\left(\rho + \frac{1}{\rho}\right)\cos\theta$$
$$y = \frac{1}{2}\left(\rho - \frac{1}{\rho}\right)\sin\theta.$$

Elimination of θ yields

$$\frac{x^2}{[\frac{1}{2}(\rho + \rho^{-1})]^2} + \frac{y^2}{[\frac{1}{2}(\rho - \rho^{-1})]^2} = 1 \tag{16}$$

and elimination of ρ

$$\frac{x^2}{\cos^2\theta} - \frac{y^2}{\sin^2\theta} = 1. \tag{17}$$

Hence the image of a circle $|w| = \rho < 1$ is an ellipse with the major axis $\rho + \rho^{-1}$ and the minor axis $\rho^{-1} - \rho$. The image of a radius is half a branch of a hyperbola. The ellipses (16) and the hyperbolas (17) are confocal. The correspondence is illustrated in Fig. 12.

Clearly, the transformation (15) allows us to include in our list of elementary conformal mappings the mapping of the outside of an ellipse or the region between the branches of a hyperbola onto a circular region. It does not, however, allow us to map the inside of an ellipse or the inside of a hyperbolic branch.

As a final and less trivial example we shall study the mapping defined by a cubic polynomial $w = a_0z^3 + a_1z^2 + a_2z + a_3$. The familiar transformation $z = z_1 - a_1/3a_0$ allows us to get rid of the quadratic term,

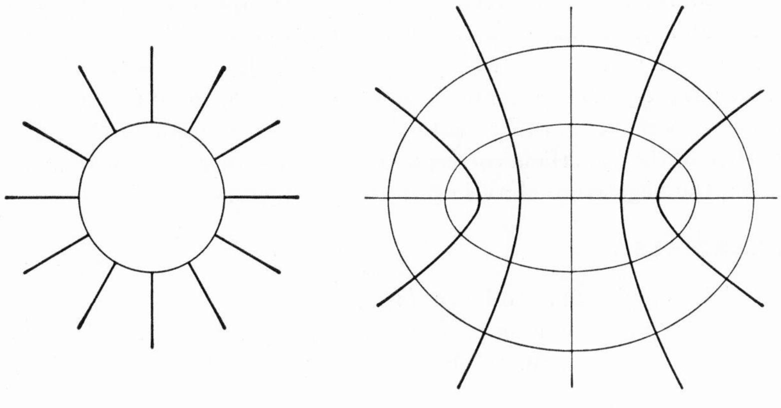

FIG. 12. Mapping by $z = \frac{1}{2}(w + w^{-1})$.

and by obvious normalizations we can reduce the polynomial to the form $w = z^3 - 3z$. The coefficient for z is chosen so as to make the derivative vanish for $z = \pm 1$.

Making use of the transformation (15) we introduce an auxiliary variable ζ defined by

$$z = \zeta + \frac{1}{\zeta}. \tag{18}$$

Our cubic polynomial takes then the simple form

$$w = \zeta^3 + \frac{1}{\zeta^3}. \tag{19}$$

We note that each z determines two values ζ, but they are reciprocal and yield the same value of w. In order to obtain a unique ζ we may impose the condition $|\zeta| < 1$, but then the segment $(-2,2)$ must be excluded from the z-plane.

It is now easy to visualize the correspondence between the z- and w-planes. To the circle $|\zeta| = \rho < 1$ corresponds an ellipse with the semiaxes $\rho^{-1} \pm \rho$ in the z-plane, and one with the semiaxes $\rho^{-3} \pm \rho^3$ in the w-plane. Similarly, a radius $\arg \zeta = \theta$ corresponds to hyperbolic branches in the z- and w-planes; the one in the z-plane has an asymptote which makes the angle $-\theta$ with the positive real axis, and in the w-plane the corresponding angle is -3θ. The whole pattern of confocal ellipses and hyperbolas remains invariant, but when z describes an ellipse w will trace the corresponding larger ellipse three times. The situation is thus very similar to the one in the case of the simpler mapping $w = z^3$. For orientation the reader may lean on Fig. 12, except that the foci are not ± 2.

For the region between two hyperbolic branches whose asymptotes make an angle $\leqq 2\pi/3$ the mapping is one to one. We note in particular that the six regions into which the hyperbola $3x^2 - y^2 = 3$ and the x-axis divide the z-plane are mapped onto half planes, three of them onto the upper half plane and three onto the lower. The inside of the right-hand branch of the hyperbola corresponds to the whole w-plane with an incision along the negative real axis up to the point -2.

EXERCISES

All mappings are to be conformal.

1. Map the common part of the disks $|z| < 1$ and $|z - 1| < 1$ on the inside of the unit circle. Choose the mapping so that the two symmetries are preserved.

2. Map the region between $|z| = 1$ and $|z - \frac{1}{2}| = \frac{1}{2}$ on a half plane.

3. Map the complement of the arc $|z| = 1, y \geqq 0$ on the outside of the unit circle so that the points at ∞ correspond to each other.

4. Map the outside of the parabola $y^2 = 2px$ on the disk $|w| < 1$ so that $z = 0$ and $z = -p/2$ correspond to $w = 1$ and $w = 0$. (Lindelöf.)

5. Map the inside of the right-hand branch of the hyperbola $x^2 - y^2 = a^2$ on the disk $|w| < 1$ so that the focus corresponds to $w = 0$ and the vertex to $w = -1$. (Lindelöf.)

6. Map the inside of the lemniscate $|z^2 - a^2| = \rho^2 (\rho > a)$ on the disk $|w| < 1$ so that symmetries are preserved. (Lindelöf.)

7. Map the outside of the ellipse $(x/a)^2 + (y/b)^2 = 1$ onto $|w| < 1$ with preservation of symmetries.

8. Map the part of the z-plane to the left of the right-hand branch of the hyperbola $x^2 - y^2 = 1$ on a half plane. (Lindelöf.)

Hint: Consider on one side the mapping of the upper half of the region by $w = z^2$, on the other side the mapping of a quadrant by

$$w = z^3 - 3z.$$

4.3. Elementary Riemann Surfaces. The visualization of a function by means of the corresponding mapping is completely clear only when the mapping is one to one. If this is not the case, we can still give our imagination the necessary support by the introduction of generalized regions in which distinct points may have the same coordinates. In order to do this it is necessary to suppose that points which occupy the same place can be distinguished by other characteristics, for instance a tag or a color. Points with the same tag are considered to lie in the same *sheet* or *layer*.

This idea leads to the notion of a *Riemann surface.* It is not our intention to give, in this connection, a rigorous definition of this notion. For our purposes it is sufficient to introduce Riemann surfaces in a purely descriptive manner. We are free to do so as long as we use them merely for purposes of illustration, and never in logical proofs.

The simplest Riemann surface is connected with the mapping by a power $w = z^n$, where $n > 1$ is an integer. We know that there is a one-to-one correspondence between each angle $(k - 1)(2\pi/n) < \arg z < k(2\pi/n)$, $k = 1, \ldots, n$, and the whole w-plane except for the positive real axis. The image of each angle is thus obtained by performing a "cut" along the positive axis; this cut has an upper and a lower "edge." Corresponding to the n angles in the z-plane we consider n identical copies of the w-plane with the cut. They will be the "sheets" of the Riemann surface, and they are distinguished by a tag k which serves to identify the corresponding angle. When z moves in its plane, the corresponding point w should be free to move on the Riemann surface. For this reason we must attach the lower edge of the first sheet to the upper edge of the second sheet, the lower edge of the second sheet to the upper edge of the third, and so on. In the last step the lower edge of the nth sheet is attached to the upper edge of the first sheet, completing the cycle. In a physical sense this is not possible without self-intersection, but the idealized model shall be free from this discrepancy. The result of the construction is a Riemann surface whose points are in one-to-one correspondence with the points of the z-plane. What is more, this correspondence is continuous if continuity is defined in the sense suggested by the construction.

The cut along the positive axis could be replaced by a cut along any simple arc from 0 to ∞; the Riemann surface obtained in this way should be considered as identical with the one originally constructed. In other words, the cuts are in no way distinguished lines on the surface, but the introduction of specific cuts is necessary for descriptive purposes.

The point $w = 0$ is in a special position. It connects all the sheets, and a curve must wind n times around the origin before it closes. A point of this kind is called a *branch point*. If our Riemann surface is considered over the extended plane, the point at ∞ is also a branch point. In more general cases a branch point need not connect all the sheets; if it connects h sheets, it is said to be of order $h - 1$.

The Riemann surface corresponding to $w = e^z$ is of similar nature. In this case the function maps each parallel strip $(k - 1)2\pi < y < k \cdot 2\pi$ onto a sheet with a cut along the positive axis. The sheets are attached to each other so that they form an endless screw. The origin will *not* be a point of the Riemann surface, corresponding to the fact that e^z is never zero.

The reader will find it easy to construct other Riemann surfaces. We will illustrate the procedure by consideration of the Riemann surface defined by $w = \cos z$. A region which is mapped in a one-to-one manner onto the whole plane, except for one or more cuts, is called a *fundamental region*. For fundamental regions of $w = \cos z$ we may choose the strips $(k - 1)\pi < x < k\pi$. Each strip is mapped onto the whole w-plane with cuts along the real axis from $-\infty$ to -1 and from 1 to ∞. The line $x = k\pi$ corresponds to both edges of the positive cut if k is even, and

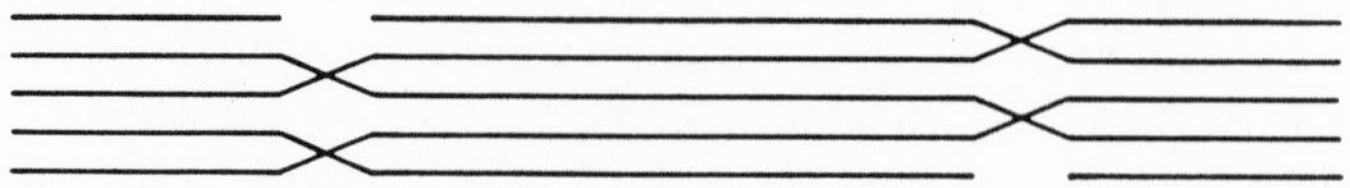

FIG. 13. The Riemann surface of $\cos z$.

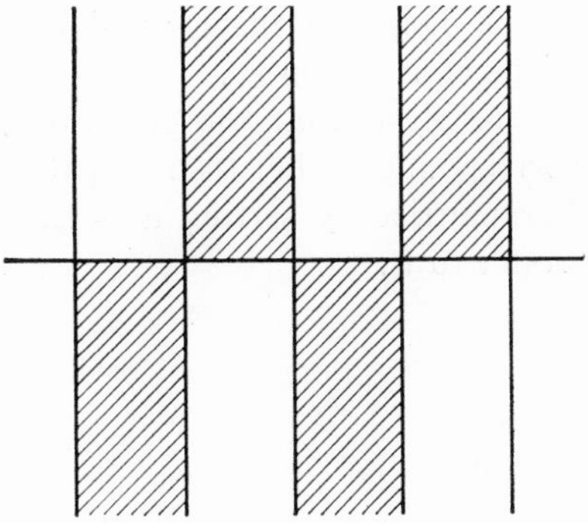

FIG. 14. Fundamental regions of $\cos z$.

to the edges of the negative cut if k is odd. If we consider the two strips which are adjacent along the line $x = k\pi$, we find that the edges of the corresponding cuts must be joined crosswise so as to generate a simple branch point at $w = \pm 1$. The resulting surface has infinitely many simple branch points over $w = 1$ and $w = -1$ which alternatingly connect the odd and even sheets.

An attempt to illustrate the connection between the sheets is made in Fig. 13. It represents a cross section of the surface in the case that the cuts are chosen parallel to each other. The reader should bear in mind that any two points on the same level can be joined by an arc which does not intersect any of the cuts.

Whatever the advantage of such representations may be, the clearest picture of the Riemann surface is obtained by direct consideration of the fundamental regions in the z-plane. The interpretation is even simpler if, as in Fig. 14, we introduce the subregions which correspond to the upper and lower half plane. The shaded regions are those in which $\cos z$ has a positive imaginary part. Each region corresponds to a half plane on which we mark the boundary points 1 and -1. For any two adjacent regions, one white and one shaded, the half planes must be joined across one of the three intervals $(-\infty,-1)$, $(-1,1)$, $(1,\infty)$. The choice of the correct junction is automatic from a glance at the corresponding situation in the z-plane.

EXERCISES

1. Describe the Riemann surface associated with the function

$$w = \frac{1}{2}\left(z + \frac{1}{z}\right).$$

2. Same problem for $w = (z^2 - 1)^2$.

3. Same problem for $w = z^3 - 3z$.

4. Describe the general nature of the Riemann surface associated with the function e^{e^z}.

5. Show that the equation $w^3 + z^3 - wz = 0$ defines a one-to-one correspondence between two Riemann surfaces with three sheets. *Hint:* Parametrize by setting $w = tz$. Describe the mapping from t to z and from t to w.

4 COMPLEX INTEGRATION

1. FUNDAMENTAL THEOREMS

Many important properties of analytic functions are very difficult to prove without use of complex integration. For instance, it is only quite recently that it became possible to prove, without resorting to complex integrals or equivalent tools, that the derivative of an analytic function is continuous, or that the higher derivatives exist. At present the integration-free proofs are, to say the least, much more difficult than the classical proofs.

As in the real case we distinguish between *definite* and *indefinite integrals.* An indefinite integral is a function whose derivative equals a given analytic function in a region; in many elementary cases indefinite integrals can be found by inversion of known derivation formulas. The definite integrals are taken over differentiable or piecewise differentiable arcs and are not limited to analytic functions. They can be defined by a limit process which mimics the definition of a real definite integral. Actually, we shall prefer to define complex definite integrals in terms of real integrals. This will save us from repeating existence proofs which are essentially the same as in the real case. Naturally, the reader must be thoroughly familiar with the theory of definite integrals of real continuous functions.

1.1. Line Integrals. The most immediate generalization of a real integral is to the definite integral of a complex function over a real interval. If $f(t) = u(t) + iv(t)$ is a continuous function, defined in an interval (a,b), we set by definition

$$\int_a^b f(t)\,dt = \int_a^b u(t)\,dt + i\int_a^b v(t)\,dt. \tag{1}$$

This integral has most of the properties of the real integral. In particular, if $c = \alpha + i\beta$ is a complex constant we obtain

$$\int_a^b cf(t)\,dt = c\int_a^b f(t)\,dt, \tag{2}$$

for both members are equal to

$$\int_a^b (\alpha u - \beta v)\,dt + i\int_a^b (\alpha v + \beta u)\,dt.$$

When $a \leqq b$, the fundamental inequality

$$\left|\int_a^b f(t)\,dt\right| \leqq \int_a^b |f(t)|\,dt \tag{3}$$

holds for arbitrary complex $f(t)$. To see this we choose $c = e^{-i\theta}$ with a real θ in (2) and find

$$\mathrm{Re}\left[e^{-i\theta}\int_a^b f(t)\,dt\right] = \int_a^b \mathrm{Re}\,[e^{-i\theta}f(t)]\,dt \leqq \int_a^b |f(t)|\,dt.$$

For $\theta = \arg \int_a^b f(t)\,dt$ the expression on the left reduces to the absolute value of the integral, and (3) results.†

We consider now a piecewise differentiable arc γ with the equation $z = z(t)$, $a \leqq t \leqq b$. If the function $f(z)$ is defined and continuous on γ, then $f(z(t))$ is also continuous and we can set

$$\int_\gamma f(z)\,dz = \int_a^b f(z(t))z'(t)\,dt. \tag{4}$$

This is our *definition* of the complex line integral of $f(z)$ extended over the arc γ. In the right-hand member of (4), if $z'(t)$ is not continuous throughout, the interval of integration has to be subdivided in the obvious manner. Whenever a line integral over an arc γ is considered, let it be tacitly understood that γ is piecewise differentiable.

The most important property of the integral (4) is its invariance under a change of parameter. A change of parameter is determined by an increasing function $t = t(\tau)$ which maps an interval $\alpha \leqq \tau \leqq \beta$ onto $a \leqq t \leqq b$; we assume that $t(\tau)$ is piecewise differentiable. By the rule

† θ is not defined if $\int_a^b f\,dt = 0$, but then there is nothing to prove.

for changing the variable of integration we have

$$\int_a^b f(z(t))z'(t)\,dt = \int_\alpha^\beta f(z(t(\tau)))z'(t(\tau))t'(\tau)\,d\tau.$$

But $z'(t(\tau))t'(\tau)$ is the derivative of $z(t(\tau))$ with respect to τ, and hence the integral (4) has the same value whether γ be represented by the equation $z = z(t)$ or by the equation $z = z(t(\tau))$.

In Chap. 3, Sec. 2.1, we defined the opposite arc $-\gamma$ by the equation $z = z(-t)$, $-b \leqq t \leqq -a$. We have thus

$$\int_{-\gamma} f(z)\,dz = \int_{-b}^{-a} f(z(-t))(-z'(-t))\,dt,$$

and by a change of variable the last integral can be brought to the form

$$\int_b^a f(z(t))z'(t)\,dt.$$

We conclude that

$$\int_{-\gamma} f(z)\,dz = -\int_\gamma f(z)\,dz. \tag{5}$$

The integral (4) has also a very obvious additive property. It is quite clear what is meant by subdividing an arc γ into a finite number of subarcs. A subdivision can be indicated by a symbolic equation

$$\gamma = \gamma_1 + \gamma_2 + \cdots + \gamma_n,$$

and the corresponding integrals satisfy the relation

$$\int_{\gamma_1+\gamma_2+\cdots+\gamma_n} f\,dz = \int_{\gamma_1} f\,dz + \int_{\gamma_2} f\,dz + \cdots + \int_{\gamma_n} f\,dz. \tag{6}$$

Finally, the integral over a closed curve is also invariant under a shift of parameter. The old and the new initial point determine two subarcs γ_1, γ_2, and the invariance follows from the fact that the integral over $\gamma_1 + \gamma_2$ is equal to the integral over $\gamma_2 + \gamma_1$.

In addition to integrals of the form (4) we can also consider line integrals with respect to $\bar{z}$. The most convenient definition is by double conjugation

$$\int_\gamma f\,\overline{dz} = \overline{\int_\gamma \bar{f}\,dz}.$$

Using this notation, line integrals with respect to x or y can be introduced by

$$\int_\gamma f\,dx = \frac{1}{2}\left(\int_\gamma f\,dz + \int_\gamma f\,\overline{dz}\right)$$

$$\int_\gamma f\,dy = \frac{1}{2i}\left(\int_\gamma f\,dz - \int_\gamma f\,\overline{dz}\right).$$

With $f = u + iv$ we find that the integral (4) can be written in the form

$$\int_\gamma (u\,dx - v\,dy) + i\int_\gamma (u\,dy + v\,dx) \tag{7}$$

which separates the real and imaginary part.

Of course we could just as well have started by defining integrals of the form

$$\int_\gamma p\,dx + q\,dy,$$

in which case formula (7) would serve as definition of the integral (4). It is a matter of taste which one prefers.

An essentially different line integral is obtained by integration with respect to *arc length*. Two notations are in common use, and the definition is

$$\int_\gamma f\,ds = \int_\gamma f|dz| = \int_\gamma f(z(t))|z'(t)|\,dt. \tag{8}$$

This integral is again independent of the choice of parameter. In contrast to (5) we have now

$$\int_{-\gamma} f|dz| = \int_\gamma f|dz|$$

while (6) remains valid in the same form. The inequality

$$\left|\int_\gamma f\,dz\right| \leqq \int_\gamma |f|\cdot|dz| \tag{9}$$

is a consequence of (3).

For $f = 1$ the integral (8) reduces to $\int_\gamma |dz|$ which is by definition the *length* of γ. As an example we compute the length of a circle. From the parametric equation $z = z(t) = a + \rho e^{it}$, $0 \leqq t \leqq 2\pi$, of a full circle we obtain $z'(t) = i\rho e^{it}$ and hence

$$\int_0^{2\pi} |z'(t)|\,dt = \int_0^{2\pi} \rho\,dt = 2\pi\rho$$

as expected.

1.2. Rectifiable Arcs. The length of an arc can also be defined as the least upper bound of all sums

$$|z(t_1) - z(t_0)| + |z(t_2) - z(t_1)| + \cdots + |z(t_n) - z(t_{n-1})| \tag{10}$$

where $a = t_0 < t_1 < \cdots < t_n = b$. If this least upper bound is finite we say that the arc is *rectifiable*. It is quite easy to show that piecewise differentiable arcs are rectifiable, and that the two definitions of length coincide.

Because $|x(t_k) - x(t_{k-1})| \leqq |z(t_k) - z(t_{k-1})|$, $|y(t_k) - y(t_{k-1})| \leqq |z(t_k) - z(t_{k-1})|$ and $|z(t_k) - z(t_{k-1})| \leqq |x(t_k) - x(t_{k-1})| + |y(t_k) - y(t_{k-1})|$ it is clear that the sums (10) and the corresponding sums

$$|x(t_1) - x(t_0)| + \cdots + |x(t_n) - x(t_{n-1})|$$
$$|y(t_1) - y(t_0)| + \cdots + |y(t_n) - y(t_{n-1})|$$

are bounded at the same time. When the latter sums are bounded, one says that the functions $x(t)$ and $y(t)$ are of *bounded variation.* *An arc $z = z(t)$ is rectifiable if and only if the real and imaginary parts of $z(t)$ are of bounded variation.*

If γ is rectifiable and $f(z)$ continuous on γ it is possible to define integrals of type (8) as a limit

$$\int_\gamma f\,ds = \lim \sum_{k=1}^{n} f(z(t_k))|z(t_k) - z(t_{k-1})|.$$

Here the limit is of the same kind as that encountered in the definition of a definite integral.

Integrals over rectifiable arcs are seldom needed in the theory of analytic functions, and certainly not in its elementary parts. However, the notion is one that every mathematician should know.

1.3. Line Integrals as Functions of Arcs. General line integrals of the form $\int_\gamma p\,dx + q\,dy$ are often studied as functions (or *functionals*) of the arc γ. It is then assumed that p and q are defined and continuous in a region Ω and that γ is free to vary in Ω. An important class of integrals is characterized by the property that the integral over an arc depends only on its end points. In other words, if γ_1 and γ_2 have the same initial point and the same end point, we require that $\int_{\gamma_1} p\,dx + q\,dy = \int_{\gamma_2} p\,dx + q\,dy$. To say that an integral depends only on the end points is equivalent to saying that the integral over any closed curve is zero. Indeed, if γ is a closed curve, then γ and $-\gamma$ have the same end points, and if the integral depends only on the end points, we obtain

$$\int_\gamma = \int_{-\gamma} = -\int_\gamma$$

and consequently $\int_\gamma = 0$. Conversely, if γ_1 and γ_2 have the same end points, then $\gamma_1 - \gamma_2$ is a closed curve, and if the integral over any closed curve vanishes, it follows that $\int_{\gamma_1} = \int_{\gamma_2}$.

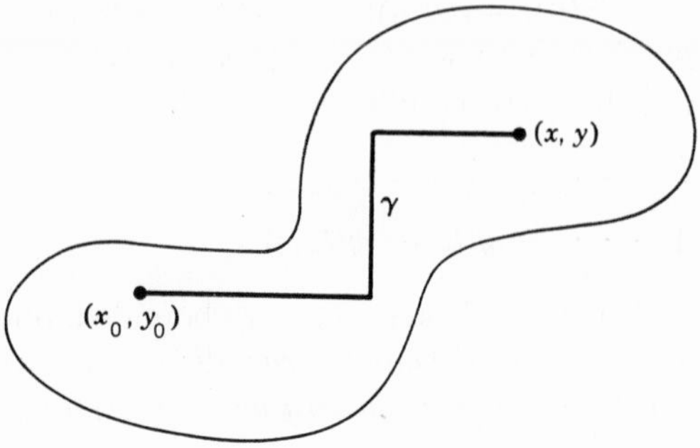

FIG. 15

The following theorem gives a necessary and sufficient condition under which a line integral depends only on the end points.

Theorem 1. *The line integral* $\int_\gamma p\,dx + q\,dy$*, defined in* Ω*, depends only on the end points of* γ *if and only if there exists a function* $U(x,y)$ *in* Ω *with the partial derivatives* $\partial U/\partial x = p$*,* $\partial U/\partial y = q$*.*

The sufficiency follows at once, for if the condition is fulfilled we can write, with the usual notations,

$$\int_\gamma p\,dx + q\,dy = \int_a^b \left(\frac{\partial U}{\partial x}x'(t) + \frac{\partial U}{\partial y}y'(t)\right)dt = \int_a^b \frac{d}{dt}U(x(t),y(t))\,dt$$
$$= U(x(b),y(b)) - U(x(a),y(a)),$$

and the value of this difference depends only on the end points. To prove the necessity we choose a fixed point $(x_0,y_0) \in \Omega$, join it to (x,y) by a polygon γ, contained in Ω, whose sides are parallel to the coordinate axes (Fig. 15) and define a function by

$$U(x,y) = \int_\gamma p\,dx + q\,dy.$$

Since the integral depends only on the end points, the function is well defined. Moreover, if we choose the last segment of γ horizontal, we can keep y constant and let x vary without changing the other segments. On the last segment we can choose x for parameter and obtain

$$U(x,y) = \int^x p(x,y)\,dx + \text{const.},$$

the lower limit of the integral being irrelevant. From this expression it follows at once that $\partial U/\partial x = p$. In the same way, by choosing the last segment vertical, we can show that $\partial U/\partial y = q$.

It is customary to write $dU = (\partial U/\partial x)\,dx + (\partial U/\partial y)\,dy$ and to say that an expression $p\,dx + q\,dy$ which can be written in this form is an *exact differential.* Thus an integral depends only on the end points if and only if the integrand is an exact differential. Observe that p, q and U can be either real or complex. The function U, if it exists, is uniquely determined up to an additive constant, for if two functions have the same partial derivative their difference must be constant.

When is $f(z)\,dz = f(z)\,dx + if(z)\,dy$ an exact differential? According to the definition there must exist a function $F(z)$ in Ω with the partial derivatives

$$\frac{\partial F(z)}{\partial x} = f(z)$$
$$\frac{\partial F(z)}{\partial y} = if(z).$$

If this is so, $F(z)$ fulfills the Cauchy-Riemann equation

$$\frac{\partial F}{\partial x} = -i\frac{\partial F}{\partial y};$$

since $f(z)$ is by assumption continuous (otherwise $\int_\gamma f\,dz$ would not be defined) $F(z)$ is analytic with the derivative $f(z)$ (Chap. 2, Sec. 1.2).

The integral $\int_\gamma f\,dz$, *with continuous* f, *depends only on the end points of* γ *if and only if* f *is the derivative of an analytic function in* Ω.

Under these circumstances we shall prove later that $f(z)$ is itself analytic.

As an immediate application of the above result we find that

$$\int_\gamma (z-a)^n\,dz = 0 \tag{11}$$

for all closed curves γ, provided that the integer n is $\geqq 0$. In fact, $(z-a)^n$ is the derivative of $(z-a)^{n+1}/(n+1)$, a function which is analytic in the whole plane. If n is negative, but $\neq -1$, the same result holds for all closed curves which do not pass through a, for in the complementary region of the point a the indefinite integral is still analytic and single-valued. For $n = -1$, (11) does not always hold. Consider a circle C with the center a, represented by the equation $z = a + \rho e^{it}$, $0 \leqq t \leqq 2\pi$. We obtain

$$\int_C \frac{dz}{z-a} = \int_0^{2\pi} i\,dt = 2\pi i.$$

This result shows that it is impossible to define a single-valued branch of $\log (z - a)$ in an annulus $\rho_1 < |z - a| < \rho_2$. On the other hand, if the closed curve γ is contained in a half plane which does not contain a, the integral vanishes, for in such a half plane a single-valued and analytic branch of $\log (z - a)$ can be defined.

EXERCISES

1. Compute

$$\int_\gamma x\,dz$$

where γ is the directed line segment from 0 to $1 + i$.

2. Compute

$$\int_{|z|=r} x\,dz,$$

for the positive sense of the circle, in two ways: first, by use of a parameter, and second, by observing that $x = \frac{1}{2}(z + \bar{z}) = \frac{1}{2}\left(z + \frac{r^2}{z}\right)$ on the circle.

3. Compute

$$\int_{|z|=2} \frac{dz}{z^2 - 1}$$

for the positive sense of the circle.

4. Compute

$$\int_{|z|=1} |z - 1| \cdot |dz|.$$

5. Suppose that $f(z)$ is analytic on a closed curve γ (i.e., f is analytic in a region that contains γ). Show that

$$\int_\gamma \overline{f(z)} f'(z)\,dz$$

is purely imaginary. (The continuity of $f'(z)$ is taken for granted.)

6. Assume that $f(z)$ is analytic and satisfies the inequality $|f(z) - 1| < 1$ in a region Ω. Show that

$$\int_\gamma \frac{f'(z)}{f(z)}\,dz = 0$$

for every closed curve in Ω. (The continuity of $f'(z)$ is taken for granted.)

7. If $P(z)$ is a polynomial and C denotes the circle $|z - a| = R$, what is the value of $\int_C P(z)\,d\bar{z}$? *Answer:* $-2\pi i R^2 P'(a)$.

8. Describe a set of circumstances under which the formula

$$\int_\gamma \log z \, dz = 0$$

is meaningful and true.

1.4. Cauchy's Theorem for a Rectangle. There are several forms of Cauchy's theorem, but they differ in their topological rather than in their analytical content. It is natural to begin with a case in which the topological considerations are trivial.

We consider, specifically, a rectangle R defined by inequalities $a \leqq x \leqq b, c \leqq y \leqq d$. Its perimeter can be considered as a simple closed curve consisting of four line segments whose direction we choose so that R lies to the left of the directed segments. The order of the vertices is thus (a,c), (b,c), (b,d), (a,d). We refer to this closed curve as the *boundary curve* or *contour* of R, and we denote it by ∂R.†

We emphasize that R is chosen as a closed point set and, hence, is not a region. In the theorem that follows we consider a function which is analytic on the rectangle R. We recall to the reader that such a function is by definition defined and analytic in a region which contains R.

The following is a preliminary version of *Cauchy's theorem:*

Theorem 2. *If the function $f(z)$ is analytic on R, then*

$$\int_{\partial R} f(z) \, dz = 0. \tag{12}$$

The proof is based on the method of bisection. Let us introduce the notation

$$\eta(R) = \int_{\partial R} f(z) \, dz$$

which we will also use for any rectangle contained in the given one. If R is divided into four congruent rectangles $R^{(1)}$, $R^{(2)}$, $R^{(3)}$, $R^{(4)}$, we find that

$$\eta(R) = \eta(R^{(1)}) + \eta(R^{(2)}) + \eta(R^{(3)}) + \eta(R^{(4)}), \tag{13}$$

for the integrals over the common sides cancel each other. It is important to note that this fact can be verified explicitly and does not make illicit use of geometric intuition. Nevertheless, a reference to Fig. 16 is helpful.

† This is standard notation, and we shall use it repeatedly. Note that by earlier convention ∂R is also the boundary of R as a point set (Chap. 3, Sec. 1.2).

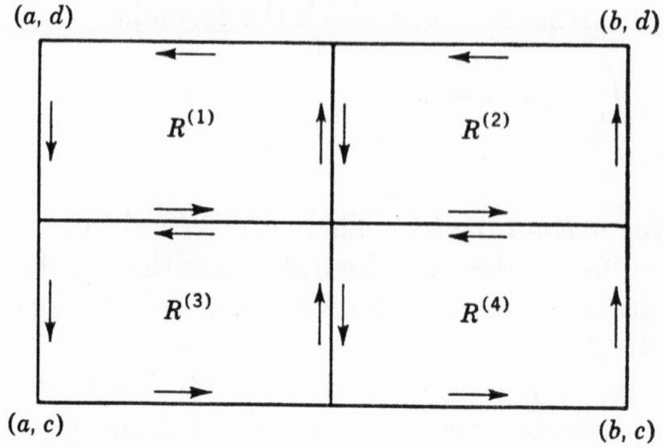

FIG. 16. Bisection of rectangle.

It follows from (13) that at least one of the rectangles $R^{(k)}$, $k = 1, 2, 3, 4$, must satisfy the condition

$$|\eta(R^{(k)})| \geqq \tfrac{1}{4}|\eta(R)|.$$

We denote this rectangle by R_1; if several $R^{(k)}$ have this property, the choice shall be made according to some definite rule.

This process can be repeated indefinitely, and we obtain a sequence of nested rectangles $R \supset R_1 \supset R_2 \supset \cdots \supset R_n \supset \cdots$ with the property

$$|\eta(R_n)| \geqq \tfrac{1}{4}|\eta(R_{n-1})|$$

and hence

$$|\eta(R_n)| \geqq 4^{-n}|\eta(R)|. \tag{14}$$

The rectangles R_n converge to a point $z^* \in R$ in the sense that R_n will be contained in a prescribed neighborhood $|z - z^*| < \delta$ as soon as n is sufficiently large. First of all, we choose δ so small that $f(z)$ is defined and analytic in $|z - z^*| < \delta$. Secondly, if $\varepsilon > 0$ is given, we can choose δ so that

$$\left|\frac{f(z) - f(z^*)}{z - z^*} - f'(z^*)\right| < \varepsilon$$

or

$$|f(z) - f(z^*) - (z - z^*)f'(z^*)| < \varepsilon|z - z^*| \tag{15}$$

for $|z - z^*| < \delta$. We assume that δ satisfies both conditions and that R_n is contained in $|z - z^*| < \delta$.

We make now the observation that

$$\int_{\Gamma(R_n)} dz = 0$$
$$\int_{\Gamma(R_n)} z\,dz = 0.$$

These trivial special cases of our theorem have already been proved in Sec. 1.1. We recall that the proof depended on the fact that 1 and z are the derivatives of z and $z^2/2$, respectively.

By virtue of these equations we are able to write

$$\eta(R_n) = \int_{\Gamma(R_n)} [f(z) - f(z^*) - (z - z^*)f'(z^*)]\,dz,$$

and it follows by (15) that

$$|\eta(R_n)| \leqq \varepsilon \int_{\Gamma(R_n)} |z - z^*| \cdot |dz|. \tag{16}$$

In the last integral $|z - z^*|$ is at most equal to the diagonal d_n of R_n. If L_n denotes the length of the perimeter of R_n, the integral is hence $\leqq d_nL_n$. But if d and L are the corresponding quantities for the original rectangle R, it is clear that $d_n = 2^{-n}d$ and $L_n = 2^{-n}L$. By (16) we have hence

$$|\eta(R_n)| \leqq 4^{-n}\, dL\, \varepsilon,$$

and comparison with (14) yields

$$|\eta(R)| \leqq dL\, \varepsilon.$$

Since ε is arbitrary, we can only have $\eta(R) = 0$, and the theorem is proved.

This beautiful proof, which could hardly be simpler, is essentially due to É. Goursat who discovered that the classical hypothesis of a continuous $f'(z)$ is redundant. At the same time the proof is simpler than the earlier proofs inasmuch as it leans neither on double integration nor on differentiation under the integral sign.

The hypothesis in Theorem 2 can be weakened considerably. We shall prove at once the following stronger theorem which will find very important use.

Theorem 3. *Let $f(z)$ be analytic on the set R' obtained from a rectangle R by omitting a finite number of interior points ζ_j. If it is true that*

$$\lim_{z\to\zeta_j}(z - \zeta_j)f(z) = 0$$

for all j, then

$$\int_{\partial R} f(z)\,dz = 0.$$

It is sufficient to consider the case of a single exceptional point ζ, for evidently R can be divided into smaller rectangles which contain at most one ζ_j.

We divide R into nine rectangles, as shown in Fig. 17, and apply

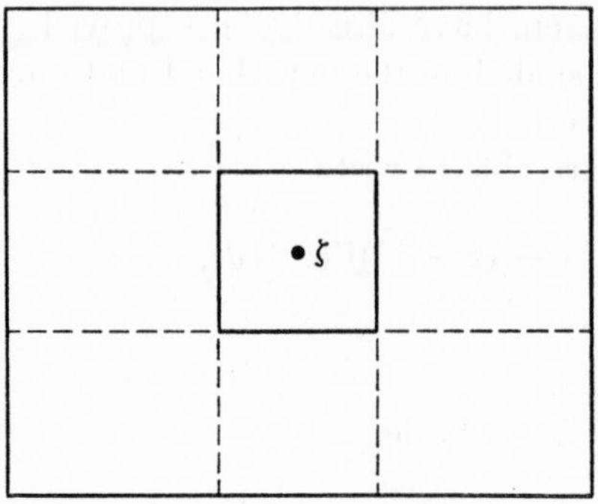

FIG. 17

Theorem 2 to all but the rectangle R_0 in the center. If the corresponding equations (12) are added, we obtain, after cancellations,

$$\int_{\partial R} f\,dz = \int_{\partial R_0} f\,dz. \tag{17}$$

If $\varepsilon > 0$ we can choose the rectangle R_0 so small that

$$|f(z)| \leqq \frac{\varepsilon}{|z - \zeta|}$$

on ∂R_0. By (17) we have thus

$$\left| \int_{\partial R} f\,dz \right| \leqq \varepsilon \int_{\partial R_0} \frac{|dz|}{|z - \zeta|}.$$

If we assume, as we may, that R_0 is a square of center ζ, elementary estimates show that

$$\int_{\partial R_0} \frac{|dz|}{|z - \zeta|} < 8.$$

Thus we obtain

$$\left| \int_{\partial R} f\,dz \right| < 8\varepsilon,$$

and since ε is arbitrary the theorem follows.

We observe that the hypothesis of the theorem is certainly fulfilled if $f(z)$ is analytic and *bounded* on R'.

1.5. Cauchy's Theorem in a Circular Disk. It is not true that the integral of an analytic function over a closed curve is always zero.

Indeed, we have found that

$$\int_C \frac{dz}{z - a} = 2\pi i$$

when C is a circle about a. In order to make sure that the integral vanishes, it is necessary to make a special assumption concerning the region Ω in which $f(z)$ is known to be analytic and to which the curve γ is restricted. We are not yet in a position to formulate this condition, and for this reason we must restrict attention to a very special case. In what follows we assume that Ω is an open circular disk $|z - z_0| < \rho$ to be denoted by Δ.

Theorem 4. *If $f(z)$ is analytic in an open disk Δ, then*

(18) $$\int_\gamma f(z)\,dz = 0$$

for every closed curve γ in Δ.

The proof is a repetition of the argument used in proving the second half of Theorem 1. We define a function $F(z)$ by

(19) $$F(z) = \int_\sigma f\,dz$$

where σ consists of the horizontal line segment from the center (x_0,y_0) to (x,y_0) and the vertical segment from (x,y_0) to (x,y); it is immediately seen that $\partial F/\partial y = if(z)$. On the other hand, by Theorem 2 σ can be replaced by a path consisting of a vertical segment followed by a horizontal segment. This choice defines the same function $F(z)$, and we obtain $\partial F/\partial x = f(z)$. Hence $F(z)$ is analytic in Δ with the derivative $f(z)$, and $f(z)\,dz$ is an exact differential.

Clearly, the same proof would go through for any region which contains the rectangle with the opposite vertices z_0 and z as soon as it contains z. A rectangle, a half plane, or the inside of an ellipse all have this property, and hence Theorem 4 holds for any of these regions. By this method we cannot, however, reach full generality.

For the applications it is very important that the conclusion of Theorem 4 remains valid under the weaker condition of Theorem 3. We state this as a separate theorem.

Theorem 5. *Let $f(z)$ be analytic in the region Δ' obtained by omitting a finite number of points ζ_j from an open disk Δ. If $f(z)$ satisfies the condition $\lim_{z\to\zeta_j}(z - \zeta_j)f(z) = 0$ for all j, then (17) holds for any closed curve γ in Δ'.*

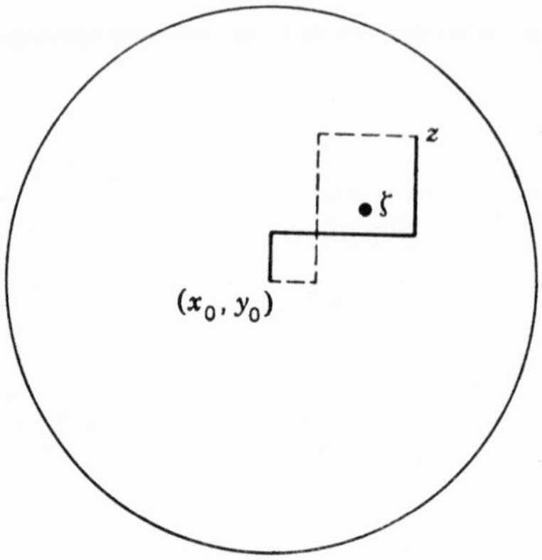

FIG. 18

The proof must be modified, for we cannot let σ pass through the exceptional points. Assume first that no ζ_j lies on the lines $x = x_0$ and $y = y_0$. It is then possible to avoid the exceptional points by letting σ consist of three segments (Fig. 18). By an obvious application of Theorem 3 we find that the value of $F(z)$ in (18) is independent of the choice of the middle segment; moreover, the last segment can be either vertical or horizontal. We conclude as before that $F(z)$ is an indefinite integral of $f(z)$, and the theorem follows.

In case there are exceptional points on the lines $x = x_0$ and $y = y_0$ the reader will easily convince himself that a similar proof can be carried out, provided that we use four line segments in the place of three.

2. CAUCHY'S INTEGRAL FORMULA

Through a very simple application of Cauchy's theorem it becomes possible to represent an analytic function $f(z)$ as a line integral in which the variable z enters as a parameter. This representation, known as *Cauchy's integral formula*, has numerous important applications. Above all, it enables us to study the local properties of an analytic function in great detail.

2.1. The Index of a Point with Respect to a Closed Curve. As a preliminary to the derivation of Cauchy's formula we must define a notion which in a precise way indicates how many times a closed curve winds around a fixed point not on the curve. If the curve is piecewise differentiable, as we shall assume without serious loss of generality, the definition can be based on the following lemma:

Lemma 1. *If the piecewise differentiable closed curve γ does not pass through the point a, then the value of the integral*

$$\int_\gamma \frac{dz}{z-a}$$

is a multiple of $2\pi i$.

This lemma may seem trivial, for we can write

$$\int_\gamma \frac{dz}{z-a} = \int_\gamma d \log (z-a) = \int_\gamma d \log |z-a| + i \int_\gamma d \arg (z-a).$$

When z describes a closed curve, $\log |z-a|$ returns to its initial value and $\arg (z-a)$ increases or decreases by a multiple of 2π. This would seem to imply the lemma, but more careful thought shows that the reasoning is of no value unless we define $\arg (z-a)$ in a unique way.

The simplest proof is computational. If the equation of γ is $z = z(t)$, $\alpha \leqq t \leqq \beta$, let us consider the function

$$h(t) = \int_\alpha^t \frac{z'(t)}{z(t)-a}\,dt.$$

It is defined and continuous on the closed interval $[\alpha,\beta]$, and it has the derivative

$$h'(t) = \frac{z'(t)}{z(t)-a}$$

whenever $z'(t)$ is continuous. From this equation it follows that the derivative of $e^{-h(t)}(z(t)-a)$ vanishes except perhaps at a finite number of points, and since this function is continuous it must reduce to a constant. We have thus

$$e^{h(t)} = \frac{z(t)-a}{z(\alpha)-a}.$$

Since $z(\beta) = z(\alpha)$ we obtain $e^{h(\beta)} = 1$, and therefore $h(\beta)$ must be a multiple of $2\pi i$. This proves the lemma.

We can now define *the index of the point a with respect to the curve γ* by the equation

$$n(\gamma,a) = \frac{1}{2\pi i}\int_\gamma \frac{dz}{z-a}.$$

With a suggestive terminology the index is also called the *winding number* of γ with respect to a.

It is clear that $n(-\gamma,a) = -n(\gamma,a)$.

The following property is an immediate consequence of Theorem 4:

(i) *If γ lies inside of a circle, then $n(\gamma,a) = 0$ for all points a outside of the same circle.*

As a point set γ is closed and bounded. Its complement is open and can be represented as a union of disjoint regions, the components of the complement. We shall say, for short, that γ *determines* these regions. If the complementary regions are considered in the extended plane, there is exactly one which contains the point at infinity. Consequently, γ determines one and only one unbounded region.

(ii) *As a function of a the index $n(\gamma,a)$ is constant in each of the regions determined by γ, and zero in the unbounded region.*

Any two points in the same region determined by γ can be joined by a polygon which does not meet γ. For this reason it is sufficient to prove that $n(\gamma,a) = n(\gamma,b)$ if γ does not meet the line segment from a to b. Outside of this segment the function $(z - a)/(z - b)$ is never real and $\leqq 0$. For this reason the principal branch of $\log [(z - a)/(z - b)]$ is analytic in the complement of the segment. Its derivative is equal to $(z - a)^{-1} - (z - b)^{-1}$, and if γ does not meet the segment we must have

$$\int_\gamma \left(\frac{1}{z-a} - \frac{1}{z-b}\right) dz = 0;$$

hence $n(\gamma,a) = n(\gamma,b)$. If $|a|$ is sufficiently large, γ is contained in a disk $|z| < \rho < |a|$ and we conclude by (i) that $n(\gamma,a) = 0$. This proves that $n(\gamma,a) = 0$ in the unbounded region.

We shall find the case $n(\gamma,a) = 1$ particularly important, and it is desirable to formulate a geometric condition which leads to this consequence. For simplicity we take $a = 0$.

Lemma 2. *Let z_1, z_2 be two points on a closed curve γ which does not pass through the origin. Denote the subarc from z_1 to z_2 in the direction of the curve by γ_1, and the subarc from z_2 to z_1 by γ_2. Suppose that z_1 lies in the lower half plane and z_2 in the upper half plane. If γ_1 does not meet the negative real axis and γ_2 does not meet the positive real axis, then $n(\gamma,0) = 1$.*

For the proof we draw the half lines L_1 and L_2 from the origin through z_1 and z_2 (Fig. 19). Let ζ_1, ζ_2 be the points in which L_1, L_2 intersect a circle C about the origin. If C is described in the positive sense, the arc C_1 from ζ_1 to ζ_2 does not intersect the negative axis, and the arc C_2 from ζ_2 to ζ_1 does not intersect the positive axis. Denote the directed line segments from z_1 to ζ_1 and from z_2 to ζ_2 by δ_1, δ_2. Introducing the closed curves $\sigma_1 = \gamma_1 + \delta_2 - C_1 - \delta_1$, $\sigma_2 = \gamma_2 + \delta_1 - C_2 - \delta_2$ we find that $n(\gamma,0) = n(C,0) + n(\sigma_1,0) + n(\sigma_2,0)$ because of cancellations. But σ_1 does not meet the negative axis. Hence the origin belongs to the

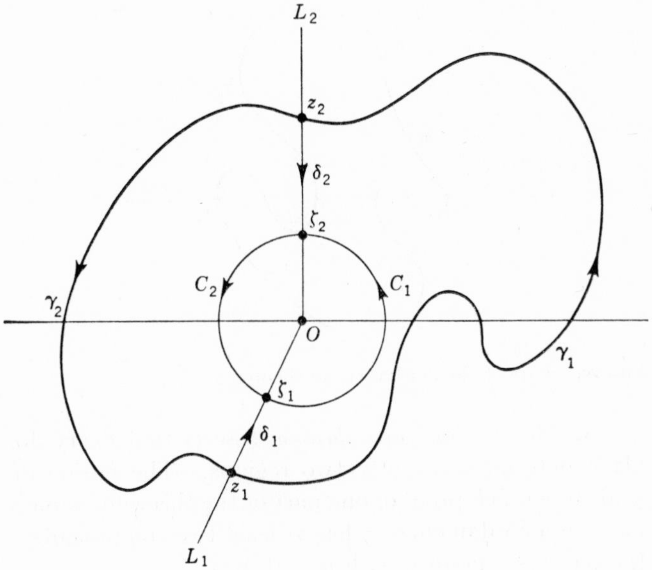

FIG. 19

unbounded region determined by σ_1, and we obtain $n(\sigma_1,0) = 0$. For a similar reason $n(\sigma_2,0) = 0$, and we obtain $n(\gamma,0) = n(C,0) = 1$.

*EXERCISES

These are not routine exercises. They serve to illustrate the topological use of winding numbers.

1. Give an alternate proof of Lemma 1 by dividing γ into a finite number of subarcs such that there exists a single-valued branch of $\arg(z - a)$ on each subarc. Pay particular attention to the compactness argument that is needed to prove the existence of such a subdivision.

2. It is possible to define $n(\gamma,a)$ for any continuous closed curve γ that does not pass through a, whether piecewise differentiable or not. For this purpose γ is divided into subarcs $\gamma_1, \ldots, \gamma_n$, each contained in a circular disk that does not include a. Let σ_k be the directed line segment from the initial to the terminal point of γ_k, and set $\sigma = \sigma_1 + \cdots + \sigma_n$. We define $n(\gamma,a)$ to be the value of $n(\sigma,a)$.

To justify the definition, prove the following:

(*a*) the result is independent of the subdivision;

(*b*) if γ is piecewise differentiable the new definition is equivalent to the old;

(*c*) the properties (i) and (ii) of the text continue to hold.

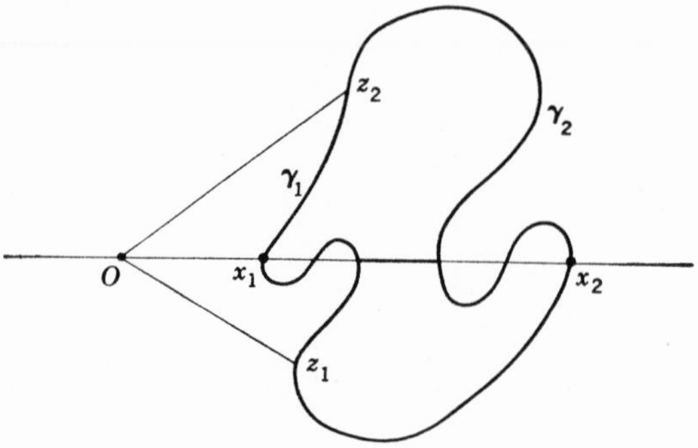

FIG. 20. Part of the Jordan curve theorem.

3. The *Jordan curve theorem* asserts that every Jordan curve in the plane determines exactly two regions. The notion of winding number leads to a quick proof of one part of the theorem, namely that the complement of a Jordan curve γ has at least two components. This will be so if there exists a point a with $n(\gamma,a) \neq 0$.

We may assume that $\text{Re } z > 0$ on γ, and that there are points z_1, $z_2 \in \gamma$ with $\text{Im } z_1 < 0$, $\text{Im } z_2 > 0$. These points may be chosen so that there are no other points of γ on the line segments from 0 to z_1 and from 0 to z_2. Let γ_1 and γ_2 be the arcs of γ from z_1 to z_2 (excluding the end points).

Let σ_1 be the closed curve that consists of the line segment from 0 to z_1 followed by γ_1 and the segment from z_2 to 0, and let σ_2 be constructed in the same way with γ_2 in the place of γ_1. Then $\sigma_1 - \sigma_2 = \pm\gamma$.

The positive real axis intersects both γ_1 and γ_2 (why?). Choose the notation so that the intersection x_2 farthest to the right is with γ_2 (Fig. 20). Prove the following:

(*a*) $n(\sigma_1,x_2) = 0$, hence $n(\sigma_1,z) = 0$ for $z \in \gamma_2$;

(*b*) $n(\sigma_1,x) = n(\sigma_2,x) = 1$ for small $x > 0$ (Lemma 2);

(*c*) the first intersection x_1 of the positive real axis with γ lies on γ_1;

(*d*) $n(\sigma_2,x_1) = 1$, hence $n(\sigma_2,z) = 1$ for $z \in \gamma_1$;

(*e*) there exists a segment of the positive real axis with one end point on γ_1, the other on γ_2, and no other points on γ. The points x between the end points satisfy $n(\gamma,x) = \pm 1$.

2.2. The Integral Formula. Let $f(z)$ be analytic in an open circular disk Δ. Consider a closed curve γ in Δ and a point $a \in \Delta$ which does not lie on γ. We apply Cauchy's theorem to the function

$$F(z) = \frac{f(z) - f(a)}{z - a}.$$

This function is analytic for $z \neq a$. For $z = a$ it is not defined, but it satisfies the condition

$$\lim_{z \to a} F(z)(z - a) = \lim_{z \to a} (f(z) - f(a)) = 0$$

which is the condition of Theorem 5. We conclude that

$$\int_\gamma \frac{f(z) - f(a)}{z - a}\, dz = 0.$$

This equation can be written in the form

$$\int_\gamma \frac{f(z)\, dz}{z - a} = f(a) \int_\gamma \frac{dz}{z - a},$$

and we observe that the integral in the right-hand member is by definition $2\pi i \cdot n(\gamma,a)$. We have thus proved:

Theorem 6. *Suppose that $f(z)$ is analytic in an open disk Δ, and let γ be a closed curve in Δ. For any point a not on γ*

$$n(\gamma,a) \cdot f(a) = \frac{1}{2\pi i} \int_\gamma \frac{f(z)\, dz}{z - a}, \tag{20}$$

where $n(\gamma,a)$ is the index of a with respect to γ.

In this statement we have suppressed the requirement that a be a point in Δ. We have done so in view of the obvious interpretation of the formula (20) for the case that a is not in Δ. Indeed, in this case $n(\gamma,a)$ and the integral in the right-hand member are both zero, and the formula remains correct whatever value we wish to assign to $f(a)$.

It is clear that Theorem 6 remains valid for any region Ω to which Theorem 5 can be applied. The presence of exceptional points ζ_j is permitted, provided none of them coincides with a.

The most common application is to the case where $n(\gamma,a) = 1$. We have then

$$f(a) = \frac{1}{2\pi i} \int_\gamma \frac{f(z)\, dz}{z - a}, \tag{21}$$

and this we interpret as a *representation formula.* Indeed, it permits us to compute $f(a)$ as soon as the values of $f(z)$ on γ are given, together with the fact that $f(z)$ is analytic in Δ. In (21) we may let a take different values, provided that the order of a with respect to γ remains equal to 1. We may thus treat a as a variable, and it is convenient to change the notation and rewrite (21) in the form

$$f(z) = \frac{1}{2\pi i} \int_\gamma \frac{f(\zeta)\, d\zeta}{\zeta - z}. \tag{22}$$

It is this formula which is usually referred to as *Cauchy's integral formula.* We must remember that it is valid only when $n(\gamma,z) = 1$, and that we have proved it only when $f(z)$ is analytic in a disk.

EXERCISES

1. Compute

$$\int_{|z|=1} \frac{e^z}{z}\,dz.$$

2. Compute

$$\int_{|z|=2} \frac{dz}{z^2+1}$$

by decomposition of the integrand in partial fractions.

3. Compute

$$\int_{|z|=\rho} \frac{|dz|}{|z-a|^2}$$

under the condition $|a| \neq \rho$. *Hint:* make use of the equations $z\bar{z} = \rho^2$ and

$$|dz| = -i\rho\,\frac{dz}{z}.$$

2.3. Higher Derivatives. The representation formula (22) gives us an ideal tool for the study of the local properties of analytic functions. In particular we can now show that an analytic function has derivatives of all orders, which are then also analytic.

We consider a function $f(z)$ which is analytic in an arbitrary region Ω. To a point $a \in \Omega$ we determine a δ-neighborhood Δ contained in Ω, and in Δ a circle C about a. Theorem 6 can be applied to $f(z)$ in Δ. Since $n(C,a) = 1$ we have $n(C,z) = 1$ for all points z inside of C. For such z we obtain by (22)

$$f(z) = \frac{1}{2\pi i}\int_C \frac{f(\zeta)\,d\zeta}{\zeta - z}.$$

Provided that the integral can be differentiated under the sign of integration we find

$$f'(z) = \frac{1}{2\pi i}\int_C \frac{f(\zeta)\,d\zeta}{(\zeta - z)^2} \tag{23}$$

and

$$f^{(n)}(z) = \frac{n!}{2\pi i}\int_C \frac{f(\zeta)\,d\zeta}{(\zeta - z)^{n+1}}. \tag{24}$$

If the differentiations can be justified, we shall have proved the existence of all derivatives at the points inside of C. Since every point in Ω lies inside of some such circle, the existence will be proved in the whole region Ω. At the same time we shall have obtained a convenient representation formula for the derivatives.

For the justification we could either refer to corresponding theorems in the real case, or we could prove a general theorem concerning line integrals whose integrand depends analytically on a parameter. Actually, we shall prove only the following lemma which is all we need in the present case:

Lemma 3. *Suppose that $\varphi(\zeta)$ is continuous on the arc γ. Then the function*

$$F_n(z) = \int_\gamma \frac{\varphi(\zeta)\, d\zeta}{(\zeta - z)^n}$$

is analytic in each of the regions determined by γ, and its derivative is $F'_n(z) = nF_{n+1}(z)$.

We prove first that $F_1(z)$ is continuous. Let z_0 be a point not on γ, and choose the neighborhood $|z - z_0| < \delta$ so that it does not meet γ. By restricting z to the smaller neighborhood $|z - z_0| < \delta/2$ we attain that $|\zeta - z| > \delta/2$ for all $\zeta \in \gamma$. From

$$F_1(z) - F_1(z_0) = (z - z_0) \int_\gamma \frac{\varphi(\zeta)\, d\zeta}{(\zeta - z)(\zeta - z_0)}$$

we obtain at once

$$|F_1(z) - F_1(z_0)| < |z - z_0| \cdot \frac{2}{\delta^2} \int_\gamma |\varphi|\, |d\zeta|,$$

and this inequality proves the continuity of $F_1(z)$ at z_0.

From this part of the lemma, applied to the function $\varphi(\zeta)/(\zeta - z_0)$, we conclude that the difference quotient

$$\frac{F_1(z) - F_1(z_0)}{z - z_0} = \int_\gamma \frac{\varphi(\zeta)\, d\zeta}{(\zeta - z)(\zeta - z_0)}$$

tends to the limit $F_2(z_0)$ as $z \to z_0$. Hence it is proved that $F'_1(z) = F_2(z)$.

The general case is proved by induction. Suppose we have shown that $F'_{n-1}(z) = (n - 1)F_n(z)$. From the identity

$$F_n(z) - F_n(z_0)$$
$$= \left[\int_\gamma \frac{\varphi\, d\zeta}{(\zeta - z)^{n-1}(\zeta - z_0)} - \int_\gamma \frac{\varphi\, d\zeta}{(\zeta - z_0)^n}\right] + (z - z_0) \int_\gamma \frac{\varphi\, d\zeta}{(\zeta - z)^n(\zeta - z_0)}$$

we can conclude that $F_n(z)$ is continuous. Indeed, by the induction hypothesis, applied to $\varphi(\zeta)/(\zeta - z_0)$, the first term tends to zero for $z \to z_0$, and in the second term the factor of $z - z_0$ is bounded in a neighborhood of z_0. Now, if we divide the identity by $z - z_0$ and let z tend to z_0, the quotient in the first term tends to a derivative which by the induction hypothesis equals $(n - 1)F_{n+1}(z_0)$. The remaining factor in the second term is continuous, by what we have already proved, and has the limit $F_{n+1}(z_0)$. Hence $F_n'(z_0)$ exists and equals $nF_{n+1}(z_0)$.

It is clear that Lemma 3 is just what is needed in order to deduce (23) and (24) in a rigorous way. We have thus proved that an analytic function has derivatives of all orders which are analytic and can be represented by the formula (24).

Among the consequences of this result we like to single out two classical theorems. The first is known as *Morera's theorem*, and it can be stated as follows:

If $f(z)$ is defined and continuous in a region Ω, and if $\int_\gamma f\,dz = 0$ for all closed curves γ in Ω, then $f(z)$ is analytic in Ω.

The hypothesis implies, as we have already remarked in Sec. 1.3, that $f(z)$ is the derivative of an analytic function $F(z)$. We know now that $f(z)$ is then itself analytic.

A second classical result goes under the name of *Liouville's theorem:*

A function which is analytic and bounded in the whole plane must reduce to a constant.

For the proof we make use of a simple estimate derived from (24). Let the radius of C be r, and assume that $|f(\zeta)| \leqq M$ on C. If we apply (24) with $z = a$, we obtain at once

$$|f^{(n)}(a)| \leqq Mn!r^{-n}. \tag{25}$$

For Liouville's theorem we need only the case $n = 1$. The hypothesis means that $|f(\zeta)| \leqq M$ on all circles. Hence we can let r tend to ∞, and (25) leads to $f'(a) = 0$ for all a. We conclude that the function is constant.

Liouville's theorem leads to an almost trivial proof of the *fundamental theorem of algebra*. Suppose that $P(z)$ is a polynomial of degree > 0. If $P(z)$ were never zero, the function $1/P(z)$ would be analytic in the whole plane. We know that $P(z) \to \infty$ for $z \to \infty$, and therefore $1/P(z)$ tends to zero. This implies boundedness (the absolute value is continuous on the Riemann sphere and has thus a finite maximum), and by Liouville's theorem $1/P(z)$ would be constant. Since this is not so, the equation $P(z) = 0$ must have a root.

The inequality (25) is known as *Cauchy's estimate*. It shows above all that the successive derivatives of an analytic function cannot be arbitrary; there must always exist an M and an r so that (25) is fulfilled. In order to make the best use of the inequality it is important that r be judiciously chosen, the object being to minimize the function $M(r)r^{-n}$, where $M(r)$ is the maximum of $|f|$ on $|\zeta - a| = r$.

EXERCISES

1. Compute

$$\int_{|z|=1} e^z z^{-n}\,dz, \qquad \int_{|z|=2} z^n(1-z)^m\,dz, \qquad \int_{|z|=\rho} |z-a|^{-4}\,|dz|\ (|a| \neq \rho).$$

2. Prove that a function which is analytic in the whole plane and satisfies an inequality $|f(z)| < |z|^n$ for some n and all sufficiently large $|z|$ reduces to a polynomial.

3. If $f(z)$ is analytic and $|f(z)| \leqq M$ for $|z| \leqq R$, find an upper bound for $|f^{(n)}(z)|$ in $|z| \leqq \rho < R$.

4. If $f(z)$ is analytic for $|z| < 1$ and $|f(z)| \leqq 1/(1 - |z|)$, find the best estimate of $|f^{(n)}(0)|$ that Cauchy's inequality will yield.

5. Show that the successive derivatives of an analytic function at a point can never satisfy $|f^{(n)}(z)| > n!n^n$. Formulate a sharper theorem of the same kind.

***6.** A more general form of Lemma 3 reads as follows:

Let the function $\varphi(z,t)$ be continuous as a function of both variables when z lies in a region Ω and $\alpha \leqq t \leqq \beta$. Suppose further that $\varphi(z,t)$ is analytic as a function of $z \in \Omega$ for any fixed t. Then

$$F(z) = \int_\alpha^\beta \varphi(z,t)\,dt$$

is analytic in z and

$$F'(z) = \int_\alpha^\beta \frac{\partial\varphi(z,t)}{\partial z}\,dt. \tag{26}$$

To prove this represent $\varphi(z,t)$ as a Cauchy integral

$$\varphi(z,t) = \frac{1}{2\pi i}\int_C \frac{\varphi(\zeta,t)}{\zeta - z}\,d\zeta.$$

Fill in the necessary details to obtain

$$F(z) = \int_C \left(\frac{1}{2\pi i}\int_\alpha^\beta \varphi(\zeta,t)\,dt\right)\frac{d\zeta}{\zeta - z}$$

and use Lemma 3 to prove (26).

Remark: It is interesting to note that the powerful Cauchy theorem makes it unnecessary to assume that $\partial F/\partial z$ is a uniform limit of the difference quotient.

3. LOCAL PROPERTIES OF ANALYTIC FUNCTIONS

We have already proved that an analytic function has derivatives of all orders. In this section we will make a closer study of the local properties. It will include a classification of the *isolated singularities* of analytic functions.

3.1. Removable Singularities. Taylor's Theorem. In Theorem 3 we introduced a weaker condition which could be substituted for analyticity at a finite number of points without affecting the end result. We showed moreover, in Theorem 5, that Cauchy's theorem in a circular disk remains true under these weaker conditions. This was an essential point in our derivation of Cauchy's integral formula, for we were required to apply Cauchy's theorem to a function of the form $(f(z) - f(a))/(z - a)$.

Finally, it was pointed out that Cauchy's integral formula remains valid in the presence of a finite number of exceptional points, all satisfying the fundamental condition of Theorem 3, provided that none of them coincides with a. This remark is more important than it may seem on the surface. Indeed, Cauchy's formula provides us with a representation of $f(z)$ through an integral which in its dependence on z has the same character at the exceptional points as everywhere else. It follows that the exceptional points are such only by lack of information, and not by their intrinsic nature. Points with this character are called *removable singularities.* We shall prove the following precise theorem:

Theorem 7. *Suppose that $f(z)$ is analytic in the region Ω' obtained by omitting a point a from a region Ω. A necessary and sufficient condition that there exist an analytic function in Ω which coincides with $f(z)$ in Ω' is that $\lim_{z\to a} (z - a)f(z) = 0$. The extended function is uniquely determined.*

The necessity and the uniqueness are trivial since the extended function must be continuous at a. To prove the sufficiency we draw a circle C about a so that C and its inside are contained in Ω. Cauchy's formula is valid, and we can write

$$f(z) = \frac{1}{2\pi i}\int_C \frac{f(\zeta)\,d\zeta}{\zeta - z}$$

for all $z \neq a$ inside of C. But the integral in the right-hand member represents an analytic function of z throughout the inside of C. Consequently, the function which is equal to $f(z)$ for $z \neq a$ and which has the value

$$\frac{1}{2\pi i}\int_C \frac{f(\zeta)\,d\zeta}{\zeta - a} \tag{27}$$

for $z = a$ is analytic in Ω. It is natural to denote the extended function by $f(z)$ and the value (27) by $f(a)$.

We apply this result to the function

$$F(z) = \frac{f(z) - f(a)}{z - a}$$

used in the proof of Cauchy's formula. It is not defined for $z = a$, but it satisfies the condition $\lim_{z\to a} (z - a)F(z) = 0$. The limit of $F(z)$ as z tends to a is $f'(a)$. Hence there exists an analytic function which is equal to $F(z)$ for $z \neq a$ and equal to $f'(a)$ for $z = a$. Let us denote this function by $f_1(z)$. Repeating the process we can define an analytic function $f_2(z)$ which equals $(f_1(z) - f_1(a))/(z - a)$ for $z \neq a$ and $f_1'(a)$ for $z = a$, and so on.

The recursive scheme by which $f_n(z)$ is defined can be written in the form

$$\begin{aligned} f(z) &= f(a) + (z - a)f_1(z) \\ f_1(z) &= f_1(a) + (z - a)f_2(z) \\ &\cdots\cdots\cdots\cdots\cdots \\ f_{n-1}(z) &= f_{n-1}(a) + (z - a)f_n(z). \end{aligned}$$

From these equations which are trivially valid also for $z = a$ we obtain

$$f(z) = f(a) + (z - a)f_1(a) + (z - a)^2 f_2(a) + \cdots + (z - a)^{n-1} f_{n-1}(a) + (z - a)^n f_n(z).$$

Differentiating n times and setting $z = a$ we find

$$f^{(n)}(a) = n! f_n(a).$$

This determines the coefficients $f_n(a)$, and we obtain the following form of *Taylor's theorem:*

Theorem 8. *If $f(z)$ is analytic in a region Ω, containing a, it is possible to write*

$$f(z) = f(a) + \frac{f'(a)}{1!}(z - a) + \frac{f''(a)}{2!}(z - a)^2 + \cdots + \frac{f^{(n-1)}(a)}{(n - 1)!}(z - a)^{n-1} + f_n(z)(z - a)^n, \tag{28}$$

where $f_n(z)$ is analytic in Ω.

This finite development must be well distinguished from the infinite *Taylor series* which we will study later. It is, however, the finite development (28) which is the most useful for the study of the local properties of $f(z)$. Its usefulness is enhanced by the fact that $f_n(z)$ has a simple explicit expression as a line integral.

Using the same circle C as before we have first

$$f_n(z) = \frac{1}{2\pi i}\int_C \frac{f_n(\zeta)\,d\zeta}{\zeta - z}.$$

For $f_n(\zeta)$ we substitute the expression obtained from (26). There will be one main term containing $f(\zeta)$. The remaining terms are, except for constant factors, of the form

$$F_\nu(a) = \int_C \frac{d\zeta}{(\zeta - a)^\nu(\zeta - z)}, \qquad \nu \geqq 1.$$

But

$$F_1(a) = \frac{1}{z - a}\int_C \left(\frac{1}{\zeta - z} - \frac{1}{\zeta - a}\right) d\zeta = 0,$$

identically for all a inside of C. By Lemma 3 we have $F_{\nu+1}(a) = F_1^{(\nu)}(a)/\nu!$ and thus $F_\nu(a) = 0$ for all $\nu \geqq 1$. Hence the expression for $f_n(z)$ reduces to

$$f_n(z) = \frac{1}{2\pi i}\int_C \frac{f(\zeta)\,d\zeta}{(\zeta - a)^n(\zeta - z)}. \tag{29}$$

The representation is valid inside of C.

3.2. Zeros and Poles. If $f(a)$ and all derivatives $f^{(\nu)}(a)$ vanish, we can write by (28)

$$f(z) = f_n(z)(z - a)^n \tag{30}$$

for any n. An estimate for $f_n(z)$ can be obtained by (29). The disk with the circumference C has to be contained in the region Ω in which $f(z)$ is defined and analytic. The absolute value $|f(z)|$ has a maximum M on C; if the radius of C is denoted by R, we find

$$|f_n(z)| \leqq \frac{M}{R^{n-1}(R - |z - a|)}$$

for $|z - a| < R$. By (28) we have thus

$$|f(z)| \leqq \left(\frac{|z - a|}{R}\right)^n \cdot \frac{MR}{R - |z - a|}.$$

But $(|z - a|/R)^n \to 0$ for $n \to \infty$, since $|z - a| < R$. Hence $f(z) = 0$ inside of C.

We show now that $f(z)$ is identically zero in all of Ω. Let E_1 be the set on which $f(z)$ and all derivatives vanish and E_2 the set on which the function or one of the derivatives is different from zero. E_1 is open by the above reasoning, and E_2 is open because the function and all derivatives are continuous. Therefore either E_1 or E_2 must be empty. If E_2 is empty, the function is identically zero. If E_1 is empty, $f(z)$ can never vanish together with all its derivatives.

Assume that $f(z)$ is not identically zero. Then, if $f(a) = 0$, there exists a first derivative $f^{(h)}(a)$ which is different from zero. We say then that a is a *zero of order* h, and the result that we have just proved expresses that there are no zeros of infinite order. In this respect an analytic function has the same local behavior as a polynomial, and just as in the case of polynomials we find that it is possible to write $f(z) = (z - a)^h f_h(z)$ where $f_h(z)$ is analytic and $f_h(a) \neq 0$.

In the same situation, since $f_h(z)$ is continuous, $f_h(z) \neq 0$ in a neighborhood of a and $z = a$ is the only zero of $f(z)$ in this neighborhood. In other words, the zeros of an analytic function which does not vanish identically are *isolated*. This property can also be formulated as a uniqueness theorem: *If $f(z)$ and $g(z)$ are analytic in Ω, and if $f(z) = g(z)$ on a set which has an accumulation point in Ω, then $f(z)$ is identically equal to $g(z)$.* The conclusion follows by consideration of the difference $f(z) - g(z)$.

Particular instances of this result which deserve to be quoted are the following: If $f(z)$ is identically zero in a subregion of Ω, then it is identically zero in Ω, and the same is true if $f(z)$ vanishes on an arc which does not reduce to a point. We can also say that an analytic function is uniquely determined by its values on any set with an accumulation point in the region of analyticity. This does not mean that we know of any way in which the values of the function can be computed.

We consider now a function $f(z)$ which is analytic in a neighborhood of a, except perhaps at a itself. In other words, $f(z)$ shall be analytic in a region $0 < |z - a| < \delta$. The point a is called an *isolated singularity* of $f(z)$. We have already treated the case of a removable singularity. Since we can then define $f(a)$ so that $f(z)$ becomes analytic in the disk $|z - a| < \delta$, it needs no further consideration.†

If $\lim_{z \to a} f(z) = \infty$, the point a is said to be a *pole* of $f(z)$, and we set $f(a) = \infty$. There exists a $\delta' \leqq \delta$ such that $f(z) \neq 0$ for $0 < |z - a| < \delta'$. In this region the function $g(z) = 1/f(z)$ is defined and analytic. But the singularity of $g(z)$ at a is removable, and $g(z)$ has an analytic exten-

† If a is a removable singularity, $f(z)$ is frequently said to be *regular* at a; this term is sometimes used as a synonym for analytic.

sion with $g(a) = 0$. Since $g(z)$ does not vanish identically, the zero at a has a finite order, and we can write $g(z) = (z - a)^h g_h(z)$ with $g_h(a) \neq 0$. The number h is the *order* of the pole, and $f(z)$ has the representation $f(z) = (z - a)^{-h} f_h(z)$ where $f_h(z) = 1/g_h(z)$ is analytic and different from zero in a neighborhood of a. The nature of a pole is thus exactly the same as in the case of a rational function.

A function $f(z)$ which is analytic in a region Ω, except for poles, is said to be *meromorphic* in Ω. More precisely, to every $a \in \Omega$ there shall exist a neighborhood $|z - a| < \delta$, contained in Ω, such that either $f(z)$ is analytic in the whole neighborhood, or else $f(z)$ is analytic for $0 < |z - a| < \delta$, and the isolated singularity is a pole. Observe that the poles of a meromorphic function are isolated *by definition*. The quotient $f(z)/g(z)$ of two analytic functions in Ω is a meromorphic function in Ω, provided that $g(z)$ is not identically zero. The only possible poles are the zeros of $g(z)$, but a common zero of $f(z)$ and $g(z)$ can also be a removable singularity. If this is the case, the value of the quotient must be determined by continuity. More generally, the sum, the product, and the quotient of two meromorphic functions are meromorphic. The case of an identically vanishing denominator must be excluded, unless we wish to consider the constant ∞ as a meromorphic function.

For a more detailed discussion of isolated singularities, we consider the conditions (1) $\lim_{z \to a} |z - a|^\alpha |f(z)| = 0$, (2) $\lim_{z \to a} |z - a|^\alpha |f(z)| = \infty$, for real values of α. If (1) holds for a certain α, then it holds for all larger α, and hence for some integer m. Then $(z - a)^m f(z)$ has a removable singularity and vanishes for $z = a$. Either $f(z)$ is identically zero, in which case (1) holds for all α, or $(z - a)^m f(z)$ has a zero of finite order k. In the latter case it follows at once that (1) holds for all $\alpha > h = -m - k$, while (2) holds for all $\alpha < h$. Assume now that (2) holds for some α; then it holds for all smaller α, and hence for some integer n. The function $(z - a)^n f(z)$ has a pole of finite order l, and setting $h = n + l$ we find again that (1) holds for $\alpha > h$ and (2) for $\alpha < h$. The discussion shows that there are three possibilities: (i) condition (1) holds for all α, and $f(z)$ vanishes identically; (ii) there exists an integer h such that (1) holds for $\alpha > h$ and (2) for $\alpha < h$; (iii) neither (1) nor (2) holds for any α.

Case (i) is uninteresting. In case (ii) h may be called the *algebraic order* of $f(z)$ at a. It is positive in case of a pole, negative in case of a zero, and zero if $f(z)$ is analytic but $\neq 0$ at a. The remarkable thing is that the order is always an integer; there is no single-valued analytic function which tends to 0 or ∞ like a fractional power of $|z - a|$.

In the case of a pole of order h, let us apply Theorem 8 to the analytic function $(z - a)^h f(z)$. We obtain a development of the form

$$(z - a)^h f(z) = B_h + B_{h-1}(z - a) + \cdots + B_1(z - a)^{h-1} + \varphi(z)(z - a)^h$$

where $\varphi(z)$ is analytic at $z = a$. For $z \neq a$ we can divide by $(z - a)^h$ and find

$$f(z) = B_h(z - a)^{-h} + B_{h-1}(z - a)^{-h+1} + \cdots + B_1(z - a)^{-1} + \varphi(z).$$

The part of this development which precedes $\varphi(z)$ is called the *singular part* of $f(z)$ at $z = a$. A pole has thus not only an order, but also a well-defined singular part. The difference of two functions with the same singular part is analytic at a.

In case (iii) the point a is an *essential isolated singularity.* In the neighborhood of an essential singularity $f(z)$ is at the same time unbounded and comes arbitrarily close to zero. As a characterization of the complicated behavior of a function in the neighborhood of an essential singularity, we prove the following classical theorem of Weierstrass:

Theorem 9. *An analytic function comes arbitrarily close to any complex value in every neighborhood of an essential singularity.*

If the assertion were not true, we could find a complex number A and a $\delta > 0$ such that $|f(z) - A| > \delta$ in a neighborhood of a (except for $z = a$). For any $\alpha < 0$ we have then $\lim_{z \to a} |z - a|^\alpha |f(z) - A| = \infty$. Hence a would not be an essential singularity of $f(z) - A$. Accordingly, there exists a β with $\lim_{z \to a} |z - a|^\beta |f(z) - A| = 0$, and we are free to choose $\beta > 0$. Since in that case $\lim_{z \to a} |z - a|^\beta |A| = 0$ it would follow that $\lim_{z \to a} |z - a|^\beta |f(z)| = 0$, and a would not be an essential singularity of $f(z)$. The contradiction proves the theorem.

The notion of isolated singularity applies also to functions which are analytic in a neighborhood $|z| > R$ of ∞. Since $f(\infty)$ is not defined, we treat ∞ as an isolated singularity, and by convention it has the same character of removable singularity, pole, or essential singularity as the singularity of $g(z) = f(1/z)$ at $z = 0$. If the singularity is nonessential, $f(z)$ has an algebraic order h such that $\lim_{z \to \infty} z^{-h} f(z)$ is neither zero nor infinity, and for a pole the singular part is a polynomial in z. If ∞ is an essential singularity, the function has the property expressed by Theorem 9 in every neighborhood of infinity.

EXERCISES

1. If $f(z)$ and $g(z)$ have the algebraic orders h and k at $z = a$, show that fg has the order $h + k$, f/g the order $h - k$, and $f + g$ an order which does not exceed max (h,k).

2. Show that a function which is analytic in the whole plane and has a nonessential singularity at ∞ reduces to a polynomial.

3. Show that the functions e^z, $\sin z$ and $\cos z$ have essential singularities at ∞.

4. Show that any function which is meromorphic in the extended plane is rational.

5. Show that an isolated singularity of $f(z)$ cannot be a pole of $\exp f(z)$. Deduce that an isolated singularity is removable as soon as $\operatorname{Re} f(z)$ is bounded above or below.

3.3. The Local Mapping. We begin with the proof of a general formula which enables us to determine the number of zeros of an analytic function. We are considering a function $f(z)$ which is analytic in an open disk Δ. Let γ be a closed curve in Δ such that $f(z) \neq 0$ on γ. For the sake of simplicity we suppose first that $f(z)$ has only a finite number of zeros in Δ, and we agree to denote them by $z_1, z_2, \ldots, z_n$ where each zero is repeated as many times as its order indicates.

By repeated applications of Theorem 8, or rather its consequence (30), it is clear that we can write $f(z) = (z - z_1)(z - z_2) \cdots (z - z_n)g(z)$ where $g(z)$ is analytic and $\neq 0$ in Δ. Forming the logarithmic derivative we obtain

$$\frac{f'(z)}{f(z)} = \frac{1}{z - z_1} + \frac{1}{z - z_2} + \cdots + \frac{1}{z - z_n} + \frac{g'(z)}{g(z)}$$

for $z \neq z_j$, and particularly on γ. Since $g(z) \neq 0$ in Δ, Cauchy's theorem yields

$$\int_\gamma \frac{g'(z)}{g(z)}\,dz = 0.$$

Recalling the definition of $n(\gamma,z_j)$ we find

$$n(\gamma,z_1) + n(\gamma,z_2) + \cdots + n(\gamma,z_n) = \frac{1}{2\pi i}\int_\gamma \frac{f'(z)}{f(z)}\,dz. \tag{31}$$

This is still true if $f(z)$ has infinitely many zeros in Δ. It is clear that γ is contained in a concentric disk Δ' smaller than Δ. Unless $f(z)$ is identically zero, a case which must obviously be excluded, it has only a finite number of zeros in Δ'. This is an obvious consequence of the Bolzano-Weierstrass theorem, for if there were infinitely many zeros they would have an accumulation point in the closure of Δ', and this is impossible. We can now apply (31) to the disk Δ'. The zeros outside of Δ' satisfy $n(\gamma,z_j) = 0$ and hence do not contribute to the sum in (31). We have thus proved:

Theorem 10. *Let z_j be the zeros of a function $f(z)$ which is analytic in a circular disk Δ and does not vanish identically, each zero being counted as many times as its order indicates. For every closed curve γ in Δ which does not pass through a zero*

$$\sum_j n(\gamma,z_j) = \frac{1}{2\pi i}\int_\gamma \frac{f'(z)}{f(z)}\,dz, \tag{32}$$

where the sum has only a finite number of terms $\neq 0$.

The function $w = f(z)$ maps γ onto a closed curve Γ in the w-plane, and we find

$$\int_\Gamma \frac{dw}{w} = \int_\gamma \frac{f'(z)}{f(z)}\,dz.$$

The formula (32) has thus the following interpretation:

$$n(\Gamma,0) = \sum_j n(\gamma,z_j). \tag{33}$$

The simplest and most useful application is to the case where it is known beforehand that each $n(\gamma,z_j)$ must be either 0 or 1. Then (32) yields a formula for the *total number of zeros* enclosed by γ. This is evidently the case when γ is a circle.

Let a be an arbitrary complex value, and apply Theorem 10 to $f(z) - a$. The zeros of $f(z) - a$ are the roots of the equation $f(z) = a$, and we denote them by $z_j(a)$. In the place of (32) we obtain the formula

$$\sum_j n(\gamma,z_j(a)) = \frac{1}{2\pi i}\int_\gamma \frac{f'(z)}{f(z) - a}\,dz$$

and (33) takes the form

$$n(\Gamma,a) = \sum_j n(\gamma,z_j(a)).$$

It is necessary to assume that $f(z) \neq a$ on γ.

If a and b are in the same region determined by Γ, we know that $n(\Gamma,a) = n(\Gamma,b)$, and hence we have also $\sum_j n(\gamma,z_j(a)) = \sum_j n(\gamma,z_j(b))$. If γ is a circle, it follows that $f(z)$ takes the values a and b equally many times inside of γ. The following theorem on local correspondence is an immediate consequence of this result.

Theorem 11. *Suppose that $f(z)$ is analytic at z_0, $f(z_0) = w_0$, and that $f(z) - w_0$ has a zero of order n at z_0. If $\varepsilon > 0$ is sufficiently small, there exists a corresponding $\delta > 0$ such that for all a with $|a - w_0| < \delta$ the equation $f(z) = a$ has exactly n roots in the disk $|z - z_0| < \varepsilon$.*

We can choose ε so that $f(z)$ is defined and analytic for $|z - z_0| \leqq \varepsilon$ and so that z_0 is the only zero of $f(z) - w_0$ in this disk. Let γ be the circle $|z - z_0| = \varepsilon$ and Γ its image under the mapping $w = f(z)$. Since w_0 belongs to the complement of the closed set Γ, there exists a neighborhood $|w - w_0| < \delta$ which does not intersect Γ (Fig. 21). It follows immediately that all values a in this neighborhood are taken the same number of times inside of γ. The equation $f(z) = w_0$ has exactly n coinciding roots inside of γ, and hence every value a is taken n times. It is understood that multiple roots are counted according to their multiplicity, but if ε is sufficiently small we can assert that all roots of the equation $f(z) = a$ are simple for $a \neq w_0$. Indeed, it is sufficient to choose ε so that $f'(z)$ does not vanish for $0 < |z - z_0| < \varepsilon$.

Corollary 1. *A nonconstant analytic function maps open sets onto open sets.*

This is merely another way of saying that the image of every sufficiently small disk $|z - z_0| < \varepsilon$ contains a neighborhood $|w - w_0| < \delta$.

In the case $n = 1$ there is one-to-one correspondence between the disk $|w - w_0| < \delta$ and an open subset Δ of $|z - z_0| < \varepsilon$. Since open sets in the z-plane correspond to open sets in the w-plane the inverse function of $f(z)$ is continuous, and the mapping is topological. The mapping can be restricted to a neighborhood of z_0 contained in Δ, and we are able to state:

Corollary 2. *If $f(z)$ is analytic at z_0 with $f'(z_0) \neq 0$, it maps a neighborhood of z_0 conformally and topologically onto a region.*

From the continuity of the inverse function it follows in the usual way that the inverse function is analytic, and hence the inverse mapping is

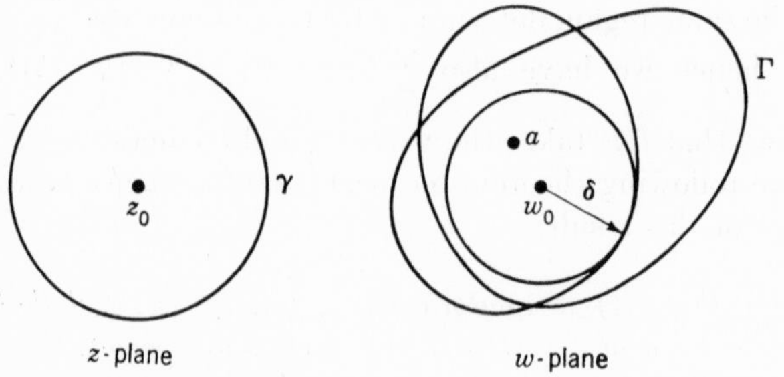

FIG. 21. Local correspondence.

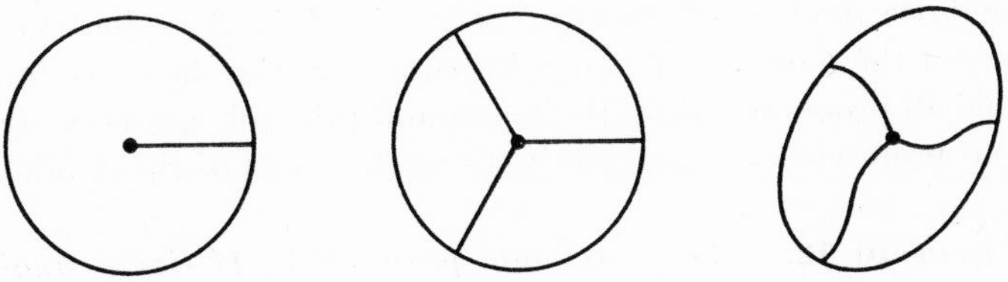

FIG. 22. Branch point: $n = 3$.

likewise conformal. Conversely, if the local mapping is one to one, Theorem 11 can hold only with $n = 1$, and hence $f'(z_0)$ must be different from zero.

For $n > 1$ the local correspondence can still be described in very precise terms. Under the assumption of Theorem 11 we can write

$$f(z) - w_0 = (z - z_0)^n g(z)$$

where $g(z)$ is analytic at z_0 and $g(z_0) \neq 0$. Choose $\varepsilon > 0$ so that $|g(z) - g(z_0)| < |g(z_0)|$ for $|z - z_0| < \varepsilon$. In this neighborhood it is possible to define a single-valued analytic branch of $\sqrt[n]{g(z)}$, which we denote by $h(z)$. We have thus

$$f(z) - w_0 = \zeta(z)^n$$
$$\zeta(z) = (z - z_0)h(z).$$

Since $\zeta'(z_0) = h(z_0) \neq 0$ the mapping $\zeta = \zeta(z)$ is topological in a neighborhood of z_0. On the other hand, the mapping $w = w_0 + \zeta^n$ is of an elementary character and determines n equally spaced values ζ for each value of w. By performing the mapping in two steps we obtain a very illuminating picture of the local correspondence. Figure 22 shows the inverse image of a small circular disk and the n arcs which are mapped onto the positive radius.

EXERCISES

1. Determine explicitly the largest disk about the origin whose image under the mapping $w = z^2 + z$ is one to one.

2. Same problem for $w = e^z$.

3. Apply the representation $f(z) = w_0 + \zeta(z)^n$ to $\cos z$ with $z_0 = 0$. Determine $\zeta(z)$ explicitly.

4. If $f(z)$ is analytic at the origin and $f'(0) \neq 0$, prove the existence of an analytic $g(z)$ such that $f(z^n) = f(0) + g(z)^n$ in a neighborhood of 0.

3.4. The Maximum Principle. Corollary 1 of Theorem 11 has a very important analytical consequence known as the maximum principle for analytic functions. Because of its simple and explicit formulation it is one of the most useful general theorems in the theory of functions. As a rule all proofs based on the maximum principle are very straightforward, and preference is quite justly given to proofs of this kind.

Theorem 12. *(The maximum principle.) If $f(z)$ is analytic and non-constant in a region Ω, then its absolute value $|f(z)|$ has no maximum in Ω.*

The proof is clear. If $w_0 = f(z_0)$ is any value taken in Ω, there exists a neighborhood $|w - w_0| < \varepsilon$ contained in the image of Ω. In this neighborhood there are points of modulus $> |w_0|$, and hence $|f(z_0)|$ is not the maximum of $|f(z)|$.

In a positive formulation essentially the same theorem can be stated in the form:

Theorem 12′. *If $f(z)$ is analytic on a closed bounded set E, then the maximum of $|f(z)|$ is taken on the boundary of E.*

Since E is compact $|f(z)|$ has a maximum on E. If $f(z)$ is constant, the assertion of the theorem is trivially true, for the boundary of E is not empty. Suppose that the maximum were taken at an interior point z_0. Then $|f(z_0)|$ would also be the maximum of $|f(z)|$ in a neighborhood $|z - z_0| < \delta$ contained in E. But this is impossible unless $f(z)$ is constant in this neighborhood, and then $f(z)$ is constant throughout its region of definition (we recall that $f(z)$ is analytic on E if it is defined and analytic in a *region* which contains E). Thus the maximum is always taken at a boundary point.

The maximum principle can also be proved analytically, as a consequence of Cauchy's integral formula. If the formula (22) is specialized to the case where γ is a circle of center z_0 and radius r, we can write $\zeta = z_0 + re^{i\theta}$, $d\zeta = ire^{i\theta}\,d\theta$ on γ and obtain for $z = z_0$

$$f(z_0) = \frac{1}{2\pi}\int_0^{2\pi} f(z_0 + re^{i\theta})\,d\theta. \tag{34}$$

This formula shows that the value of an analytic function at the center of a circle is equal to the arithmetic mean of its values on the circle, subject to the condition that the closed disk $|z - z_0| \leqq r$ is contained in the region of analyticity.

From (34) we derive the inequality

$$|f(z_0)| \leqq \frac{1}{2\pi}\int_0^{2\pi} |f(z_0 + re^{i\theta})|\,d\theta. \tag{35}$$

Suppose that $|f(z_0)|$ were a maximum. Then we would have $|f(z_0 + re^{i\theta})| \leqq |f(z_0)|$, and if the strict inequality held for a single value of θ it would hold, by continuity, on a whole arc. But then the mean value of $|f(z_0 + re^{i\theta})|$ would be strictly less than $|f(z_0)|$, and (35) would lead to the contradiction $|f(z_0)| < |f(z_0)|$. Thus $|f(z)|$ must be constantly equal to $|f(z_0)|$ on all sufficiently small circles $|z - z_0| = r$ and, hence, in a neighborhood of z_0. It follows easily that $f(z)$ must reduce to a constant. This reasoning provides a second proof of the maximum principle. We have given preference to the first proof because it shows that the maximum principle is a consequence of the topological properties of the mapping by an analytic function.

Returning to the formulation given in Theorem 12′ we observe that the most natural application is to the case where E is a closed region. We find that a function which is analytic on a closed region takes its maximum on the boundary of the region. For some applications it is important to notice that the hypothesis of the theorem can be weakened. It is indeed sufficient to suppose that $f(z)$ is continuous in the closed region and analytic in the open region. The continuity on the closed and bounded region ensures the existence of a maximum, and the analyticity in the open region implies that the maximum cannot be attained at an interior point unless the function reduces to a constant.

Consider now the case of a function $f(z)$ which is analytic in the open disk $|z| < R$ and continuous on the closed disk $|z| \leqq R$. If it is known that $|f(z)| \leqq M$ on $|z| = R$, then $|f(z)| \leqq M$ in the whole disk, by the preceding remark. The equality can hold only if $f(z)$ is a constant of absolute value M. Therefore, if it is known that $f(z)$ takes some value of modulus $< M$, it may be expected that a better estimate can be given. Theorems to this effect are very useful. The following particular result is known as the *lemma of Schwarz:*

Theorem 13. *If $f(z)$ is analytic for $|z| < 1$ and satisfies the conditions $|f(z)| \leqq 1, f(0) = 0$, then $|f(z)| \leqq |z|$ and $|f'(0)| \leqq 1$. Equality holds only if $f(z) = cz$ with a constant c of absolute value* 1.

We apply the maximum principle to the function $f_1(z)$ which is equal to $f(z)/z$ for $z \neq 0$ and to $f'(0)$ for $z = 0$. On the circle $|z| = r < 1$ it is of absolute value $\leqq 1/r$, and hence $|f_1(z)| \leqq 1/r$ for $|z| \leqq r$. Letting r tend to 1 we find that $|f_1(z)| \leqq 1$ for all z, and this is the assertion of the theorem. If the equality holds at a single point, it means that $|f_1(z)|$ attains its maximum and, hence, that $f_1(z)$ must reduce to a constant.

The rather specialized assumptions of Theorem 13 are not essential, but should be looked upon as the result of a normalization. For instance, if $f(z)$ is known to satisfy the conditions of the theorem in a disk of radius R, the original form of the theorem can be applied to the function $f(Rz)$. As a result we obtain $|f(Rz)| \leqq |z|$, which can be rewritten as $|f(z)| \leqq |z|/R$. Similarly, if the upper bound of the modulus is M instead of 1, we apply the theorem to $f(z)/M$ or, in the more general case, to $f(Rz)/M$. The resulting inequality is $|f(z)| \leqq M|z|/R$.

Still more generally, we may replace the condition $f(0) = 0$ by an arbitrary condition $f(z_0) = w_0$ where $|z_0| < R$ and $|w_0| < M$. Let $\zeta = Tz$ be a linear transformation which maps $|z| < R$ onto $|\zeta| < 1$ with z_0 going into the origin, and let Sw be a linear transformation with $Sw_0 = 0$ which maps $|w| < M$ onto $|Sw| < 1$. It is clear that the function $Sf(T^{-1}\zeta)$ satisfies the hypothesis of the original theorem. Hence we obtain $|Sf(T^{-1}\zeta)| \leqq |\zeta|$, or $|Sf(z)| \leqq |Tz|$. Explicitly, this inequality can be written in the form

$$\left| \frac{M(f(z) - w_0)}{M^2 - \bar{w}_0 f(z)} \right| \leqq \left| \frac{R(z - z_0)}{R^2 - \bar{z}_0 z} \right|. \tag{36}$$

EXERCISES

1. Show by use of (36), or directly, that $|f(z)| \leqq 1$ for $|z| \leqq 1$ implies

$$\frac{|f'(z)|}{(1 - |f(z)|^2)} \leqq \frac{1}{1 - |z|^2}.$$

2. If $f(z)$ is analytic and $\operatorname{Im} f(z) \geqq 0$ for $\operatorname{Im} z > 0$, show that

$$\frac{|f(z) - f(z_0)|}{|f(z) - \overline{f(z_0)}|} \leqq \frac{|z - z_0|}{|z - \bar{z}_0|}$$

and

$$\frac{|f'(z)|}{\operatorname{Im} f(z)} \leqq \frac{1}{y} \qquad (z = x + iy).$$

3. In Ex. 1 and 2, prove that equality implies that $f(z)$ is a linear transformation.

4. Derive corresponding inequalities if $f(z)$ maps $|z| < 1$ into the upper half plane.

5. Prove by use of Schwarz's lemma that every one-to-one conformal mapping of a circular disk onto another (or a half plane) is given by a linear transformation.

***6.** If γ is a piecewise differentiable arc contained in $|z| < 1$ the integral

$$\int_\gamma \frac{|dz|}{1 - |z|^2}$$

is called the *noneuclidean length* (or hyperbolic length) of γ. Show that an analytic function $f(z)$ with $|f(z)| < 1$ for $|z| < 1$ maps every γ on an arc with smaller or equal noneuclidean length.

Deduce that a linear transformation of the unit disk onto itself preserves noneuclidean lengths, and check the result by explicit computation.

***7.** Prove that the arc of smallest noneuclidean length that joins two given points in the unit disk is a circular arc which is orthogonal to the unit circle. (Make use of a linear transformation that carries one end point to the origin, the other to a point on the positive real axis.)

The shortest noneuclidean length is called the *noneuclidean distance* between the end points. Derive a formula for the noneuclidean distance between z_1 and z_2. *Answer:*

$$\frac{1}{2}\log\frac{1+\left|\dfrac{z_1-z_2}{1-\bar{z}_1z_2}\right|}{1-\left|\dfrac{z_1-z_2}{1-\bar{z}_1z_2}\right|}.$$

***8.** How should noneuclidean length in the upper half plane be defined?

4. THE GENERAL FORM OF CAUCHY'S THEOREM

In our preliminary treatment of Cauchy's theorem and the integral formula we considered only the case of a circular region. For the purpose of studying the local properties of analytic functions this was quite adequate, but from a more general point of view we cannot be satisfied with a result which is so obviously incomplete. The generalization can proceed in two directions. For one thing we can seek to characterize the regions in which Cauchy's theorem has universal validity. Secondly, we can consider an arbitrary region and look for the curves γ for which the assertion of Cauchy's theorem is true.

4.1. *Chains and Cycles.*

In the first place we must generalize the notion of line integral. To this end we examine the equation

$$\int_{\gamma_1+\gamma_2+\cdots+\gamma_n} f\,dz = \int_{\gamma_1} f\,dz + \int_{\gamma_2} f\,dz + \cdots + \int_{\gamma_n} f\,dz \tag{37}$$

which is valid when $\gamma_1, \gamma_2, \ldots, \gamma_n$ form a subdivision of the arc γ. Since the right-hand member of (37) has a meaning for any finite collection, nothing prevents us from considering an arbitrary formal sum $\gamma_1 + \gamma_2 + \cdots + \gamma_n$, which need not be an arc, and we define the corresponding integral by means of equation (37). Such formal sums of arcs are called *chains*. It is clear that nothing is lost and much may be gained by considering line integrals over arbitrary chains.

Just as there is nothing unique about the way in which an arc can be subdivided, it is clear that different formal sums can represent the same chain. The guiding principle is that two chains should be considered identical if they yield the same line integrals for all functions f. If this principle is analyzed, we find that the following operations do not change the identity of a chain: (1) permutation of two arcs, (2) subdivision of an arc, (3) fusion of subarcs to a single arc, (4) reparametrization of an arc, (5) cancellation of opposite arcs. On this basis it would be easy to formulate a logical equivalence relation which defines the identity of chains in a formal manner. Inasmuch as the situation does not involve any logical pitfalls, we shall dispense with this formalization.

The sum of two chains is defined in the obvious way by juxtaposition. It is clear that the additive property (37) of line integrals remains valid for arbitrary chains. When identical chains are added, it is convenient to denote the sum as a multiple. With this notation every chain can be written in the form

$$\gamma = a_1\gamma_1 + a_2\gamma_2 + \cdots + a_n\gamma_n \tag{38}$$

where the a_j are positive integers and the γ_j are all different. For opposite arcs we are allowed to write $a(-\gamma) = -a\gamma$ and continue the reduction of (38) until no two γ_j are opposite. The coefficients will be arbitrary integers, and terms with zero coefficients can be added at will. The last device enables us to express any two chains in terms of the same arcs, and their sum is obtained by adding corresponding coefficients. The zero chain is either an empty sum or a sum with all coefficients equal to zero.

A chain is a *cycle* if it can be represented as a sum of closed curves. Very simple combinatorial considerations show that a chain is a cycle if and only if in any representation the initial and end points of the individual arcs are identical in pairs. Thus it is immediately possible to tell whether a chain is a cycle or not.

In the applications we shall consider chains which are contained in a given region Ω. By this we mean that the chains have a representation by arcs in Ω and that only such representations will be considered. It is clear that all theorems which we have heretofore formulated only for closed curves in a region are in fact valid for arbitrary cycles in a region. In particular, *the integral of an exact differential over any cycle is zero.*

The index of a point with respect to a cycle is defined in exactly the same way as in the case of a single closed curve. It has the same properties, and in addition we can formulate the obvious but important additive law expressed by the equation $n(\gamma_1 + \gamma_2,a) = n(\gamma_1,a) + n(\gamma_2,a)$.

4.2. Simple Connectivity. There is little doubt that all readers will know what we mean if we speak about a region without holes. Such regions are said to be *simply connected,* and it is for simply connected regions that Cauchy's theorem is universally valid. The suggestive language we have used cannot take the place of a mathematical definition, but fortunately very little is needed to make the term precise. Indeed, a region without holes is obviously one whose complement consists of a single piece. We are thus led to the following definition:

Definition 1. *A region is simply connected if its complement with respect to the extended plane is connected.*

At this point we warn the reader that this definition is not the one that is commonly accepted, the main reason being that our definition cannot be used in more than two real dimensions. In the course of our work we shall find, however, that the property expressed by Definition 1 is equivalent to a number of other properties, more or less equally important. One of these states that any closed curve can be contracted to a point, and this condition is usually chosen as definition. Our choice has the advantage of leading very quickly to the essential results in complex integration theory.

It is easy to see that a circular disk, a half plane, and a parallel strip are simply connected. The last example shows the importance of taking the complement with respect to the extended plane, for the complement of the strip in the finite plane is evidently not connected. The definition can be applied to regions on the Riemann sphere, and this is evidently the most symmetric situation. For our purposes it is nevertheless better to agree that all regions lie in the finite plane unless the contrary is explicitly stated. According to this convention the outside of a circle is not simply connected, for its complement consists of a closed disk and the point at infinity.

Theorem 14. *A region Ω is simply connected if and only if $n(\gamma,a) = 0$ for all cycles γ in Ω and all points a which do not belong to Ω.*

This alternative condition is also very suggestive. It states that a closed curve in a simply connected region cannot wind around any point which does not belong to the region. It seems quite evident that this condition is not fulfilled in the case of a region with a hole.

The necessity of the condition is almost trivial. Let γ be any cycle in Ω. If the complement of Ω is connected, it must be contained in one of the regions determined by γ, and inasmuch as ∞ belongs to the comple-

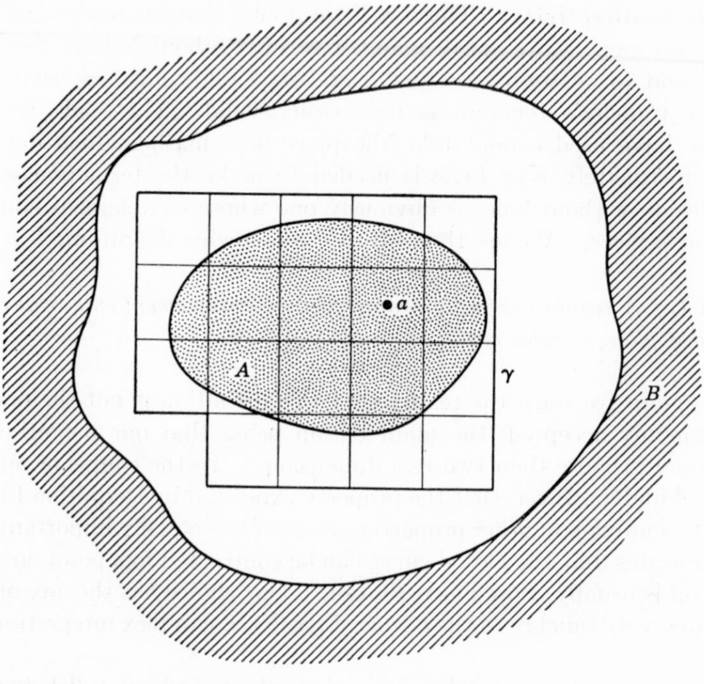

FIG. 23. Curve with index 1.

ment this must be the unbounded region. Consequently $n(\gamma,a) = 0$ for all finite points in the complement.

For the precise proof of the sufficiency an explicit construction is needed. We assume that the complement of Ω can be represented as the union $A \cup B$ of two disjoint closed sets. One of these sets contains ∞, and the other is consequently bounded; let A be the bounded set. The sets A and B have a shortest distance $\delta > 0$. Cover the whole plane with a net of squares Q of side $< \delta/\sqrt{2}$. We are free to choose the net so that a certain point $a \in A$ lies at the center of a square. The boundary curve of Q is denoted by ∂Q; we assume explicitly that the squares Q are closed and that the interior of Q lies to the left of the directed line segments which make up ∂Q.

Consider now the cycle

$$\gamma = \sum_j \partial Q_j \tag{39}$$

where the sum ranges over all squares Q_j in the net which have a point in common with A (Fig. 23). Because a is contained in one and only one of these squares, it is evident that $n(\gamma,a) = 1$. Furthermore, it is clear that γ does not meet B. But if the cancellations are carried out, it is equally clear that γ does not meet A. Indeed, any side which meets A is a common side of two squares included in the sum (39), and since the directions are opposite the side does not appear in the reduced expression of γ. Hence γ is contained in Ω, and our theorem is proved.

We remark now that Cauchy's theorem is certainly not valid for regions which are not simply connected. In fact, if there is a cycle γ in Ω such that $n(\gamma,a) \neq 0$ for some a outside of Ω, then $1/(z - a)$ is analytic in Ω while its integral

$$\int_\gamma \frac{dz}{z - a} = 2\pi i n(\gamma,a) \neq 0.$$

4.3. Exact Differentials in Simply Connected Regions. We will now prove that Cauchy's theorem holds in an arbitrary simply connected region. In view of Theorem 1 we need only prove that $f(z)\,dz$ is an exact differential. This is known to be so when attention is restricted to a circular disk contained in Ω. Therefore, our task is to prove that a differential which is exact in a neighborhood of each point is also exact in the whole region Ω, provided that Ω is simply connected. In this form the statement is not limited to differentials of the form $f\,dz$, and we prefer to prove the following proposition:

Theorem 15. *The differential $p\,dx + q\,dy$ whose coefficients are defined and continuous in a simply connected region Ω is exact in Ω if and only if*

$$\int_{\partial R} p\,dx + q\,dy = 0$$

for every rectangle R contained in Ω.

We choose a point $z_0 \in \Omega$ and define $U(z)$ by

$$U(z) = \int_\sigma p\,dx + q\,dy$$

where σ is a polygon from z_0 to z, contained in Ω, with sides parallel to the axes. If we can show that $U(z)$ is independent of the choice of σ, it follows in the same way as in the proof of Theorem 1 that $\partial U/\partial x = p$, $\partial U/\partial y = q$. The difference $\gamma = \sigma_1 - \sigma_2$ of two polygons from z_0 to z is a closed polygon in Ω with vertical and horizontal sides, and we have to show that the integral of $p\,dx + q\,dy$ over γ is zero.

For the proof we use a rectangular net obtained by drawing lines parallel to both axes through all the vertices of γ (Fig. 24). There will be some finite rectangles R_i and some unbounded regions R'_j which

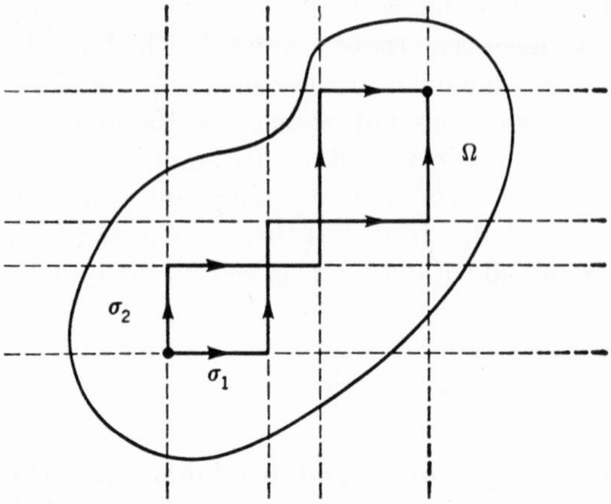

FIG. 24

may be considered as infinite rectangles. Inasmuch as we need not consider the trivial case in which γ lies on a vertical or horizontal line, we may assume that there is at least one finite rectangle R_i.

Choose a point a_i from the interior of each R_i, and form the cycle

$$\gamma_0 = \sum_i n(\gamma,a_i)\,\partial R_i \tag{40}$$

where the sum ranges over all finite rectangles; the coefficients $n(\gamma,a_i)$ are well determined, for no a_i can lie on γ. In the discussion that follows we shall also make use of points a'_j chosen from the interior of each R'_j, although they are not needed for the construction of γ_0.

The choice of γ_0, defined by (40), is dictated by a definite purpose. It is clear that $n(\partial R_i,a_k) = 1$ if $k = i$ and 0 if $k \neq i$; similarly, $n(\partial R_i,a'_j) = 0$ for all j. With this in mind we obtain from (40) $n(\gamma_0,a_i) = n(\gamma,a_i)$ and $n(\gamma_0,a'_j) = 0$. It is also true that $n(\gamma,a'_j) = 0$, for evidently the interior of R'_j must belong to the unbounded region determined by γ. We have thus shown that $n(\gamma - \gamma_0,a) = 0$ for all $a = a_i$ and $a = a'_j$.

From this property of $\gamma - \gamma_0$ we wish to conclude that γ_0 is identical with γ. Let σ_{ik} be the common side of two adjacent rectangles R_i, R_k; we choose the orientation so that R_i lies to the left of σ_{ik}. Suppose that the reduced expression of $\gamma - \gamma_0$ contains the multiple $c\sigma_{ik}$. Then the cycle $\gamma - \gamma_0 - c\,\partial R_i$ does not contain σ_{ik}, and it follows that a_i and a_k must have the same index with respect to this cycle. On the other hand, the respective indices are evidently $-c$ and 0; we conclude that $c = 0$. The same reasoning applies if σ_{ij} is the common side of a finite rectangle

R_i and an infinite rectangle R'_j. In the presence of at least one finite rectangle it is clear that no two infinite rectangles can have a finite side in common, and we have proved conclusively that $\gamma - \gamma_0$ must be identically zero. This means that γ can be represented in the form

$$\gamma = \sum_i n(\gamma,a_i)\ \partial R_i. \tag{41}$$

We prove now that the representation (41) is a representation *in* Ω; more precisely, we show that the rectangles R_i whose corresponding coefficient $n(\gamma,a_i)$ is different from 0 are contained in Ω. This is a consequence of the simple connectivity of Ω. Indeed, suppose that a point a in the closed rectangle R_i were not in Ω. Then $n(\gamma,a) = 0$, by Theorem 14. On the other hand, the line segment between a and a_i does not intersect γ, and hence $n(\gamma,a_i) = n(\gamma,a)$, contradicting the hypothesis $n(\gamma,a_i) \neq 0$.

It follows that the hypothesis of Theorem 15 applies to each $\Gamma(R_i)$ which occurs effectively in (41). Consequently,

$$\int_\gamma p\,dx + q\,dx = 0,$$

and the theorem is proved.

The most important consequence is Cauchy's theorem for simply connected regions:

Theorem 16. *If $f(z)$ is analytic in a simply connected region Ω, then*

$$\int_\gamma f(z)\,dz = 0$$

for every cycle γ in Ω.

The following corollary is of frequent use:

Corollary. *If $f(z)$ is analytic and $\neq 0$ in a simply connected region Ω, a single-valued analytic branch of* $\log f(z)$ *can be defined in Ω.*

By the preceding theorem the function $f'(z)/f(z)$ has an indefinite integral $F(z)$ in Ω. The function $f(z)e^{-F(z)}$ has then the derivative 0 and must reduce to a constant. Choosing a point $z_0 \in \Omega$ and an arbitrary value of $\log f(z_0)$ we find that

$$e^{F(z)-F(z_0)+\log f(z_0)} = f(z),$$

and consequently we can set $\log f(z) = F(z) - F(z_0) + \log f(z_0)$.

Under the same circumstances we can also determine a single-valued branch of an arbitrary power $f(z)^\mu = e^{\mu \log f(z)}$.

4.4. Multiply Connected Regions. The proof of Theorem 15 includes more than we have stated. As a matter of fact the hypothesis of simple connectivity was used merely to conclude that $n(\gamma,a) = 0$ for all points a not in Ω. For particular polygons this condition may well be fulfilled even when the region Ω is not simply connected. In an arbitrary region we have in effect proved that

$$\int_\gamma p\,dx + q\,dy = 0$$

for any closed polygon γ which does not wind around any outside points, and it is reasonable to expect that this result is not restricted to polygons. However, the transition from a polygon with horizontal and vertical sides to an arbitrary cycle must be based on a different argument, for we can no longer be sure that the differential is exact.

Before we proceed with this proof it is convenient to introduce a name for the type of cycles with which we shall be concerned.

Definition 2. *A cycle γ in Ω is said to be homologous to zero with respect to Ω if and only if $n(\gamma,a) = 0$ for all points a not in Ω.*

In symbols we write $\gamma \sim 0 \pmod{\Omega}$. When it is clear to what region we are referring, Ω need not be mentioned explicitly. The notation $\gamma_1 \sim \gamma_2$ shall be equivalent to $\gamma_1 - \gamma_2 \sim 0$. It is clear that homologies can be added and subtracted. Moreover, $\gamma \sim 0 \pmod{\Omega}$ implies $\gamma \sim 0$ $\pmod{\Omega'}$ for every $\Omega' \supset \Omega$.

Again, our terminology does not quite agree with standard practice. It was E. Artin who discovered that the characterization of homology by vanishing winding numbers ties in precisely with what is needed for Cauchy's theorem. This idea has led to a remarkable simplification of earlier proofs.

Theorem 17. *If $p\,dx + q\,dy$ is locally exact in Ω, i.e., if*

$$\int_\gamma p\,dx + q\,dy = 0 \tag{42}$$

for $\gamma = \partial R$, R being any rectangle contained in Ω, then (42) *holds for every cycle γ which is homologous to zero in Ω.*

For the proof it is sufficient to show that γ can be replaced by a polygon σ with horizontal and vertical sides such that every locally exact differential has the same integral over σ as over γ. This property implies, in particular, $n(\sigma,a) = n(\gamma,a)$, and hence $\sigma \sim 0$. The proof of Theorem 15 applies to σ, and we may conclude that γ satisfies condition (42).

We construct σ as an approximation of γ. Let the distance from γ to the complement of Ω be $\geqq \rho > 0$. If the equation of γ is $z = z(t)$, $a \leqq t \leqq b$, the function $z(t)$ is uniformly continuous on the closed interval (a,b). We determine $\delta < 0$ so that $|z(t) - z(t')| < \rho$ for $|t - t'| < \delta$ and divide (a,b) in subintervals of length $<\delta$. The corresponding subarcs of γ, which we denote by γ_i, have the property that each γ_i is contained in a disk of radius ρ which lies entirely in Ω. The end points of γ_i can be joined within the same disk by a polygon σ_i consisting of a horizontal and a vertical segment. Since our differential is exact in the disk,

$$\int_{\sigma_i} p\,dx + q\,dy = \int_{\gamma_i} p\,dx + a\,dy,$$

and setting $\sigma = \Sigma\,\sigma_i$ we obtain

$$\int_{\sigma} p\,dx + q\,dy = \int_{\gamma} p\,dx + q\,dy;$$

this completes the proof.

Theorem 17 characterizes the cycles which are homologous to zero. We have proved, in effect, that if the integral over γ vanishes for all differentials of the special form $dz/(z - a)$ with a outside Ω, then it vanishes for all locally exact differentials.† In particular, it vanishes for the differentials of the form $f(z)\,dz$ where $f(z)$ is analytic in Ω. This is the final and most complete form of Cauchy's theorem.

Theorem 18. *If $f(z)$ is analytic in Ω, then*

$$\int_{\gamma} f(z)\,dz = 0$$

for every cycle γ which is homologous to zero in Ω.

A region which is not simply connected is called multiply connected. More precisely, Ω is said to have the finite connectivity n if the complement of Ω has exactly n components and infinite connectivity if the complement has infinitely many components. In a less precise but more suggestive language, a region of connectivity n arises by punching n holes in the Riemann sphere.

In the case of finite connectivity, let $A_1, A_2, \ldots, A_n$ be the components of the complement of Ω, and assume that ∞ belongs to A_n. If

† As in the hypothesis of Theorem 17 a differential is said to be *locally exact* in a region Ω if it is exact in some neighborhood of each point in Ω.

γ is an arbitrary cycle in Ω, we can prove, just as in Theorem 14, that $n(\gamma,a)$ is constant when a varies over any one of the components A_i and that $n(\gamma,a) = 0$ in A_n. Moreover, duplicating the construction used in the proof of the same theorem we can find cycles γ_i, $i = 1, \ldots, n-1$, such that $n(\gamma_i,a) = 1$ for $a \in A_i$ and $n(\gamma_i,a) = 0$ for all other points outside of Ω.

For a given cycle γ in Ω, let c_i be the constant value of $n(\gamma,a)$ for $a \in A_i$. We find that any point outside of Ω has the index zero with respect to the cycle $\gamma - c_1\gamma_1 - c_2\gamma_2 - \cdots - c_{n-1}\gamma_{n-1}$. In other words,

$$\gamma \sim c_1\gamma_1 + c_2\gamma_2 + \cdots + c_{n-1}\gamma_{n-1}.$$

Every cycle is thus homologous to a linear combination of the cycles $\gamma_1, \gamma_2, \ldots, \gamma_{n-1}$. This linear combination is uniquely determined, for if two linear combinations were homologous to the same cycle their difference would be a linear combination which is homologous to zero. But it is clear that the cycle $c_1\gamma_1 + c_2\gamma_2 + \cdots + c_{n-1}\gamma_{n-1}$ winds c_i times around the points in A_i; hence it cannot be homologous to zero unless all the c_i vanish.

In view of these circumstances the cycles $\gamma_1, \gamma_2, \ldots, \gamma_{n-1}$ are said to form a *homology basis* for the region Ω. It is not the only homology basis, but by an elementary theorem in linear algebra we may conclude that every homology basis has the same number of elements. We find that every region with a finite homology basis has finite connectivity, and the number of basis elements is one less than the connectivity.

By Theorem 18 we obtain, for any analytic function $f(z)$ in Ω,

$$\int_\gamma f\,dz = c_1 \int_{\gamma_1} f\,dz + c_2 \int_{\gamma_2} f\,dz + \cdots + c_{n-1} \int_{\gamma_{n-1}} f\,dz.$$

The numbers

$$P_i = \int_{\gamma_i} f\,dz$$

depend only on the function, and not on γ. They are called *modules of periodicity* of the differential $f\,dz$, or, with less accuracy, the *periods* of the indefinite integral. We have found that the integral of $f(z)$ over any cycle is a linear combination of the periods with integers as coefficients, and the integral along an arc from z_0 to z is determined up to additive multiples of the periods. The vanishing of the periods is a necessary and sufficient condition for the existence of a single-valued indefinite integral.

In order to illustrate, let us consider the extremely simple case of an annulus, defined by $r_1 < |z| < r_2$. The complement has the components $|z| \leqq r_1$ and $|z| \geqq r_2$; we include the degenerate cases $r_1 = 0$ and $r_2 = \infty$. The annulus is doubly connected, and a homology basis is formed by any circle $|z| = r$, $r_1 < r < r_2$. If this circle is denoted by C, any cycle in the annulus satisfies $\gamma \sim nC$ where $n = n(\gamma,0)$. The integral of an analytic function over a cycle is a multiple of the single period

$$P = \int_C f\,dz$$

whose value is of course independent of the radius r.

EXERCISES

1. Prove that the region obtained from a simply connected region by removing m points has the connectivity $m + 1$, and find a homology basis.

2. Show that the bounded regions determined by a closed curve are simply connected, while the unbounded region is doubly connected.

3. Show that single-valued analytic branches of $\log z$, z^α and z^z can be defined in any simply connected region which does not contain the origin.

4. Show that a single-valued analytic branch of $\sqrt{1 - z^2}$ can be defined in any region such that the points ± 1 are in the same component of the complement. What are the possible values of

$$\int \frac{dz}{\sqrt{1 - z^2}}$$

over a closed curve in the region?

5. THE CALCULUS OF RESIDUES

The results of the preceding section have shown that the determination of line integrals of analytic functions over closed curves can be reduced to the determination of periods. Under certain circumstances it turns out that the periods can be found without or with very little computation. We are thus in possession of a method which in many cases permits us to evaluate integrals without resorting to explicit calculation. This is of great value for practical purposes as well as for the further development of the theory.

In order to make this method more systematic a simple formalism, known as the calculus of residues, was introduced by Cauchy, the founder of complex integration theory. From the point of view adopted in this book the use of residues amounts essentially to an application of the results proved in Sec. 4 under particularly simple circumstances.

5.1. The Residue Theorem. Our first task is to review earlier results in the light of the more general theorems of Sec. 4. Clearly, all results which were derived as consequences of Cauchy's theorem for a disk remain valid in arbitrary regions for all cycles which are homologous to zero. For instance, and this application is typical, Cauchy's integral formula can now be expressed in the following form:

If $f(z)$ is analytic in a region Ω, then

$$n(\gamma,a)f(a) = \frac{1}{2\pi i}\int_\gamma \frac{f(z)\,dz}{z-a}$$

for every cycle γ which is homologous to zero in Ω.

The proof is a repetition of the proof of Theorem 6. In this connection we point out that there is of course no longer any need to give a separate proof of Theorem 16 in the presence of removable singularities. Indeed, our discussion of the local behavior has already shown that all removable singularities can simply be ignored.

We turn now to the discussion of a function $f(z)$ which is analytic in a region Ω except for isolated singularities. For a first orientation, let us assume that there are only a finite number of singular points, denoted by $a_1, a_2, \ldots, a_n$. The region obtained by excluding the points a_j will be denoted by Ω'.

To each a_j there exists a $\delta_j > 0$ such that the doubly connected region $0 < |z - a_j| < \delta_j$ is contained in Ω'. Draw a circle C_j about a_j of radius $<\delta_j$, and let

$$P_j = \int_{C_j} f(z)\,dz \tag{43}$$

be the corresponding period of $f(z)$. The particular function $1/(z - a_j)$ has the period $2\pi i$. Therefore, if we set $R_j = P_j/2\pi i$, the combination

$$f(z) - \frac{R_j}{z - a_j}$$

has a vanishing period. The constant R_j which produces this result is called the *residue* of $f(z)$ at the point a_j. We repeat the definition in the following form:

Definition 3. *The residue of $f(z)$ at an isolated singularity a is the unique complex number R which makes $f(z) - R/(z - a)$ the derivative of a single-valued analytic function in an annulus $0 < |z - a| < \delta$.*

It is helpful to use such self-explanatory notations as $R = \mathrm{Res}_{z=a} f(z)$.

Let γ be a cycle in Ω' which is homologous to zero with respect to Ω. Then γ satisfies the homology

$$\gamma \sim \sum_j n(\gamma,a_j)C_j$$

with respect to Ω'; indeed, we can easily verify that the points a_j as well as all points outside of Ω have the same order with respect to both cycles.

By virtue of the homology we obtain, with the notation (43),

$$\int_\gamma f\,dz = \sum_j n(\gamma,a_j)P_j,$$

and since $P_j = 2\pi i \cdot R_j$ finally

$$\frac{1}{2\pi i}\int_\gamma f\,dz = \sum_j n(\gamma,a_j)R_j.$$

This is the *residue theorem*, except for the restrictive assumption that there are only a finite number of singularities. In the general case we need only prove that $n(\gamma,a_j) = 0$ except for a finite number of points a_j, for then the same proof can be applied. The assertion follows by routine reasoning. The set of all points a with $n(\gamma,a) = 0$ is open and contains all points outside of a large circle. The complement is consequently a compact set, and as such it cannot contain more than a finite number of the isolated points a_j. Therefore $n(\gamma,a_j) \neq 0$ only for a finite number of the singularities, and we have proved:

Theorem 19. *Let $f(z)$ be analytic except for isolated singularities a_j in a region Ω. Then*

$$\frac{1}{2\pi i}\int_\gamma f(z)\,dz = \sum_j n(\gamma,a_j)\,\mathrm{Res}_{z=a_j} f(z) \tag{44}$$

for any cycle γ which is homologous to zero in Ω and does not pass through any of the points a_j.

In the applications it is frequently the case that each $n(\gamma,a_j)$ is either 0 or 1. Then we have simply

$$\frac{1}{2\pi i}\int_\gamma f(z)\,dz = \sum_j \mathrm{Res}_{z=a_j} f(z)$$

where the sum is extended over all singularities enclosed by γ.

The residue theorem is of little value unless we have at our disposal a simple procedure to determine the residues. For essential singularities there is no such procedure of any practical value, and thus it is not surprising that the residue theorem is comparatively seldom used in the presence of essential singularities. With respect to poles the situation is entirely different. We need only look at the expansion

$$f(z) = B_h(z-a)^{-h} + \cdots + B_1(z-a)^{-1} + \varphi(z)$$

to recognize that the residue equals the coefficient B_1. Indeed, when the term $B_1(z-a)^{-1}$ is omitted, the remainder is evidently a derivative.

Since the principal part at a pole is always either given or can be easily found, we have thus a very simple method for finding the residues.

For simple poles the method is even more immediate, for then the residue equals the value of the function $(z - a)f(z)$ for $z = a$. For instance, let it be required to find the residues of the function

$$\frac{e^z}{(z-a)(z-b)}$$

at the poles a and $b \neq a$. The residue at a is obviously $e^a/(a - b)$, and the residue at b is $e^b/(b - a)$. If $b = a$, the situation is slightly more complicated. We must then expand e^z by Taylor's theorem in the form $e^z = e^a + e^a(z - a) + f_2(z)(z - a)^2$. Dividing by $(z - a)^2$ we find that the residue of $e^z/(z - a)^2$ at $z = a$ is e^a.

Remark. In presentations of Cauchy's theorem, the integral formula and the residue theorem which follow more classical lines, there is no mention of homology, nor is the notion of index used explicitly. Instead, the curve γ to which the theorems are applied is supposed to form the complete boundary of a subregion of Ω, and the orientation is chosen so that the subregion lies to the left of Ω. In rigorous texts considerable effort is spent on proving that these intuitive notions have a precise meaning. The main objection to this procedure is the necessity to allot time and attention to rather delicate questions which are peripheral in comparison with the main issues.

With the general point of view that we have adopted it is still possible, and indeed quite easy, to isolate the classical case. All that is needed is to accept the following definition:

Definition 4. *A cycle γ is said to bound the region Ω if and only if $n(\gamma,a)$ is defined and equal to 1 for all points $a \in \Omega$ and either undefined or equal to zero for all points a not in Ω.*

If γ bounds Ω, and if $\Omega + \gamma$ is contained in a larger region Ω', then it is clear that γ is homologous to zero with respect to Ω'. The following statements are therefore trivial consequences of Theorems 18 and 19:

If γ bounds Ω and $f(z)$ is analytic on the set $\Omega + \gamma$, then

$$\int_\gamma f(z)\,dz = 0$$

and

$$f(z) = \frac{1}{2\pi i}\int_\gamma \frac{f(\zeta)\,d\zeta}{\zeta - z}$$

for all $z \in \Omega$.

If $f(z)$ is analytic on $\Omega + \gamma$ except for isolated singularities in Ω, then

$$\frac{1}{2\pi i}\int_\gamma f(z)\,dz = \sum_j \operatorname{Res}_{z=a_j} f(z)$$

where the sum ranges over the singularities $a_j \in \Omega$.

We observe that a cycle γ which bounds Ω must contain the set theoretic boundary of Ω. Indeed, if z_0 lies on the boundary of Ω, then every neighborhood of z_0 contains points from Ω and points not in Ω. If such a neighborhood were free from points of γ, $n(\gamma,z)$ would be defined and constant in the neighborhood. This contradicts the definition, and hence every neighborhood of z_0 must meet γ; since γ is closed, z_0 must lie on γ.

The converse of the preceding statement is not true, for a point on γ may well have a neighborhood which does not meet Ω. Normally, one would try to choose γ so that it is identical with the boundary of Ω, but for Cauchy's theorem and related considerations this assumption is not needed.

5.2. The Argument Principle. Cauchy's integral formula can be considered as a special case of the residue theorem. Indeed, the function $f(z)/(z-a)$ has a simple pole at $z = a$ with the residue $f(a)$, and when we apply (44), the integral formula results.

Another application of the residue theorem occurred in the proof of Theorem 10 which served to determine the number of zeros of an analytic function, For a zero of order h we can write $f(z) = (z-a)^h f_h(z)$, with $f_h(a) \neq 0$, and obtain $f'(z) = h(z-a)^{h-1}f_h(z) + (z-a)^h f_h'(z)$. Consequently $f'(z)/f(z) = h/(z-a) + f_h'(z)/f_h(z)$, and we see that f'/f has a simple pole with the residue h. In the formula (32) this residue is accounted for by a corresponding repetition of terms.

We can now generalize Theorem 10 to the case of a meromorphic function. If f has a pole of order h, we find by the same calculation as above, with $-h$ replacing h, that f'/f has the residue $-h$. The following theorem results:

Theorem 20. *If $f(z)$ is meromorphic in Ω with the zeros a_j and the poles b_k, then*

$$\frac{1}{2\pi i}\int_\gamma \frac{f'(z)}{f(z)}\,dz = \sum_j n(\gamma,a_j) - \sum_k n(\gamma,b_k) \tag{45}$$

for every cycle γ which is homologous to zero in Ω and does not pass through any of the zeros or poles.

It is understood that multiple zeros and poles have to be repeated as many times as their order indicates; the sums in (45) are finite.

Theorem 20 is usually referred to as the *argument principle.* The name refers to the interpretation of the left-hand member of (45) as $n(\Gamma,0)$ where Γ is the image cycle of γ. If Γ lies in a disk which does not contain the origin, then $n(\Gamma,0) = 0$. This observation is the basis for the following corollary, known as *Rouché's theorem:*

Corollary. *Let γ be homologous to zero in Ω and such that $n(\gamma,z)$ is either* 0 *or* 1 *for any point z not on γ. Suppose that $f(z)$ and $g(z)$ are analytic in Ω and satisfy the inequality $|f(z) - g(z)| < |f(z)|$ on γ. Then $f(z)$ and $g(z)$ have the same number of zeros enclosed by γ.*

The assumption implies that $f(z)$ and $g(z)$ are zero-free on γ. Moreover, they satisfy the inequality

$$\left|\frac{g(z)}{f(z)} - 1\right| < 1$$

on γ. The values of $F(z) = g(z)/f(z)$ on γ are thus contained in the open disk of center 1 and radius 1. When Theorem 20 is applied to $F(z)$, we have thus $n(\Gamma,0) = 0$, and the assertion follows.

A typical application of Rouché's theorem would be the following. Suppose that we wish to find the number of zeros of a function $f(z)$ in the disk $|z| \leqq R$. Using Taylor's theorem we can write

$$f(z) = P_{n-1}(z) + z^n f_n(z)$$

where P_{n-1} is a polynomial of degree $n - 1$. For a suitably chosen n it may happen that we can prove the inequality $R^n|f_n(z)| < |P_{n-1}(z)|$ on $|z| = R$. Then $f(z)$ has the same number of zeros in $|z| \leqq R$ as $P_{n-1}(z)$, and this number can be determined by approximate solution of the polynomial equation $P_{n-1}(z) = 0$.

Theorem 20 can be generalized in the following manner. If $g(z)$ is analytic in Ω, then $g(z)\dfrac{f'(z)}{f(z)}$ has the residue $hg(a)$ at a zero a of order h and the residue $-hg(a)$ at a pole. We obtain thus the formula

$$\frac{1}{2\pi i}\int_\gamma g(z)\frac{f'(z)}{f(z)}\,dz = \sum_j n(\gamma,a_j)g(a_j) - \sum_k n(\gamma,b_k)g(b_k). \tag{46}$$

This result is important for the study of the inverse function. With the notations of Theorem 11 we know that the equation $f(z) = w$, $|w - w_0| < \delta$ has n roots $z_j(w)$ in the disk $|z - z_0| < \varepsilon$. If we apply

(46) with $g(z) = z$, we obtain

$$\sum_{j=1}^{n} z_j(w) = \frac{1}{2\pi i} \int_{|z-z_0|=\epsilon} \frac{f'(z)}{f(z) - w} z\,dz. \tag{47}$$

For $n = 1$ the inverse function $f^{-1}(w)$ can thus be represented explicitly by

$$f^{-1}(w) = \frac{1}{2\pi i} \int_{|z-z_0|=\epsilon} \frac{f'(z)}{f(z) - w} z\,dz.$$

If (46) is applied with $g(z) = z^m$, equation (47) is replaced by

$$\sum_{j=1}^{n} z_j(w)^m = \frac{1}{2\pi i} \int_{|z-z_0|=\epsilon} \frac{f'(z)}{f(z) - w} z^m\,dz.$$

It is not difficult to show that the right-hand member represents an analytic function of w for $|w - w_0| < \delta$. Thus the power sums of the roots $z_j(w)$ are single-valued analytic functions of w. But it is well known that the elementary symmetric functions can be expressed as polynomials in the power sums. Hence they are also analytic, and we find that the $z_j(w)$ are the roots of a polynomial equation

$$z^n + a_1(w)z^{n-1} + \cdots + a_{n-1}(w)z + a_n(w) = 0$$

whose coefficients are analytic functions of w in $|w - w_0| < \delta$.

5.3. Evaluation of Definite Integrals. The calculus of residues provides a very efficient tool for the evaluation of definite integrals. It is particularly important when it is impossible to find the indefinite integral explicitly, but even if the ordinary methods of calculus can be applied the use of residues is frequently a laborsaving device. The fact that the calculus of residues yields complex rather than real integrals is no disadvantage, for clearly the evaluation of a complex integral is equivalent to the evaluation of two definite integrals.

There are, however, some serious limitations, and the method is far from infallible. In the first place, the integrand must be closely connected with some analytic function. This is not very serious, for usually we are only required to integrate elementary functions, and they can all be extended to the complex domain. It is much more serious that the technique of complex integration applies only to closed curves, while a real integral is always extended over an interval. A special device must be used in order to reduce the problem to one which concerns integration over a closed curve. There are a number of ways in which this can be accomplished, but they all apply under rather special circumstances.

The technique can be learned at the hand of typical examples, but even complete mastery does not guarantee success.

1. All integrals of the form

$$\int_0^{2\pi} R(\cos\theta, \sin\theta)\, d\theta \tag{48}$$

where the integrand is a rational function of $\cos\theta$ and $\sin\theta$ can be easily evaluated by means of residues. Of course these integrals can also be computed by explicit integration, but this technique is usually very laborious. It is very natural to make the substitution $z = e^{i\theta}$ which immediately transforms (48) into the line integral

$$-i \int_{|z|=1} R\left[\frac{1}{2}\left(z + \frac{1}{z}\right), \frac{1}{2i}\left(z - \frac{1}{z}\right)\right] \frac{dz}{z}.$$

It remains only to determine the residues which correspond to the poles of the integrand inside the unit circle.

As an example, let us compute

$$\int_0^{\pi} \frac{d\theta}{a + \cos\theta}, \qquad a > 1.$$

This integral is not extended over $(0,2\pi)$, but since $\cos\theta$ takes the same values in the intervals $(0,\pi)$ and $(\pi,2\pi)$ is is clear that the integral from 0 to π is one-half of the integral from 0 to 2π. Taking this into account we find that the integral equals

$$-i \int_{|z|=1} \frac{dz}{z^2 + 2az + 1}$$

The denominator can be factored into $(z - \alpha)(z - \beta)$ with

$$\alpha = -a + \sqrt{a^2 - 1}, \qquad \beta = -a - \sqrt{a^2 - 1}.$$

Evidently $|\alpha| < 1$, $|\beta| > 1$, and the residue at α is $1/(\alpha - \beta)$. The value of the integral is found to be $\pi/\sqrt{a^2 - 1}$.

2. An integral of the form

$$\int_{-\infty}^{\infty} R(x)\, dx$$

converges if and only if in the rational function $R(x)$ the degree of the denominator is at least two units higher than the degree of the numerator, and if no pole lies on the real axis. The standard procedure is to integrate the complex function $R(z)$ over a closed curve consisting of a line segment $(-\rho,\rho)$ and the semicircle from ρ to $-\rho$ in the upper half plane.

If ρ is large enough this curve encloses all poles in the upper half plane, and the corresponding integral is equal to $2\pi i$ times the sum of the residues in the upper half plane. As $\rho \to \infty$ obvious estimates show that the integral over the semicircle tends to 0, and we obtain

$$\int_{-\infty}^{\infty} R(x)\,dx = 2\pi i \sum_{y>0} \text{Res}\,R(z).$$

3. The same method can be applied to an integral of the form

$$\int_{-\infty}^{\infty} R(x)e^{ix}\,dx \tag{49}$$

whose real and imaginary parts determine the important integrals

$$\int_{-\infty}^{\infty} R(x)\cos x\,dx, \qquad \int_{-\infty}^{\infty} R(x)\sin x\,dx. \tag{50}$$

Since $|e^{iz}| = e^{-y}$ is bounded in the upper half plane, we can again conclude that the integral over the semicircle tends to zero, provided that the rational function $R(z)$ has a zero of at least order 2 at infinity. We obtain

$$\int_{-\infty}^{\infty} R(x)e^{ix}\,dx = 2\pi i \sum_{y>0} \text{Res}\,R(z)e^{iz}.$$

It is less obvious that the same result holds when $R(z)$ has only a simple zero at infinity. In this case it is not convenient to use semicircles. For one thing, it is not so easy to estimate the integral over the semicircle, and secondly, even if we were successful we would only have proved that the integral

$$\int_{-\rho}^{\rho} R(x)e^{ix}\,dx$$

over a symmetric interval has the desired limit for $\rho \to \infty$. In reality we are of course required to prove that

$$\int_{-X_1}^{X_2} R(x)e^{ix}\,dx$$

has a limit when X_1 and X_2 tend independently to ∞. In the earlier examples this question did not arise because the convergence of the integral was assured beforehand.

For the proof we integrate over the perimeter of a rectangle with the vertices X_2, $X_2 + iY$, $-X_1 + iY$, $-X_1$ where $Y > 0$. As soon as X_1, X_2 and Y are sufficiently large, this rectangle contains all the poles in the upper half plane. Under the hypothesis $|zR(z)|$ is bounded. Hence the integral over the right vertical side is, except for a constant factor, less than

$$\int_0^y e^{-y} \frac{dy}{|z|} < \frac{1}{X_2} \int_0^y e^{-y}\, dy.$$

The last integral can be evaluated explicitly and is found to be < 1. Hence the integral over the right vertical side is less than a constant times $1/X_2$, and a corresponding result is found for the left vertical side. The integral over the upper horizontal side is evidently less than $e^{-Y}(X_1 + X_2)/Y$ multiplied with a constant. For fixed X_1, X_2 it tends to 0 as $Y \to \infty$, and we conclude that

$$\left| \int_{-X_1}^{X_2} R(x)e^{ix}\, dx - 2\pi i \sum_{y>0} \text{Res } R(z)e^{iz} \right| < A\left(\frac{1}{X_1} + \frac{1}{X_2}\right)$$

where A denotes a constant. This inequality proves that

$$\int_{-\infty}^{\infty} R(x)e^{ix}\, dx = 2\pi i \sum_{y>0} \text{Res } R(z)e^{iz}$$

under the sole condition that $R(\infty) = 0$.

In the discussion we have assumed, tacitly, that $R(z)$ has no poles on the real axis since otherwise the integral (49) has no meaning. However, one of the integrals (50) may well exist, namely, if $R(z)$ has simple poles which coincide with zeros of $\sin x$ or $\cos x$. Let us suppose, for instance, that $R(z)$ has a simple pole at $z = 0$. Then the second integral (50) has a meaning and calls for evaluation.

We use the same method as before, but we use a path which avoids the origin by following a small semicircle of radius δ in the lower half plane (Fig. 25). It is easy to see that this closed curve encloses the poles in the upper half plane, the pole at the origin, and no others, as soon as X_1, X_2, Y are sufficiently large and δ is sufficiently small. Suppose that the residue at 0 is B, so that we can write $R(z)e^{iz} = B/z + R_0(z)$ where

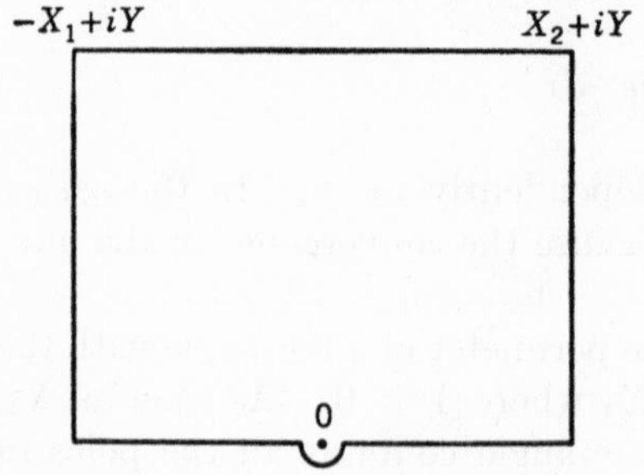

FIG. 25

$R_0(z)$ is analytic at the origin. The integral of the first term over the semicircle is πiB, while the integral of the second term tends to 0 with δ. It is clear that we are led to the result

$$\lim_{\delta\to 0} \int_{-\infty}^{-\delta} + \int_{\delta}^{\infty} R(x)e^{ix}\,dx = 2\pi i \left[\sum_{y>0} \operatorname{Res} R(z)e^{iz} + \tfrac{1}{2}B \right].$$

The limit on the left is called the *Cauchy principal value* of the integral; it exists although the integral itself has no meaning. On the right-hand side we observe that one-half of the residue at 0 has been included; this is as if one-half of the pole were counted as lying in the upper half plane.

In the general case where several poles lie on the real axis we obtain

$$\text{pr.v.} \int_{-\infty}^{\infty} R(x)e^{ix}\,dx = 2\pi i \sum_{y>0} \operatorname{Res} R(z)e^{iz} + \pi i \sum_{y=0} \operatorname{Res} R(z)e^{iz}$$

where the notations are self-explanatory. It is an essential hypothesis that all the poles on the real axis be simple, and as before we must assume that $R(\infty) = 0$.

As the simplest example we have

$$\text{pr.v} \int_{-\infty}^{\infty} \frac{e^{ix}}{x}\,dx = \pi i.$$

Separating the real and imaginary part we observe that the real part of the equation is trivial by the fact that the integrand is odd. In the imaginary part it is not necessary to take the principal value, and since the integrand is even we find

$$\int_0^{\infty} \frac{\sin x}{x}\,dx = \frac{\pi}{2}.$$

We remark that integrals containing a factor $\cos^n x$ or $\sin^n x$ can be evaluated by the same technique. Indeed, these factors can be written as linear combinations of terms $\cos mx$ and $\sin mx$, and the corresponding integrals can be reduced to the form (49) by a change of variable:

$$\int_{-\infty}^{\infty} R(x)e^{imx}\,dx = \frac{1}{m}\int_{-\infty}^{\infty} R\left(\frac{x}{m}\right) e^{ix}\,dx.$$

4. The next category of integrals have the form

$$\int_0^{\infty} x^{\alpha} R(x)\,dx$$

where the exponent α is real and may be supposed to lie in the interval $0 < \alpha < 1$. For convergence $R(z)$ must have a zero of at least order two at ∞ and at most a simple pole at the origin.

The new feature is the fact that $R(z)z^\alpha$ is not single-valued. This, however, is just the circumstance which makes it possible to find the integral from 0 to ∞.

The simplest procedure is to start with the substitution $x = t^2$ which transforms the integral into

$$2 \int_0^\infty t^{2\alpha+1}R(t^2)\,dt.$$

For the function $z^{2\alpha}$ we may choose the branch whose argument lies between $-\pi\alpha$ and $3\pi\alpha$; it is well defined and analytic in the region obtained by omitting the negative imaginary axis. As long as we avoid the negative imaginary axis, we can apply the residue theorem to the function $z^{2\alpha+1}R(z^2)$. We use a closed curve consisting of two line segments along the positive and negative axis and two semicircles in the upper half plane, one very large and one very small (Fig. 26). Under our assumptions it is easy to show that the integrals over the semicircles tend to zero. Hence the residue theorem yields the value of the integral

$$\int_{-\infty}^\infty z^{2\alpha+1}R(z^2)\,dz = \int_0^\infty (z^{2\alpha+1} + (-z)^{2\alpha+1})R(z^2)\,dz.$$

However, $(-z)^{2\alpha} = e^{2\pi i\alpha}z^{2\alpha}$, and the integral equals

$$(1 - e^{2\pi i\alpha}) \int_0^\infty z^{2\alpha+1}R(z^2)\,dz.$$

Since the factor in front is $\neq 0$, we are finally able to determine the value of the desired integral.

The evaluation calls for determination of the residues of $z^{2\alpha+1}R(z^2)$ in the upper half plane. These are the same as the residues of $z^\alpha R(z)$ in the whole plane. For practical purposes it may be preferable not to use any

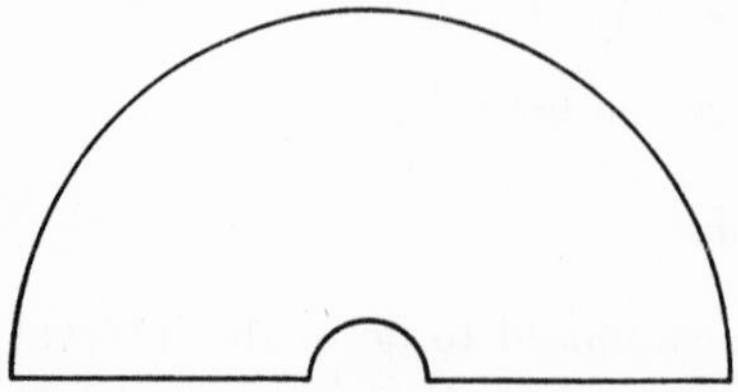

FIG. 26

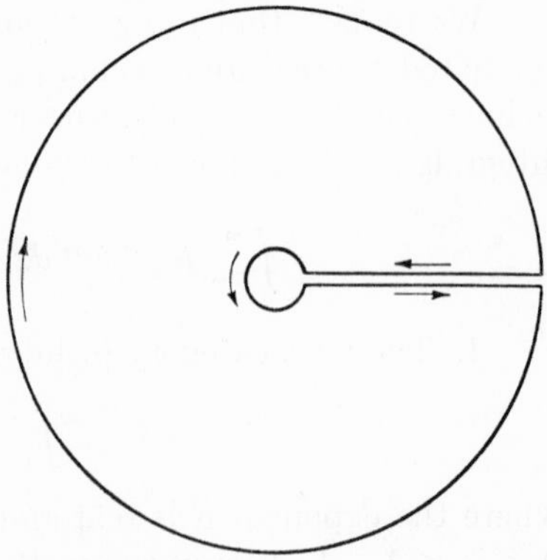

FIG. 27

preliminary substitution and integrate the function $z^\alpha R(z)$ over the closed curve shown in Fig. 27. We have then to use the branch of z^α whose argument lies between 0 and $2\pi\alpha$. This method needs some justification, for it does not conform to the hypotheses of the residue theorem. The justification is trivial.

5. As a final example we compute the special integral

$$\int_0^\pi \log \sin \theta \, d\theta.$$

Consider the function $1 - e^{2iz} = -2ie^{iz} \sin z$. From the representation $1 - e^{2iz} = 1 - e^{-2y}(\cos 2x + i \sin 2x)$, we find that this function is real and negative only for $x = n\pi$, $y \leqq 0$. In the region obtained by omitting these half lines the principal branch of $\log (1 - e^{2iz})$ is hence single-valued and analytic. We apply Cauchy's theorem to the rectangle whose vertices are $0, \pi, \pi + iY$, and iY; however, the points 0 and π have to be avoided, and we do this by following small circular quadrants of radius δ.

Because of the periodicity the integrals over the vertical sides cancel against each other. The integral over the upper horizontal side tends to 0 as $Y \to \infty$. Finally, the integrals over the quadrants can also be seen to approach zero as $\delta \to 0$. Indeed, since the imaginary part of the logarithm is bounded we need consider only the real part. Since e^{2iz} has the derivative $2i$ at the origin, we find that $|1 - e^{2iz}|/|z| \to 2$ for $z \to 0$. Hence we need only show that $\delta \log \delta$ tends to 0 with δ. For the sake of completeness we include a proof of this elementary fact. By studying the derivative we find that the function $t \log (\varepsilon/t)$ is increasing for $t \leqq \varepsilon/e$. For $\delta < \varepsilon/e$ we have thus $\delta \log (\varepsilon/\delta) < \varepsilon/e$. If we choose $\varepsilon < 1$ and let δ satisfy the additional condition $\delta < \varepsilon/[e \log (1/\varepsilon)]$, we find that $\delta \log (1/\delta) < 2\varepsilon/e$, and this proves that $\lim_{\delta \to 0} \delta \log (1/\delta) = 0$.

The same proof applies near the vertex π, and we obtain

$$\int_0^\pi \log (-2ie^{ix} \sin x) \, dx = 0$$

If we choose $\log e^{ix} = ix$, the imaginary part lies between 0 and π. Therefore, in order to obtain the principal branch with an imaginary part between $-\pi$ and π, we must choose $\log (-i) = -\pi i/2$. The equation can now be written in the form

$$\pi \log 2 - \left(\frac{\pi^2}{2}\right) i + \int_0^\pi \log \sin x \, dx + \left(\frac{\pi^2}{2}\right) i = 0,$$

and we find

$$\int_0^\pi \log \sin x \, dx = -\pi \log 2.$$

EXERCISES

Evaluate the following integrals by the method of residues:

1. $\displaystyle\int_0^{\pi/2} \frac{dx}{a + \sin^2 x}, \qquad a > 0.$
2. $\displaystyle\int_0^{\infty} \frac{x^2\,dx}{x^4 + 6x^2 + 13}.$
3. $\displaystyle\int_{-\infty}^{\infty} \frac{x^2 - x + 2}{x^4 + 10x^2 + 9}\,dx.$
4. $\displaystyle\int_0^{\infty} \frac{x^2\,dx}{(x^2 + a^2)^3}, \qquad a \text{ real}.$
5. $\displaystyle\int_0^{\infty} \frac{\cos x}{x^2 + a^2}\,dx, \qquad a \text{ real}.$
6. $\displaystyle\int_0^{\infty} \frac{x \sin x\,dx}{x^2 + a^2}, \qquad a \text{ real}.$
7. $\displaystyle\int_0^{\infty} \frac{\sin^2 kx}{x^2}\,dx, \qquad k > 0.$
8. $\displaystyle\int_0^{\infty} (1 + x^2)^{-2} \log x\,dx.$
9. $\displaystyle\int_0^{\infty} \log(1 + x^2)\,\frac{dx}{x^{1+\alpha}} \qquad (0 < \alpha < 2).$

6. HARMONIC FUNCTIONS

The real and imaginary parts of an analytic function are conjugate harmonic functions. Therefore, all theorems on analytic functions are also theorems on pairs of conjugate harmonic functions. However, harmonic functions are important in their own right, and their treatment is not always simplified by the use of complex methods. This is particularly true when the conjugate harmonic function is not single-valued.

We assemble in this section some facts about harmonic functions that are intimately connected with Cauchy's theorem. The more delicate properties of harmonic functions are postponed to a later chapter.

6.1. Definition and Basic Properties. A real-valued function $u(z)$ or $u(x,y)$, defined and single-valued in a region Ω, is said to be *harmonic* in Ω, or a *potential function*, if it is continuous together with its partial derivatives of the first two orders and satisfies *Laplace's equation*

$$\Delta u = \frac{\partial^2 u}{\partial x^2} + \frac{\partial^2 u}{\partial y^2} = 0. \tag{51}$$

We shall see later that the regularity conditions can be weakened, but this is a point of relatively minor importance.

The sum of two harmonic functions and a constant multiple of a harmonic function are again harmonic; this is due to the linear character of Laplace's equation. The simplest harmonic functions are the linear functions $ax + by$. In polar coordinates (r,θ) equation (51) takes the form

$$r \frac{\partial}{\partial r}\left(r \frac{\partial u}{\partial r}\right) + \frac{\partial^2 u}{\partial \theta^2} = 0.\dagger$$

This shows that $\log r$ is a harmonic function and that any harmonic function which depends only on r must be of the form $a \log r + b$. The argument θ is harmonic whenever it can be uniquely defined.

If u is harmonic in Ω, then

$$f(z) = \frac{\partial u}{\partial x} - i \frac{\partial u}{\partial y} \tag{52}$$

is analytic, for writing $U = \dfrac{\partial u}{\partial x}$, $V = -\dfrac{\partial u}{\partial y}$ we have

$$\frac{\partial U}{\partial x} = \frac{\partial^2 u}{\partial x^2} = -\frac{\partial^2 u}{\partial y^2} = \frac{\partial V}{\partial y}$$

$$\frac{\partial U}{\partial y} = \frac{\partial^2 u}{\partial x\, \partial y} = -\frac{\partial V}{\partial x}.$$

This, it should be remembered, is the most natural way of passing from harmonic to analytic functions.

From (52) we pass to the differential

$$f\, dz = \left(\frac{\partial u}{\partial x} dx + \frac{\partial u}{\partial y} dy\right) + i\left(-\frac{\partial u}{\partial y} dx + \frac{\partial u}{\partial x} dy\right). \tag{53}$$

In this expression the real part is the differential of u,

$$du = \frac{\partial u}{\partial x} dx + \frac{\partial u}{\partial y} dy.$$

If u has a conjugate harmonic function v, then the imaginary part can be written as

$$dv = \frac{\partial v}{\partial x} dx + \frac{\partial v}{\partial y} dy = -\frac{\partial u}{\partial y} dx + \frac{\partial u}{\partial x} dy.$$

In general, however, there is no single-valued conjugate function, and in these circumstances it is better not to use the notation dv. Instead we write

$${}^*du = -\frac{\partial u}{\partial y} dx + \frac{\partial u}{\partial x} dy$$

† This form cannot be used for $r = 0$.

and call $^*du$ the *conjugate differential* of du. We have by (53)

$$f\,dz = du + i\,{}^*du. \tag{54}$$

By Cauchy's theorem the integral of $f\,dz$ vanishes along any cycle which is homologous to zero in Ω. On the other hand, the integral of the exact differential du vanishes along all cycles. It follows by (54) that

$$\int_\gamma {}^*du = \int_\gamma -\frac{\partial u}{\partial y}\,dx + \frac{\partial u}{\partial x}\,dy = 0 \tag{55}$$

for all cycles γ which are homologous to zero in Ω.

The integral in (55) has an important interpretation which cannot be left unmentioned. If γ is a regular curve with the equation $z = z(t)$, the direction of the tangent is determined by the angle $\alpha = \arg z'(t)$, and we can write $dx = |dz| \cos \alpha$, $dy = |dz| \sin \alpha$. The normal which points to the right of the tangent has the direction $\beta = \alpha - \pi/2$, and thus $\cos \alpha = -\sin \beta$, $\sin \alpha = \cos \beta$. The expression

$$\frac{\partial u}{\partial n} = \frac{\partial u}{\partial x} \cos \beta + \frac{\partial u}{\partial y} \sin \beta$$

is a directional derivative of u, the right-hand *normal derivative* with respect to the curve γ. We obtain $^*du = (\partial u/\partial n)\,|dz|$, and (55) can be written in the form

$$\int_\gamma \frac{\partial u}{\partial n}\,|dz| = 0. \tag{56}$$

This is the classical notation. Its main advantage is that $\partial u/\partial n$ actually represents a rate of change in the direction perpendicular to γ. For instance, if γ is the circle $|z| = r$, described in the positive sense, $\partial u/\partial n$ can be replaced by the partial derivative $\partial u/\partial r$. It has the disadvantage that (56) is not expressed as an ordinary line integral, but as an integral with respect to arc length. For this reason the classical notation is less natural in connection with homology theory, and we prefer to use the notation $^*du$.

In a simply connected region the integral of $^*du$ vanishes over all cycles, and u has a single-valued conjugate function v which is determined up to an additive constant. In the multiply connected case the conjugate function has *periods*

$$\int_{\gamma_i} {}^*du = \int_{\gamma_i} \frac{\partial u}{\partial n}\,|dz|$$

corresponding to the cycles in a homology basis.

There is an important generalization of (55) which deals with a pair of harmonic functions. If u_1 and u_2 are harmonic in Ω, we claim that

$$\int_\gamma u_1 \, {}^*du_2 - u_2 \, {}^*du_1 = 0 \tag{57}$$

for every cycle γ which is homologous to zero in Ω. According to Theorem 17, Sec. 4.4, it is sufficient to prove (57) for $\gamma = \partial R$, where R is a rectangle contained in Ω. In R, u_1 and u_2 have single-valued conjugate functions v_1, v_2 and we can write

$$u_1 \, {}^*du_2 - u_2 \, {}^*du_1 = u_1 \, dv_2 - u_2 \, dv_1 = u_1 \, dv_2 + v_1 \, du_2 - d(u_2 v_1).$$

Here $d(u_2v_1)$ is an exact differential, and $u_1dv_2 + v_1du_2$ is the imaginary part of

$$(u_1 + iv_1)(du_2 + i \, dv_2).$$

The last differential can be written in the form $F_1f_2 \, dz$ where $F_1(z)$ and $f_2(z)$ are analytic on R. The integral of $F_1f_2 \, dz$ vanishes by Cauchy's theorem, and so does therefore the integral of its imaginary part. We conclude that (57) holds for $\gamma = \partial R$, and we have proved:

Theorem 21. *If u_1 and u_2 are harmonic in a region Ω, then*

$$\int_\gamma u_1 \, {}^*du_2 - u_2 \, {}^*du_1 = 0 \tag{57}$$

for every cycle γ which is homologous to zero in Ω.

For $u_1 = 1$, $u_2 = u$ the formula reduces to (55). In the classical notation (57) would be written as

$$\int_\gamma \left(u_1 \frac{\partial u_2}{\partial n} - u_2 \frac{\partial u_1}{\partial n} \right) |dz| = 0.$$

6.2. The Mean-value Property. Let us apply Theorem 21 with $u_1 = \log r$ and u_2 equal to a function u, harmonic in $|z| < \rho$. For Ω we must choose the punctured disk $0 < |z| < \rho$, and for γ we take the cycle $C_1 - C_2$ where C_i is a circle $|z| = r_i < \rho$ described in the positive sense. On a circle $|z| = r$ we have ${}^*du = r(\partial u/\partial r) \, d\theta$ and hence (57) yields

$$\log r_1 \int_{C_1} r_1 \frac{\partial u}{\partial r} \, d\theta - \int_{C_1} u \, d\theta = \log r_2 \int_{C_2} r_2 \frac{\partial u}{\partial r} \, d\theta - \int_{C_2} u \, d\theta.$$

In other words, the expression

$$\int_{|z|=r} u \, d\theta - \log r \int_{|z|=r} r \frac{\partial u}{\partial r} \, d\theta$$

is constant, and this is true even if u is only known to be harmonic in an annulus. By (55) we find in the same way that

$$\int_{|z|=r} r\frac{\partial u}{\partial r}\,d\theta$$

is constant in the case of an annulus and zero if u is harmonic in the whole disk. Combining these results we obtain:

Theorem 22. *The arithmetic mean of a harmonic function over concentric circles $|z| = r$ is a linear function of* $\log r$,

$$\frac{1}{2\pi}\int_{|z|=r} u\,d\theta = \alpha \log r + \beta, \tag{58}$$

and if u is harmonic in a disk $\alpha = 0$ and the arithmetic mean is constant.

In the latter case $\beta = u(0)$, by continuity, and changing to a new origin we find

$$u(z_0) = \frac{1}{2\pi}\int_0^{2\pi} u(z_0 + re^{i\theta})\,d\theta. \tag{59}$$

It is clear that (59) could also have been derived from the corresponding formula for analytic functions, Sec. 3.4, (34). It leads directly to the *maximum principle* for harmonic functions:

Theorem 23. *A nonconstant harmonic function has neither a maximum nor a minimum in its region of definition. Consequently, the maximum and the minimum on a closed bounded set E are taken on the boundary of E.*

The proof is the same as for the maximum principle of analytic functions and will not be repeated. It applies also to the minimum for the reason that $-u$ is harmonic together with u. In the case of analytic functions the corresponding procedure would have been to apply the maximum principle to $1/f(z)$ which is illegitimate unless $f(z) \neq 0$. Observe that the maximum principle for analytic functions follows from the maximum principle for harmonic functions by applying the latter to $\log |f(z)|$ which is harmonic when $f(z) \neq 0$.

EXERCISES

1. If u is harmonic and bounded in $0 < |z| < \rho$, show that the origin is a removable singularity in the sense that u becomes harmonic in $|z| < \rho$ when $u(0)$ is properly defined.

2. If $u(z)$ is harmonic for $0 < |z| < \rho$ and $\lim_{z\to 0} zu(z) = 0$, prove that u can be written in the form $u(z) = \alpha \log |z| + u_0(z)$ where α is a constant and u_0 is harmonic in $|z| < \rho$.

3. Suppose that $f(z)$ is analytic for $r_1 \leqq |z| \leqq r_2$, and set

$$M(r) = \max |f(z)|$$

for $|z| = r(r_1 \leqq r \leqq r_2)$. Show that

$$M(r) \leqq M(r_1)^\alpha M(r_2)^{1-\alpha}$$

where $\alpha = \log (r_2/r):\log (r_2/r_1)$ (Hadamard's three-circle theorem). Discuss cases of equality. *Hint:* Apply the maximum principle to a linear combination of $\log |f(z)|$ and $\log |z|$.

6.3. Poisson's Formula. The maximum principle has the following important consequence: If $u(z)$ is harmonic on a closed bounded set E, that is, if it is defined and harmonic in a region containing E, then it is uniquely determined by its values on the boundary of E. Indeed, if u_1 and u_2 are two harmonic functions with the same boundary values, then $u_1 - u_2$ is harmonic with the boundary values 0. Using the maximum and minimum principle we find that $u_1 - u_2$ must be identically zero on E.

There arises the problem of finding u when its boundary values are given. At this point we shall solve the problem only in the simplest case, namely for a closed disk.

Formula (59) determines the value of u at the center of the disk. But this is all we need, for there exists a linear transformation which carries any point to the center. To be explicit, suppose that $u(z)$ is harmonic in the closed disk $|z| \leqq R$. The linear transformation

$$z = S(\zeta) = \frac{R(R\zeta + a)}{R + \bar{a}\zeta}$$

maps $|\zeta| \leqq 1$ onto $|z| \leqq R$ with $\zeta = 0$ corresponding to $z = a$. The function $u(S(\zeta))$ is harmonic in $|\zeta| \leqq 1$, and by (59) we obtain

$$u(a) = \frac{1}{2\pi} \int_{|\zeta|=1} u(S(\zeta))\, d \arg \zeta.$$

From

$$\zeta = \frac{R(z - a)}{R^2 - \bar{a}z}$$

we compute

$$d \arg \zeta = -i\frac{d\zeta}{\zeta} = -i\left(\frac{1}{z - a} + \frac{\bar{a}}{R^2 - \bar{a}z}\right) dz = \left(\frac{z}{z - a} + \frac{\bar{a}z}{R^2 - \bar{a}z}\right) d\theta.$$

On substituting $R^2 = z\bar{z}$ the coefficient of $d\theta$ in the last expression can be rewritten as

$$\frac{z}{z-a} + \frac{\bar{a}}{\bar{z}-\bar{a}} = \frac{R^2 - |a|^2}{|z-a|^2}$$

or, equivalently, as

$$\frac{1}{2}\left(\frac{z+a}{z-a} + \frac{\bar{z}+\bar{a}}{\bar{z}-\bar{a}}\right) = \operatorname{Re}\frac{z+a}{z-a}.$$

We obtain the two forms

$$(60) \quad u(a) = \frac{1}{2\pi}\int_{|z|=R} \frac{R^2-|a|^2}{|z-a|^2}\,u(z)\,d\theta = \frac{1}{2\pi}\int_{|z|=R} \operatorname{Re}\frac{z+a}{z-a}\,u(z)\,d\theta$$

of *Poisson's formula.* In polar coordinates,

$$u(re^{i\varphi}) = \frac{1}{2\pi}\int_0^{2\pi} \frac{R^2-r^2}{R^2-2rR\cos(\theta-\varphi)+r^2}\,u(Re^{i\theta})\,d\theta.$$

In the derivation we have assumed that $u(z)$ is harmonic in the closed disk. However, the result remains true under the weaker condition that $u(z)$ is harmonic in the open disk and continuous in the closed disk. Indeed, if $0 < r < 1$, then $u(rz)$ is harmonic in the closed disk, and we obtain

$$u(ra) = \frac{1}{2\pi}\int_{|z|=R} \frac{R^2-|a|^2}{|z-a|^2}\,u(rz)\,d\theta.$$

Now all we need to do is to let r tend to 1. Because $u(z)$ is uniformly continuous on $|z| \leqq R$ it is true that $u(rz) \to u(z)$ uniformly for $|z| = R$, and we conclude that (60) remains valid.

We shall formulate the result as a theorem:

Theorem 24. *Suppose that $u(z)$ is harmonic for $|z| < R$, continuous for $|z| \leqq R$. Then*

$$(61) \qquad u(a) = \frac{1}{2\pi}\int_{|z|=R} \frac{R^2-|a|^2}{|z-a|^2}\,u(z)\,d\theta$$

for all $|a| < R$.

The theorem leads at once to an explicit expression for the conjugate function of u. Indeed, formula (60) gives

$$(62) \qquad u(z) = \operatorname{Re}\left[\frac{1}{2\pi i}\int_{|\zeta|=R} \frac{\zeta+z}{\zeta-z}\,u(\zeta)\,\frac{d\zeta}{\zeta}\right].$$

The bracketed expression is an analytic function of z for $|z| < R$. It follows that $u(z)$ is the real part of

$$f(z) = \frac{1}{2\pi i} \int_{|\zeta| = R} \frac{\zeta + z}{\zeta - z} u(\zeta) \frac{d\zeta}{\zeta} + iC \tag{63}$$

where C is an arbitrary real constant. This formula is known as Schwarz's formula.

As a special case of (61), note that $u = 1$ yields

$$\int_{|z| = R} \frac{R^2 - |z|^2}{|z - a|^2} \, d\theta = 2\pi \tag{64}$$

for all $|a| < R$.

6.4. Schwarz's Theorem. Theorem 24 serves to express a given harmonic function through its values on a circle. But the right-hand side of formula (61) has a meaning as soon as u is defined on $|z| = R$, provided it is sufficiently regular, for instance piecewise continuous. As in (62) the integral can again be written as the real part of an analytic function, and consequently it is a harmonic function. The question is, does it have the boundary values $u(z)$ on $|z| = R$?

There is reason to clarify the notations. Choosing $R = 1$ we define, for any piecewise continuous function $U(\theta)$ in $0 \leqq \theta \leqq 2\pi$,

$$P_U(z) = \frac{1}{2\pi} \int_0^{2\pi} \operatorname{Re} \frac{e^{i\theta} + z}{e^{i\theta} - z} U(\theta) \, d\theta$$

and call this the *Poisson integral* of U. Observe that $P_U(z)$ is not only a function of z, but also a function of the function U; as such it is called a *functional*. The functional is *linear* inasmuch as

$$P_{U+V} = P_U + P_V$$

and

$$P_{cU} = cP_U$$

for constant c. Moreover, $U \geqq 0$ implies $P_U(z) \geqq 0$; because of this property P_U is said to be a *positive* linear functional.

We deduce from (64) that $P_c = c$. From this property, together with the linear and positive character of the functional, it follows that any inequality $m \leqq U \leqq M$ implies $m \leqq P_U \leqq M$.

The question of boundary values is settled by the following fundamental theorem that was first proved by H. A. Schwarz:

Theorem 25. *The function $P_U(z)$ is harmonic for $|z| < 1$, and*

$$\lim_{z \to e^{i\theta_0}} P_U(z) = U(\theta_0) \tag{65}$$

provided that U is continuous at θ_0.

We have already remarked that P_U is harmonic. To study the boundary behavior, let C_1 and C_2 be complementary arcs of the unit circle, and denote by U_1 the function which coincides with U on C_1 and vanishes on C_2, by U_2 the corresponding function for C_2. Clearly, $P_U = P_{U_1} + P_{U_2}$.

Since P_{U_1} can be regarded as a line integral over C_1 it is, by the same reasoning as before, harmonic everywhere except on the closed arc C_1. The expression

$$\operatorname{Re} \frac{e^{i\theta} + z}{e^{i\theta} - z} = \frac{1 - |z|^2}{|e^{i\theta} - z|^2}$$

vanishes on $|z| = 1$ for $z \neq e^{i\theta}$. It follows that P_{U_1} is zero on the open arc C_2, and since it is continuous $\lim_{z \to e^{i\theta}} P_{U_1}(z) = 0$ for $e^{i\theta} \in C_2$.

In proving (65) we may suppose that $U(\theta_0) = 0$, for if this is not the case we need only replace U by $U - U(\theta_0)$. Given $\varepsilon > 0$ we can find C_1 and C_2 such that $e^{i\theta_0}$ is an interior point of C_2 and $|U(\theta)| < \varepsilon/2$ for $e^{i\theta} \in C_2$. Under this condition $|U_2(\theta)| < \varepsilon/2$ for all θ, and hence $|P_{U_2}(z)| < \varepsilon/2$ for all $|z| < 1$. On the other hand, since U_1 is continuous and vanishes at $e^{i\theta_0}$ there exists a δ such that $|P_{U_1}(z)| < \varepsilon/2$ for $|z - e^{i\theta_0}| < \delta$. It follows that $|P_U(z)| \leqq |P_{U_1}| + |P_{U_2}| < \varepsilon$ as soon as $|z| < 1$ and $|z - e^{i\theta_0}| < \delta$, which is precisely what we had to prove.

There is an interesting geometric interpretation of Poisson's formula, also due to Schwarz. Given a fixed z inside the unit circle we determine for each $e^{i\theta}$ the point $e^{i\theta^*}$ which is such that $e^{i\theta}$, z and $e^{i\theta^*}$ are in a straight

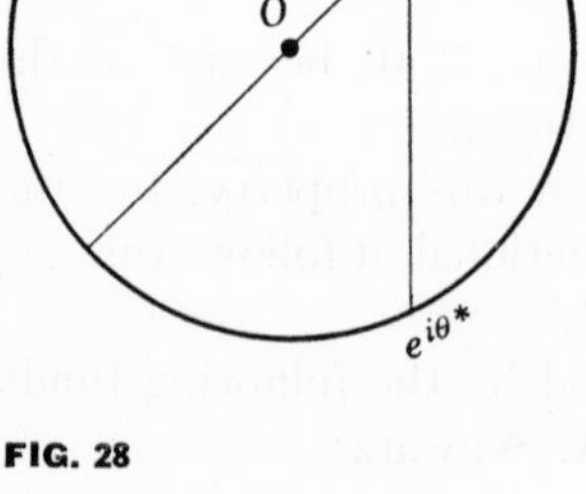

FIG. 28

line (Fig. 28). It is clear geometrically, or by simple calculation, that

$$1 - |z|^2 = |e^{i\theta} - z|\,|e^{i\theta^*} - z|. \tag{66}$$

But the ratio $(e^{i\theta} - z)/(e^{i\theta^*} - z)$ is negative, so we must have

$$1 - |z|^2 = -\,(e^{i\theta} - z)(e^{-i\theta^*} - \bar{z}).$$

We regard θ^* as a function of θ and differentiate. Since z is constant we obtain

$$\frac{e^{i\theta}\,d\theta}{e^{i\theta} - z} = \frac{e^{-i\theta^*}\,d\theta^*}{e^{-i\theta^*} - \bar{z}}$$

and, on taking absolute values,

$$\frac{d\theta^*}{d\theta} = \left|\frac{e^{i\theta^*} - z}{e^{i\theta} - z}\right|. \tag{67}$$

It follows by (66) and (67) that

$$\frac{1 - |z|^2}{|e^{i\theta} - z|^2} = \frac{d\theta^*}{d\theta}$$

and hence

$$P_U(z) = \frac{1}{2\pi}\int_0^{2\pi} U(\theta)\,d\theta^* = \frac{1}{2\pi}\int_0^{2\pi} U(\theta^*)\,d\theta.$$

In other words, to find $P_U(z)$, replace each value of $U(\theta)$ by the value at the point opposite to z, and take the average over the circle.

EXERCISES

1. Assume that $U(\xi)$ is piecewise continuous and bounded for all real ξ. Show that

$$P_U(z) = \frac{1}{\pi}\int_{-\infty}^{\infty} \frac{y}{(x - \xi)^2 + y^2}\,U(\xi)\,d\xi$$

represents a harmonic function in the upper half plane with boundary values $U(\xi)$ at points of continuity (Poisson's integral for the half plane).

2. Prove that a function which is harmonic and bounded in the upper half plane, continuous on the real axis, can be represented as a Poisson integral (Ex. 1).

Remark. The point at ∞ presents an added difficulty, for we cannot immediately apply the maximum and minimum principle to $u - P_u$. A good try would be to apply the maximum principle to $u - P_u - \varepsilon y$ for $\varepsilon > 0$, with the idea of letting ε tend to 0. This almost works, for the function tends to 0 for $y \to 0$ and to $-\infty$ for $y \to \infty$, but we lack control when $|x| \to \infty$. Show that the reasoning can be carried out successfully by application to $u - P_u - \varepsilon \operatorname{Im} (\sqrt{iz})$.

3. In Ex. 1, assume that U has a jump at 0, for instance $U(+0) = 0$, $U(-0) = 1$. Show that $P_U(z) - \frac{1}{\pi} \arg z$ tends to 0 as $z \to 0$. Generalize to arbitrary jumps and to the case of the circle.

4. If C_1 and C_2 are complementary arcs on the unit circle, set $U = 1$ on C_1, $U = 0$ on C_2. Find $P_U(z)$ explicitly and show that $2\pi P_U(z)$ equals the length of the arc, opposite to C_1, cut off by the straight lines through z and the end points of C_1.

5. Show that the mean-value formula (59) remains valid for $u = \log |1 + z|$, $z_0 = 0$, $r = 1$, and use this fact to compute

$$\int_0^\pi \log \sin \theta \, d\theta.$$

6.5. The Reflection Principle. An elementary aspect of the *symmetry principle*, or *reflection principle*, has been discussed already in connection with linear transformations (Chap. 3, Sec. 3.3). There are many more general variants first formulated by H. A. Schwarz.

The principle of reflection is based on the observation that if $u(z)$ is a harmonic function, then $u(\bar{z})$ is likewise harmonic, and if $f(z)$ is an analytic function, then $\overline{f(\bar{z})}$ is also analytic. More precisely, if $u(z)$ is harmonic and $f(z)$ analytic in a region then $u(\bar{z})$ is harmonic and $\overline{f(\bar{z})}$ analytic as functions of z in the region Ω^* obtained by reflection Ω in the real axis; that is, $z \in \Omega^*$ if and only if $\bar{z} \in \Omega$. The proofs of these statements consist in trivial verifications.

Consider the case of a symmetric region: $\Omega^* = \Omega$. Because Ω is connected it must intersect the real axis along at least one open interval. Assume now that $f(z)$ is analytic in Ω and real on at least one interval of the real axis. Since $f(z) - \overline{f(\bar{z})}$ is analytic and vanishes on an interval it must be identically zero, and we conclude that $f(z) = \overline{f(\bar{z})}$ in Ω. With the notation $f = u + iv$ we have thus $u(z) = u(\bar{z})$, $v(z) = -v(\bar{z})$.

This is important, but it is a rather weak result, for we are assuming that $f(z)$ is already known to be analytic in all of Ω. Let us denote the intersection of Ω with the upper half plane by Ω^+, and the intersection of Ω with the real axis by σ. Suppose that $f(z)$ is defined on $\Omega^+ \cup \sigma$, analytic in Ω^+, continuous and real on σ. Under these conditions we want to show that $f(z)$ is the restriction to Ω^+ of a function which is analytic in all of Ω and satisfies the symmetry condition $f(z) = \overline{f(\bar{z})}$. In other words, part of our theorem asserts that $f(z)$ has an *analytic continuation* to Ω.

Even in this formulation the assumptions are too strong. Indeed, the main thing is that the imaginary part $v(z)$ vanishes on σ, and nothing at all need to be assumed about the real part. In the definitive statement of the reflection principle the emphasis should therefore be on harmonic functions.

Theorem 26. *Let Ω^+ be the part in the upper half plane of a symmetric region Ω, and let σ be the part of the real axis in Ω. Suppose that $v(x)$ is continuous in $\Omega^+ \cup \sigma$, harmonic in Ω^+, and zero on σ. Then v has a harmonic extension to Ω which satisfies the symmetry relation $v(\bar{z}) = -v(z)$. In the same situation, if v is the imaginary part of an analytic function $f(z)$ in Ω^+, then $f(z)$ has an analytic extension which satisfies $f(z) = \overline{f(\bar{z})}$.*

For the proof we construct the function $V(z)$ which is equal to $v(z)$ in Ω^+, 0 on σ, and equal to $-v(\bar{z})$ in the mirror image of Ω^+. We have to show that V is harmonic on σ. For a point $x_0 \in \sigma$ consider a disk with center x_0 contained in Ω, and let P_V denote the Poisson integral with respect to this disk formed with the boundary values V. The difference $V - P_V$ is harmonic in the upper half of the disk. It vanishes on the half circle, by Theorem 25, and also on the diameter, because V tends to zero by definition and P_V vanishes by obvious symmetry. The maximum and minimum principle implies that $V = P_V$ in the upper half disk, and the same proof can be repeated for the lower half. We conclude that V is harmonic in the whole disk, and in particular at x_0.

For the remaining part of the theorem, let us again consider a disk with center on σ. We have already extended v to the whole disk, and v has a conjugate harmonic function $-u_0$ in the same disk which we may normalize so that $u_0 = \operatorname{Re} f(z)$ in the upper half. Consider

$$U_0(z) = u_0(z) - u_0(\bar{z}).$$

On the real diameter it is clear that $\partial U_0/\partial x = 0$ and also

$$\frac{\partial U_0}{\partial y} = 2\frac{\partial u_0}{\partial y} = -2\frac{\partial v}{\partial x} = 0.$$

It follows that the analytic function $\partial U_0/\partial x - i\,\partial U_0/\partial y$ vanishes on the real axis, and hence identically. Therefore U_0 is a constant, and this constant is evidently zero. We have proved that $u_0(z) = u_c(\bar{z})$.

The construction can be repeated for arbitrary disks. It is clear that the u_0 coincide in overlapping disks. The definition can be extended to all of Ω, and the theorem follows.

The theorem has obvious generalizations. The domain Ω can be taken to be symmetric with respect to a circle C rather than with respect to a straight line, and when z tends to C it may be assumed that $f(z)$ approaches another circle C'. Under such conditions $f(z)$ has an analytic continuation which maps symmetric points with respect to C onto symmetric points with respect to C'.

EXERCISES

1. If $f(z)$ is analytic in the whole plane and real on the real axis, purely imaginary on the imaginary axis, show that $f(z)$ is odd.

2. Show that every function f which is analytic in a symmetric region Ω can be written in the form $f_1 + if_2$ where f_1, f_2 are analytic in Ω and real on the real axis.

3. If $f(z)$ is analytic in $|z| \leqq 1$ and satisfies $|f| = 1$ on $|z| = 1$, show that $f(z)$ is rational.

4. Use (63) to derive a formula for $f'(z)$ in terms of $u(z)$.

5. If $u(z)$ is harmonic and $0 \leqq u(z) \leqq Ky$ for $y > 0$, prove that $u = ky$ with $0 \leqq k \leqq K$. [Reflect over the real axis, complete to an analytic function $f(z) = u + iv$, and use Ex. 4 to show that $f'(z)$ is bounded.]

5 SERIES AND PRODUCT DEVELOPMENTS

Very general theorems have their natural place in the theory of analytic functions, but it must also be kept in mind that the whole theory originated from a desire to be able to manipulate explicit analytic expressions. Such expressions take the form of infinite series, infinite products, and other limits. In this chapter we deal partly with the rules that govern such limits, partly with quite explicit representations of elementary transcendental functions and other specific functions.

1. POWER SERIES EXPANSIONS

In a preliminary way we have considered power series in Chap. 2, mainly for the purpose of defining the exponential and trigonometric functions. Without use of integration we were not able to prove that every analytic function has a power series expansion. This question will now be resolved in the affirmative, essentially as an application of Cauchy's theorem.

The first subsection deals with more general properties of sequences of analytic functions.

1.1. Weierstrass's Theorem. The central theorem concerning the convergence of analytic functions asserts that the limit of a uniformly convergent sequence of analytic functions is an analytic function. The precise assumptions must be carefully stated, and they should not be too restrictive.

We are considering a sequence $\{f_n(z)\}$ where each $f_n(z)$ is defined and analytic in a region Ω_n. The limit function $f(z)$ must also be considered in some region Ω, and clearly, if $f(z)$ is to be defined in Ω, each point of Ω must belong to all Ω_n for n greater than a certain n_0. In the general case n_0 will not be the same for all points of Ω, and for this reason it would not make sense to require that the convergence be uniform in Ω. In fact, in the most typical case the regions Ω_n form an increasing sequence, $\Omega_1 \subset \Omega_2 \subset \cdots \subset \Omega_n \subset \cdots$, and Ω is the union of the Ω_n. In these circumstances no single function $f_n(z)$ is defined in all of Ω; yet the limit $f(z)$ may exist at all points of Ω, although the convergence cannot be uniform.

As a very simple example take $f_n(z) = z/(2z^n + 1)$ and let Ω_n be the disk $|z| < 2^{-1/n}$. It is practically evident that $\lim_{n\to\infty} f_n(z) = z$ in the disk $|z| < 1$ which we choose as our region Ω. In order to study the uniformity of the convergence we form the difference

$$f_n(z) - z = -2z^{n+1}/(2z^n + 1).$$

For any given value of z we can make $|z^n| < \varepsilon/4$ by taking $n > \log(4/\varepsilon)/\log(1/|z|)$. If $\varepsilon < 1$ we have then $2|z|^{n+1} < \varepsilon/2$ and $|1 + 2z^n| > \frac{1}{2}$ so that $|f_n(z) - z| < \varepsilon$. It follows that the convergence is uniform in any closed disk $|z| \leqq r < 1$, or on any subset of such a closed disk.

With another formulation, in the preceding example the sequence $\{f_n(z)\}$ tends to the limit function $f(z)$ uniformly on every compact subset of the region Ω. In fact, on a compact set $|z|$ has a maximum $r < 1$ and the set is thus contained in the closed disk $|z| \leqq r$. This is the typical situation. We shall find that we can frequently prove uniform convergence on every compact subset of Ω; on the other hand, this is the natural condition in the theorem that we are going to prove.

Theorem 1. *Suppose that $f_n(z)$ is analytic in the region Ω_n, and that the sequence $\{f_n(z)\}$ converges to a limit function $f(z)$ in a region Ω, uniformly on every compact subset of Ω. Then $f(z)$ is analytic in Ω. Moreover, $f_n'(z)$ converges uniformly to $f'(z)$ on every compact subset of Ω.*

The analyticity of $f(z)$ follows most easily by use of Morera's theorem (Chap. 4, Sec. 2.3). Let $|z - a| \leqq r$ be a closed disk contained in Ω; the assumption implies that this disk lies in Ω_n for all n greater than a certain n_0.† If γ is any closed curve contained in $|z - a| < r$, we have

$$\int_\gamma f_n(z)\,dz = 0$$

† In fact, the regions Ω_n form an open covering of $|z - a| \leqq r$. The disk is compact and hence has a finite subcovering. This means that it is contained in a fixed Ω_{n_0}.

for $n > n_0$, by Cauchy's theorem. Because of the uniform convergence on γ we obtain

$$\int_\gamma f(z)\,dz = \lim_{n\to\infty} \int_\gamma f_n(z)\,dz = 0,$$

and by Morera's theorem it follows that $f(z)$ is analytic in $|z - a| < r$. Consequently $f(z)$ is analytic in the whole region Ω.

An alternative and more explicit proof is based on the integral formula

$$f_n(z) = \frac{1}{2\pi i} \int_C \frac{f_n(\zeta)\,d\zeta}{\zeta - z},$$

where C is the circle $|\zeta - a| = r$ and $|z - a| < r$. Letting n tend to ∞ we obtain by uniform convergence

$$f(z) = \frac{1}{2\pi i} \int_C \frac{f(\zeta)\,d\zeta}{\zeta - z}.$$

and this formula shows that $f(z)$ is analytic in the disk. Starting from the formula

$$f_n'(z) = \frac{1}{2\pi i} \int_C \frac{f_n(\zeta)\,d\zeta}{(\zeta - z)^2}$$

the same reasoning yields

$$\lim_{n\to\infty} f_n'(z) = \frac{1}{2\pi i} \int_C \frac{f(\zeta)\,d\zeta}{(\zeta - z)^2} = f'(z),$$

and simple estimates show that the convergence is uniform for $|z - a| \leqq \rho < r$. Any compact subset of Ω can be covered by a finite number of such closed disks, and therefore the convergence is uniform on every compact subset. The theorem is proved, and by repeated applications it follows that $f_n^{(k)}(z)$ converges uniformly to $f^{(k)}(z)$ on every compact subset of Ω.

Theorem 1 is due to Weierstrass, in an equivalent formulation. Its application to series whose terms are analytic functions is particularly important. The theorem can then be expressed as follows:

If a series with analytic terms,

$$f(z) = f_1(z) + f_2(z) + \cdots + f_n(z) + \cdots,$$

converges uniformly on every compact subset of a region Ω, then the sum $f(z)$ is analytic in Ω, and the series can be differentiated term by term.

The task of proving uniform convergence on a compact point set A can be facilitated by use of the maximum principle. In fact, with the notations of Theorem 1, the difference $|f_m(z) - f_n(z)|$ attains its maximum in A on the boundary of A. For this reason uniform convergence on the boundary of A implies uniform convergence on A. For instance, if the functions $f_n(z)$ are analytic in the disk $|z| < 1$, and if it can be shown that the sequence converges uniformly on each circle $|z| = r_m$ where $\lim_{m\to\infty} r_m = 1$, then Weierstrass's theorem applies and we can conclude that the limit function is analytic.

The following theorem is due to A. Hurwitz:

Theorem 2. *If the functions $f_n(z)$ are analytic and $\neq 0$ in a region Ω, and if $f_n(z)$ converges to $f(z)$, uniformly on every compact subset of Ω, then $f(z)$ is either identically zero or never equal to zero in Ω.*

Suppose that $f(z)$ is not identically zero. The zeros of $f(z)$ are in any case isolated. For any point $z_0 \in \Omega$ there is therefore a number $r > 0$ such that $f(z)$ is defined and $\neq 0$ for $0 < |z - z_0| \leqq r$. In particular, $|f(z)|$ has a positive minimum on the circle $|z - z_0| = r$, which we denote by C. It follows that $1/f_n(z)$ converges uniformly to $1/f(z)$ on C. Since it is also true that $f_n'(z) \to f'(z)$, uniformly on C, we may conclude that

$$\lim_{n\to\infty} \frac{1}{2\pi i}\int_C \frac{f_n'(z)}{f_n(z)}\,dz = \frac{1}{2\pi i}\int_C \frac{f'(z)}{f(z)}\,dz.$$

But the integrals on the left are all zero, for they give the number of roots of the equation $f_n(z) = 0$ inside of C. The integral on the right is therefore zero, and consequently $f(z_0) \neq 0$ by the same interpretation of the integral. Since z_0 was arbitrary, the theorem follows.

EXERCISES

1. Using Taylor's theorem applied to a branch of $\log(1 + z/n)$, prove that

$$\lim_{n\to\infty}\left(1 + \frac{z}{n}\right)^n = e^z$$

uniformly on all compact sets.

2. Show that the series

$$\zeta(z) = \sum_{n=1}^{\infty} n^{-z}$$

converges for $\operatorname{Re} z > 1$, and represent its derivative in series form.

3. Prove that

$$(1 - 2^{1-z})\zeta(z) = 1^{-z} - 2^{-z} + 3^{-z} - \cdots$$

and that the latter series represents an analytic function for $\operatorname{Re} z > 0$.

4. As a generalization of Theorem 2, prove that if the $f_n(z)$ have at most m zeros in Ω, then $f(z)$ is either identically zero or has at most m zeros.

5. Prove that

$$\sum_{n=1}^{\infty} \frac{nz^n}{1 - z^n} = \sum_{n=1}^{\infty} \frac{z^n}{(1 - z^n)^2}$$

for $|z| < 1$. (Develop in a double series and reverse the order of summation.)

1.2. The Taylor Series. We show now that every analytic function can be developed in a convergent Taylor series. This is an almost immediate consequence of the finite Taylor development given in Chap. 4, Sec. 3.1, Theorem 8, together with the corresponding representation of the remainder term. According to this theorem, if $f(z)$ is analytic in a region Ω containing z_0, we can write

$$f(z) = f(z_0) + \frac{f'(z_0)}{1!}(z - z_0) + \cdots + \frac{f^{(n)}(z_0)}{n!}(z - z_0)^n + f_{n+1}(z)(z - z_0)^{n+1}$$

with

$$f_{n+1}(z) = \frac{1}{2\pi i}\int_C \frac{f(\zeta)\,d\zeta}{(\zeta - z_0)^{n+1}(\zeta - z)}.$$

In the last formula C is any circle $|z - z_0| = \rho$ such that the closed disk $|z - z_0| \leqq \rho$ is contained in Ω.

If M denotes the maximum of $|f(z)|$ on C, we obtain at once the estimate

$$|f_{n+1}(z)(z - z_0)^{n+1}| \leqq \frac{M|z - z_0|^{n+1}}{\rho^n(\rho - |z - z_0|)}$$

We conclude that the remainder term tends uniformly to zero in every disk $|z - z_0| \leqq r < \rho$. On the other hand, ρ can be chosen arbitrarily close to the shortest distance from z_0 to the boundary of Ω. We have proved:

Theorem 3. *If $f(z)$ is analytic in the region Ω, containing z_0, then the representation*

$$f(z) = f(z_0) + \frac{f'(z_0)}{1!}(z - z_0) + \cdots + \frac{f^{(n)}(z_0)}{n!}(z - z_0)^n + \cdots$$

is valid in the largest open disk of center z_0 contained in Ω.

The radius of convergence of the Taylor series is thus at least equal to the shortest distance from z_0 to the boundary of Ω. It may well be larger, but if it is there is no guarantee that the series still represents $f(z)$ at all points which are simultaneously in Ω and in the circle of convergence.

We recall that the developments

$$e^z = 1 + z + \frac{z^2}{2} + \cdots + \frac{z^n}{n} + \cdots$$
$$\cos z = 1 - \frac{z^2}{2} + \frac{z^4}{4} - \frac{z^6}{6} + \cdots$$
$$\sin z = z - \frac{z^3}{3} + \frac{z^5}{5} - \frac{z^7}{7} + \cdots$$

served as definitions of the functions they represent. Of course, as we have remarked before, every convergent power series is its own Taylor series. We gave earlier a direct proof that power series can be differentiated term by term. This is also a direct consequence of Weierstrass's theorem.

If we want to represent a fractional power of z or $\log z$ through a power series, we must first of all choose a well-defined branch, and secondly we have to choose a center $z_0 \neq 0$. It amounts to the same thing if we develop the function $(1 + z)^\mu$ or $\log(1 + z)$ about the origin, choosing the branch which is respectively equal to 1 or 0 at the origin. Since this branch is single-valued and analytic in $|z| < 1$, the radius of convergence is at least 1. It is elementary to compute the coefficients, and we obtain

$$(1 + z)^\mu = 1 + \mu z + \binom{\mu}{2} z^2 + \cdots + \binom{\mu}{n} z^n + \cdots$$
$$\log(1 + z) = z - \frac{z^2}{2} + \frac{z^3}{3} - \frac{z^4}{4} + \frac{z^5}{5} - \cdots$$

where the binomial coefficients are defined by

$$\binom{\mu}{n} = \frac{\mu(\mu - 1) \cdots (\mu - n + 1)}{1 \cdot 2 \cdots n}.$$

If the logarithmic series had a radius of convergence greater than 1, then $\log(1 + z)$ would be bounded for $|z| < 1$. Since this is not the case, the radius of convergence must be exactly 1. Similarly, if the binomial series were convergent in a circle of radius >1, the function $(1 + z)^\mu$ and all its derivatives would be bounded in $|z| < 1$. Unless μ is a positive integer, one of the derivatives will be a negative power of $1 + z$, and hence unbounded. Thus the radius of convergence is precisely 1 except in the trivial case in which the binomial series reduces to a polynomial.

The series developments of the cyclometric functions arc tan z and arc sin z are most easily obtained by consideration of the derived series. From the expansion

$$\frac{1}{1+z^2} = 1 - z^2 + z^4 - z^6 + \cdots$$

we obtain by integration

$$\text{arc tan } z = z - \frac{z^3}{3} + \frac{z^5}{5} - \frac{z^7}{7} + \cdots$$

where the branch is uniquely determined as

$$\text{arc tan } z = \int_0^z \frac{dz}{1+z^2}$$

for any path inside the unit circle. For justification we can either rely on uniform convergence or apply Theorem 1. The radius of convergence cannot be greater than that of the derived series, and hence it is exactly 1.

If $\sqrt{1-z^2}$ is the branch with a positive real part, we have

$$\frac{1}{\sqrt{1-z^2}} = 1 + \frac{1}{2}z^2 + \frac{1 \cdot 3}{2 \cdot 4}z^4 + \frac{1 \cdot 3 \cdot 5}{2 \cdot 4 \cdot 6}z^6 + \cdots$$

for $|z| < 1$, and through integration we obtain

$$\text{arc sin } z = z + \frac{1}{2}\frac{z^3}{3} + \frac{1 \cdot 3}{2 \cdot 4}\frac{z^5}{5} + \frac{1 \cdot 3 \cdot 5}{2 \cdot 4 \cdot 6}\frac{z^7}{7} + \cdots.$$

The series represents the principal branch of arc sin z with a real part between $-\pi/2$ and $\pi/2$.

For combinations of elementary functions it is mostly not possible to find a general law for the coefficients. In order to find the first few coefficients we need not, however, calculate the successive derivatives. There are simple techniques which allow us to compute, with a reasonable amount of labor, all the coefficients that we are likely to need.

It is convenient to introduce the notation $[z^n]$ for any function which is analytic and has a zero of at least order n at the origin; less precisely, $[z^n]$ denotes a function which "contains the factor z^n." With this notation any function which is analytic at the origin can be written in the form

$$f(z) = a_0 + a_1 z + \cdots + a_n z^n + [z^{n+1}],$$

where the coefficients are uniquely determined and equal to the Taylor coefficients of $f(z)$. Thus, in order to find the first n coefficients of the Taylor expansion, it is sufficient to determine a polynomial $P_n(z)$ such that $f(z) - P_n(z)$ has a zero of at least order $n+1$ at the origin. The degree of $P_n(z)$ does not matter; it is true in any case that the coefficients of z^m, $m \leqq n$, are the Taylor coefficients of $f(z)$.

For instance, suppose that

$$f(z) = a_0 + a_1 z + a_2 z^2 + \cdots + a_n z^n + \cdots$$
$$g(z) = b_0 + b_1 z + b_2 z^2 + \cdots + b_n z^n + \cdots.$$

With an abbreviated notation we write

$$f(z) = P_n(z) + [z^{n+1}]; \qquad g(z) = Q_n(z) + [z^{n+1}].$$

It is then clear that $f(z)g(z) = P_n(z)Q_n(z) + [z^{n+1}]$, and the coefficients of the terms of degree $\leqq n$ in P_nQ_n are the Taylor coefficients of the product $f(z)g(z)$. Explicitly we obtain

$$f(z)g(z) = a_0b_0 + (a_0b_1 + a_1b_0)z + \cdots + (a_0b_n + a_1b_{n-1} + \cdots + a_nb_0)z^n + \cdots.$$

In deriving this expansion we have not even mentioned the question of convergence, but since the development is identical with the Taylor development of $f(z)g(z)$, it follows by Theorem 3 that the radius of convergence is at least equal to the smaller of the radii of convergence of the given series $f(z)$ and $g(z)$. In the practical computation of P_nQ_n it is of course not necessary to determine the terms of degree higher than n.

In the case of a quotient $f(z)/g(z)$ the same method can be applied, provided that $g(0) = b_0 \neq 0$. By use of ordinary long division, continued until the remainder contains the factor z^{n+1}, we can determine a polynomial R_n such that $P_n = Q_nR_n + [z^{n+1}]$. Then $f - R_ng = [z^{n+1}]$, and since $g(0) \neq 0$ we find that $f/g = R_n + [z^{n+1}]$. The coefficients of R_n are the Taylor coefficients of $f(z)/g(z)$. They can be determined explicitly in determinant form, but the expressions are too complicated to be of essential help.

It is also important that we know how to form the development of a composite function $f(g(z))$. In this case, if $g(z)$ is developed around z_0, the expansion of $f(w)$ must be in powers of $w - g(z_0)$. To simplify, let us assume that $z_0 = 0$ and $g(0) = 0$. We can then set

$$f(w) = a_0 + a_1 w + \cdots + a_n w^n + \cdots$$

and $g(z) = b_1 z + b_2 z^2 + \cdots + b_n z^n + \cdots$. Using the same notations as before we write $f(w) = P_n(w) + [w^{n+1}]$ and $g(z) = Q_n(z) + [z^{n+1}]$ with $Q_n(0) = 0$. Substituting $w = g(z)$ we have to observe that

$$P_n(Q_n + [z^{n+1}]) = P_n(Q_n(z)) + [z^{n+1}]$$

and that any expression of the form $[w^{n+1}]$ becomes a $[z^{n+1}]$. Thus we obtain $f(g(z)) = P_n(Q_n(z)) + [z^{n+1}]$, and the Taylor coefficients of $f(g(z))$ are the coefficients of $P_n(Q_n(z))$ for powers $\leq n$.

Finally, we must be able to expand the inverse function of an analytic function $w = g(z)$. Here we may suppose that $g(0) = 0$, and we are looking for the branch of the inverse function $z = g^{-1}(w)$ which is analytic in a neighborhood of the origin and vanishes for $w = 0$. For the existence of the inverse function it is necessary and sufficient that $g'(0) \neq 0$; hence we assume that

$$g(z) = a_1 z + a_2 z^2 + \cdots = Q_n(z) + [z^{n+1}]$$

with $a_1 \neq 0$. Our problem is to determine a polynomial $P_n(w)$ such that $P_n(Q_n(z)) = z + [z^{n+1}]$. In fact, under the assumption $a_1 \neq 0$ the notations $[z^{n+1}]$ and $[w^{n+1}]$ are interchangeable, and from $z = P_n(Q_n(z)) + [z^{n+1}]$ we obtain $z = P_n(g(z) + [z^{n+1}]) + [z^{n+1}] = P_n(w) + [w^{n+1}]$. Hence $P_n(w)$ determines the coefficients of $g^{-1}(w)$.

In order to prove the existence of a polynomial P_n we proceed by induction. Clearly, we can take $P_1(w) = w/a_1$. If P_{n-1} is given, we set $P_n = P_{n-1} + b_n z^n$ and obtain

$$\begin{aligned} P_n(Q_n(z)) &= P_{n-1}(Q_n(z)) + b_n a_1^n z^n + [z^{n+1}] \\ &= P_{n-1}(Q_{n-1}(z) + a_n z^n) + b_n a_1^n z^n + [z^{n+1}] \\ &= P_{n-1}(Q_{n-1}(z)) + P'_{n-1}(Q_{n-1}(z)) a_n z^n + b_n a_1^n z^n + [z^{n+1}]. \end{aligned}$$

In the last member the first two terms form a known polynomial of the form $z + c_n z^n + [z^{n+1}]$, and we have only to take $b_n = -c_n a_1^{-n}$.

For practical purposes the development of the inverse function is found by successive substitutions. To illustrate the method we determine the expansion of tan w from the series

$$w = \text{arc tan } z = z - \frac{z^3}{3} + \frac{z^5}{5} - \cdots.$$

If we want the development to include fifth powers, we write

$$z = w + \frac{z^3}{3} - \frac{z^5}{5} + [z^7]$$

and substitute this expression in the terms to the right. With appropriate remainders we obtain

$$\begin{aligned} z &= w + \frac{1}{3}\left(w + \frac{z^3}{3} + [w^5]\right)^3 - \frac{1}{5}(w + [w^3])^5 + [w^7] \\ &= w + \frac{1}{3}w^3 + \frac{1}{3}w^2 z^3 - \frac{1}{5}w^5 + [w^7] \\ &= w + \frac{1}{3}w^3 + \frac{1}{3}w^2(w + [w^3])^3 - \frac{1}{5}w^5 + [w^7] = w + \frac{1}{3}w^3 + \frac{2}{15}w^5 + [w^7]. \end{aligned}$$

Thus the development of tan w begins with the terms

$$\tan w = w + \frac{1}{3} w^3 + \frac{2}{15} w^5 + \cdots .$$

EXERCISES

1. Develop $1/(1 + z^2)$ in powers of $z - a$, a being a real number. Find the general coefficient and for $a = 1$ reduce to simplest form.

2. The Legendre polynomials are defined as the coefficients $P_n(\alpha)$ in the development

$$(1 - 2\alpha z + z^2)^{-\frac{1}{2}} = 1 + P_1(\alpha)z + P_2(\alpha)z^2 + \cdots .$$

Find P_1, P_2, P_3, and P_4.

3. Develop log $(\sin z/z)$ in powers of z up to the term z^6.

4. What is the coefficient of z^7 in the Taylor development of tan z?

5. The Fibonacci numbers are defined by $c_0 = 0$, $c_1 = 1$,

$$c_n = c_{n-1} + c_{n-2}.$$

Show that the c_n are Taylor coefficients of a rational function, and determine a closed expression for c_n.

1.3. The Laurent Series. A series of the form

$$b_0 + b_1 z^{-1} + b_2 z^{-2} + \cdots + b_n z^{-n} + \cdots \tag{1}$$

can be considered as an ordinary power series in the variable $1/z$. It will therefore converge outside of some circle $|z| = R$, except in the extreme case $R = \infty$; the convergence is uniform in every region $|z| \geqq \rho > R$, and hence the series represents an analytic function in the region $|z| > R$. If the series (1) is combined with an ordinary power series, we get a more general series of the form

$$\sum_{n=-\infty}^{+\infty} a_n z^n. \tag{2}$$

It will be termed convergent only if the parts consisting of nonnegative powers and negative powers are separately convergent. Since the first part converges in a disk $|z| < R_2$ and the second series in a region $|z| > R_1$, there is a common region of convergence only if $R_1 < R_2$, and (2) represents an analytic function in the annulus $R_1 < |z| < R_2$.

Conversely, we may start from an analytic function $f(z)$ whose region of definition contains an annulus $R_1 < |z| < R_2$, or more generally an annulus $R_1 < |z - a| < R_2$. We shall show that such a function can always be developed in a general power series of the form

$$f(z) = \sum_{n=-\infty}^{+\infty} A_n(z-a)^n.$$

The proof is extremely simple. All we have to show is that $f(z)$ can be written as a sum $f_1(z) + f_2(z)$ where $f_1(z)$ is analytic for $|z - a| < R_2$ and $f_2(z)$ is analytic for $|z - a| > R_1$ with a removable singularity at ∞. Under these circumstances $f_1(z)$ can be developed in nonnegative powers of $z - a$, and $f_2(z)$ can be developed in nonnegative powers of $1/(z - a)$.

To find the representation $f(z) = f_1(z) + f_2(z)$ define $f_1(z)$ by

$$f_1(z) = \frac{1}{2\pi i} \int_{|\zeta - a| = r} \frac{f(\zeta)\,d\zeta}{\zeta - z}$$

for $|z - a| < r < R_2$ and $f_2(z)$ by

$$f_2(z) = -\frac{1}{2\pi i} \int_{|\zeta - a| = r} \frac{f(\zeta)\,d\zeta}{\zeta - z}$$

for $R_1 < r < |z - a|$. In both integrals the value of r is irrelevant as long as the inequality is fulfilled, for it is an immediate consequence of Cauchy's theorem that the value of the integral does not change with r provided that the circle does not pass over the point z. For this reason $f_1(z)$ and $f_2(z)$ are uniquely defined and represent analytic functions in $|z - a| < R_2$ and $|z - a| > R_1$ respectively. Moreover, by Cauchy's integral theorem $f(z) = f_1(z) + f_2(z)$.

The Taylor development of $f_1(z)$ is

$$f_1(z) = \sum_{n=0}^{\infty} A_n(z-a)^n$$

with

(3) $$A_n = \frac{1}{2\pi i} \int_{|\zeta - a| = r} \frac{f(\zeta)\,d\zeta}{(\zeta - a)^{n+1}}.$$

In order to find the development of $f_2(z)$ we perform the transformation $\zeta = a + 1/\zeta'$, $z = a + 1/z'$. This transformation carries $|\zeta - a| = r$ into $|\zeta'| = 1/r$ with negative orientation, and by simple calculations we obtain

$$f_2\left(a + \frac{1}{z'}\right) = \frac{1}{2\pi i} \int_{|\zeta'| = \frac{1}{r}} \frac{z'}{\zeta'} \frac{f\left(a + \frac{1}{\zeta'}\right) d\zeta'}{\zeta' - z'} = \sum_{n=1}^{\infty} B_n z'^n$$

with

$$B_n = \frac{1}{2\pi i} \int\limits_{|\zeta'| = \frac{1}{r}} \frac{f\left(a + \frac{1}{\zeta'}\right) d\zeta'}{\zeta'^{n+1}} = \frac{1}{2\pi i} \int\limits_{|\zeta - a| = r} f(\zeta)(\zeta - a)^{n-1}\, d\zeta.$$

This formula shows that we can write

$$f(z) = \sum_{n=-\infty}^{+\infty} A_n(z - a)^n$$

where all the coefficients A_n are determined by (3). Observe that the integral in (3) is independent of r as long as $R_1 < r < R_2$.

If $R_1 = 0$ the point a is an isolated singularity and $A_{-1} = B_1$ is the residue at a, for $f(z) - A_{-1}(z - a)^{-1}$ is the derivative of a single-valued function in $0 < |z - a| < R_2$.

EXERCISES

1. Prove that the Laurent development is unique.

2. Let Ω be a doubly connected region whose complement consists of the components E_1, E_2. Prove that every analytic function $f(z)$ in Ω can be written in the form $f_1(z) + f_2(z)$ where $f_1(z)$ is analytic outside of E_1 and $f_2(z)$ is analytic outside of E_2. (The precise proof requires a construction like the one in Chap. 4, Sec. 4.2.)

3. The expression

$$\{f,z\} = \frac{f'''(z)}{f'(z)} - \frac{3}{2}\left(\frac{f''(z)}{f'(z)}\right)^2$$

is called the *Schwarzian derivative* of f. If f has a multiple zero or pole, find the leading term in the Laurent development of $\{f,z\}$. *Answer:* If $f(z) = a(z - z_0)^m + \cdots$, then $\{f,z\} = \frac{1}{2}(1 - m^2)(z - z_0)^{-2} + \cdots$.

4. Show that the Laurent development of $(e^z - 1)^{-1}$ at the origin is of the form

$$\frac{1}{z} - \frac{1}{2} + \sum_{1}^{\infty} (-1)^{k-1} \frac{B_k}{(2k)!} z^{2k-1}$$

where the numbers B_k, known as the Bernoulli numbers, are all positive. Calculate B_1, B_2, B_3.

5. Express the Taylor development of $\tan z$ and the Laurent development of $\cot z$ in terms of the Bernoulli numbers.

2. PARTIAL FRACTIONS AND FACTORIZATION

A rational function has two standard representations, one by partial fractions and the other by factorization of the numerator and the denominator. The present section is devoted to similar representations of arbitrary meromorphic functions.

2.1. Partial Fractions. If the function $f(z)$ is meromorphic in a region Ω, there corresponds to each pole b_ν a singular part of $f(z)$ consisting of the part of the Laurent development which contains the negative powers of $z - b_\nu$; it reduces to a polynomial $P_\nu(1/(z - b_\nu))$. It is tempting to subtract all singular parts in order to obtain a representation

$$f(z) = \sum_\nu P_\nu\left(\frac{1}{z - b_\nu}\right) + g(z) \tag{4}$$

where $g(z)$ would be analytic in Ω. However, the sum on the right-hand side is in general infinite, and there is no guarantee that the series will converge. Nevertheless, there are many cases in which the series converges, and what is more, it is frequently possible to determine $g(z)$ explicitly from general considerations. In such cases the result is very rewarding; we obtain a simple expansion which is likely to be very helpful.

If the series in (4) does not converge, the method needs to be modified. It is clear that nothing essential is lost if we subtract an analytic function $p_\nu(z)$ from each singular part P_ν. By judicious choice of the functions p_ν the series $\sum_\nu (P_\nu - p_\nu)$ can be made convergent. It is even possible to take the $p_\nu(z)$ to be polynomials.

We shall not prove the most general theorem to this effect. In the case where Ω is the whole plane we shall, however, prove that every meromorphic function has a development in partial fractions and, moreover, that the singular parts can be described arbitrarily. The theorem and its generalization to arbitrary regions are due to Mittag-Leffler.

Theorem 4. *Let $\{b_\nu\}$ be a sequence of complex numbers with $\lim_{\nu \to \infty} b_\nu = \infty$, and let $P_\nu(\zeta)$ be polynomials without constant term. Then there are functions which are meromorphic in the whole plane with poles at the points b_ν and the corresponding singular parts $P_\nu(1/(z - b_\nu))$. Moreover, the most general meromorphic function of this kind can be written in the form*

$$f(z) = \sum_\nu \left[P_\nu\left(\frac{1}{z - b_\nu}\right) - p_\nu(z)\right] + g(z) \tag{5}$$

where the $p_\nu(z)$ are suitably chosen fixed polynomials and $g(z)$ is analytic in the whole plane.

Since the function $P_\nu(1/(z - b_\nu))$ is analytic for $|z| < |b_\nu|$, it can be expanded in a Taylor series about the origin.† We choose for $p_\nu(z)$ a partial sum of this series, ending, say, with the term of degree n_ν. The difference $P_\nu - p_\nu$ can be estimated by use of the explicit expression for the remainder given in Chap. 4, Sec. 3.1. If $|P_\nu| \leqq M_\nu$ for $|z| \leqq |b_\nu|/2$, we obtain, for instance,

$$\left| P_\nu\left(\frac{1}{z - b_\nu}\right) - p_\nu(z) \right| \leqq M_\nu \left(\frac{4|z|}{|b_\nu|}\right)^{n_\nu+1} \tag{6}$$

for $|z| \leqq |b_\nu|/4$. Because of this estimate it is clear that the series in the right-hand member of (5) can be made convergent by choosing the n_ν large enough. Specifically, using the formula for the radius of convergence we find that the power series

$$\sum_\nu M_\nu \left(\frac{4z}{b_\nu}\right)^{n_\nu+1}$$

converges in the whole plane if $\lim_{\nu \to \infty} M_\nu^{1/n_\nu}/|b_\nu| = 0$; this is assured by choosing, for instance, $n_\nu > \log M_\nu$.

Consider an arbitrary closed disk $|z| \leqq R$. The series $\sum_\nu (P_\nu - p_\nu)$ has only a finite number of terms which become infinite in $|z| \leqq R$, and from a certain term on the inequality (6) will hold throughout the disk. If the terms with $|b_\nu| \leqq R$ are omitted, it follows that the remaining series converges absolutely and uniformly in $|z| \leqq R$. Since R is arbitrary, the series converges for all $z \neq b_\nu$ and represents a meromorphic function in the whole plane. It is obvious that the singular parts are $P_\nu(1/(z - b_\nu))$, and the rest of the theorem follows trivially.

As a first example we consider the function $\pi^2/\sin^2 \pi z$ which has double poles at the points $z = n$ for integral n. The singular part at the origin is $1/z^2$, and since $\sin^2 \pi(z - n) = \sin^2 \pi z$ the singular part at $z = n$ is $1/(z - n)^2$. The series

$$\sum_{n=-\infty}^{+\infty} \frac{1}{(z - n)^2} \tag{7}$$

is convergent for $z \neq n$, as seen by comparison with the familiar series $\sum_1^\infty 1/n^2$. It is uniformly convergent on any compact set after omission of

† We suppose, for simplicity, that no b_ν equals zero.

the terms which become infinite on the set. For this reason we can write

$$\frac{\pi^2}{\sin^2 \pi z} = \sum_{n=-\infty}^{+\infty} \frac{1}{(z-n)^2} + g(z) \tag{8}$$

where $g(z)$ is analytic in the whole plane. We contend that $g(z)$ is identically zero.

To prove this we observe that the function $\pi^2/\sin^2 \pi z$ and the series (7) are both periodic with the period 1. Therefore the function $g(z)$ has the same period. For $z = x + iy$ we have (Chap. 2, Sec. 3.2, Ex. 4)

$$|\sin \pi z|^2 = \cosh^2 y - \cos^2 x$$

and hence $\pi^2/\sin^2 \pi z$ tends uniformly to 0 as $|y| \to \infty$. But it is easy to see that the function (7) has the same property. Indeed, the convergence is uniform for $|y| \geqq 1$, say, and the limit for $|y| \to \infty$ can thus be obtained by taking the limit in each term. We conclude that $g(z)$ tends uniformly to 0 for $|y| \to \infty$. This is sufficient to infer that $|g(z)|$ is bounded in a period strip $0 \leqq x \leqq 1$, and because of the periodicity $|g(z)|$ will be bounded in the whole plane. By Liouville's theorem $g(z)$ must reduce to a constant, and since the limit is 0 the constant must vanish. We have thus proved the identity

$$\frac{\pi^2}{\sin^2 \pi z} = \sum_{-\infty}^{\infty} \frac{1}{(z-n)^2}. \tag{9}$$

From this equation a related identity can be obtained by integration. The left-hand member is the derivative of $-\pi \cot \pi z$, and the terms on the right are derivatives of $-1/(z-n)$. The series with the general term $1/(z-n)$ diverges, and a partial sum of the Taylor series must be subtracted from all the terms with $n \neq 0$. As it happens it is sufficient to subtract the constant terms, for the series

$$\sum_{n \neq 0} \left(\frac{1}{z-n} + \frac{1}{n} \right) = \sum_{n \neq 0} \frac{z}{n(z-n)}$$

is comparable with $\sum_1^\infty 1/n^2$ and hence convergent. The convergence is uniform on every compact set, provided that we omit the terms which become infinite. For this reason termwise differentiation is permissible, and we obtain

$$\pi \cot \pi z = \frac{1}{z} + \sum_{n \neq 0} \left(\frac{1}{z-n} + \frac{1}{n} \right) \tag{10}$$

except for an additive constant. If the terms corresponding to n and $-n$ are bracketed together, (10) can be written in the equivalent forms

$$(11)\qquad \pi \cot \pi z = \lim_{m\to\infty} \sum_{n=-m}^{m} \frac{1}{z-n} = \frac{1}{z} + \sum_{n=1}^{\infty} \frac{2z}{z^2-n^2}.$$

With this way of writing it becomes evident that both members of the equation are odd functions of z, and for this reason the integration constant must vanish. The equations (10) and (11) are thus correctly stated.

Let us now reverse the procedure and try to evaluate the analogous sum

$$(12)\qquad \lim_{m\to\infty} \sum_{-m}^{m} \frac{(-1)^n}{z-n} = \frac{1}{z} + \sum_{1}^{\infty} (-1)^n \frac{2z}{z^2-n^2}$$

which evidently represents a meromorphic function. It is very natural to separate the odd and even terms and write

$$\sum_{-(2k+1)}^{2k+1} \frac{(-1)^n}{z-n} = \sum_{n=-k}^{k} \frac{1}{z-2n} - \sum_{n=-k-1}^{k} \frac{1}{z-1-2n}.$$

By comparison with (11) we find that the limit is

$$\frac{\pi}{2} \cot \frac{\pi z}{2} - \frac{\pi}{2} \cot \frac{\pi(z-1)}{2} = \frac{\pi}{\sin \pi z},$$

and we have proved that

$$(13)\qquad \frac{\pi}{\sin \pi z} = \lim_{m\to\infty} \sum_{-m}^{m} (-1)^n \frac{1}{z-n}.$$

EXERCISES

1. Comparing coefficients in the Laurent developments of $\cot \pi z$ and of its expression as a sum of partial fractions, find the values of

$$\sum_{1}^{\infty} \frac{1}{n^2}, \quad \sum_{1}^{\infty} \frac{1}{n^4}, \quad \sum_{1}^{\infty} \frac{1}{n^6}.$$

Give a complete justification of the steps that are needed.

2. Express

$$\sum_{-\infty}^{\infty} \frac{1}{z^3-n^3}$$

in closed form.

3. Use (13) to find the partial fraction development of $1/\cos \pi z$, and show that it leads to $\pi/4 = 1 - \frac{1}{3} + \frac{1}{5} - \frac{1}{7} + \cdots$.

4. What is the value of

$$\sum_{-\infty}^{\infty} \frac{1}{(z+n)^2 + a^2}?$$

2.2. *Infinite Products.* An infinite product of complex numbers

$$p_1 p_2 \cdots p_n \cdots = \prod_{n=1}^{\infty} p_n \tag{14}$$

is evaluated by taking the limit of the partial products $P_n = p_1 p_2 \cdots p_n$. It is said to converge to the value $P = \lim_{n\to\infty} P_n$ if this limit exists and is different from zero. There are good reasons for excluding the value zero. For one thing, if the value $P = 0$ were permitted, any infinite product with one factor 0 would converge, and the convergence would not depend on the whole sequence of factors. On the other hand, in certain connections this convention is too radical. In fact, we wish to express a function as an infinite product, and this must be possible even if the function has zeros. For this reason we make the following agreement: The infinite product (14) is said to converge if and only if at most a finite number of the factors are zero, and if the partial products formed by the nonvanishing factors tend to a finite limit which is different from zero.

In a convergent product the general factor p_n tends to 1; this is clear by writing $p_n = P_n/P_{n-1}$, the zero factors being omitted. In view of this fact it is preferable to write all infinite products in the form

$$\prod_{n=1}^{\infty} (1 + a_n) \tag{15}$$

so that $a_n \to 0$ is a necessary condition for convergence.

If no factor is zero, it is natural to compare the product (15) with the infinite series

$$\sum_{n=1}^{\infty} \log (1 + a_n). \tag{16}$$

Since the a_n are complex we must agree on a definite branch of the logarithms, and we decide to choose the principal branch in each term. Denote the partial sums of (16) by S_n. Then $P_n = e^{S_n}$, and if $S_n \to S$ it follows that P_n tends to the limit $P = e^S$ which is $\neq 0$. In other words, the convergence of (16) is a sufficient condition for the convergence of (15).

In order to prove that the condition is also necessary, suppose that $P_n \to P \neq 0$, and choose a fixed value of $\log P$, for instance the value of the principal branch. With the corresponding value of $\arg P$ determine $\arg P_n$ by the condition $\arg P - \pi < \arg P_n \leqq \arg P + \pi$, and set $\log P_n = \log |P_n| + i \arg P_n$. We know that $S_n = \log P_n + h_n \cdot 2\pi i$, where h_n is a well-determined integer. For two consecutive terms we obtain

$$(h_{n+1} - h_n)2\pi i = \log (1 + a_{n+1}) + \log P_n - \log P_{n+1}.$$

We need pay attention only to the imaginary parts. As n is sufficiently large we have for instance $|\arg (1 + a_{n+1})| < 2\pi/3$, $|\arg P_n - \arg P| < 2\pi/3$, and $|\arg P_{n+1} - \arg P| < 2\pi/3$. These inequalities imply $|h_{n+1} - h_n| < 1$, and thus we conclude that $h_{n+1} = h_n$ for all sufficiently large n. Ultimately h_n is therefore constantly equal to a certain integer h, and we find that S_n tends to the limit $S = \log P + h \cdot 2\pi i$. We have proved:

Theorem 5. *The infinite product* $\prod_1^\infty (1 + a_n)$ *with* $1 + a_n \neq 0$ *converges simultaneously with the series* $\sum_1^\infty \log (1 + a_n)$ *whose terms represent the values of the principal branch of the logarithm.*

The question of convergence of a product can thus be reduced to the more familiar question concerning the convergence of a series. It can be further reduced by observing that the series (16) converges absolutely at the same time as the simpler series $\Sigma |a_n|$. This is an immediate consequence of the fact that

$$\lim_{z \to 0} \frac{\log (1 + z)}{z} = 1.$$

If either the series (16) or $\sum_1^\infty |a_n|$ converges, we have $a_n \to 0$, and for a given $\varepsilon > 0$ the double inequality

$$(1 - \varepsilon)|a_n| < |\log (1 + a_n)| < (1 + \varepsilon)|a_n|$$

will hold for all sufficiently large n. It follows immediately that the two series are in fact simultaneously absolutely convergent.

An infinite product is said to be absolutely convergent if and only if the corresponding series (16) converges absolutely. With this terminology we can state our result in the following terms:

Theorem 6. *A necessary and sufficient condition for the absolute convergence of the product* $\prod_1^\infty (1 + a_n)$ *is the convergence of the series* $\sum_1^\infty |a_n|$.

In the last theorem the emphasis is on absolute convergence. By simple examples it can be shown that the convergence of $\sum_1^\infty a_n$ is neither sufficient nor necessary for the convergence of the product $\prod_1^\infty (1 + a_n)$.

It is clear what to understand by a uniformly convergent infinite product whose factors are functions of a variable. The presence of zeros may cause some slight difficulties which can usually be avoided by considering only sets on which at most a finite number of the factors can vanish. If these factors are omitted, it is sufficient to study the uniform convergence of the remaining product. Theorems 5 and 6 have obvious counterparts for uniform convergence. If we examine the proofs, we find that all estimates can be made uniform, and the conclusions lead to uniform convergence.

EXERCISES

1. Show that

$$\prod_{n=2}^{\infty} \left(1 - \frac{1}{n^2}\right) = \frac{1}{2}.$$

2. Prove that for $|z| < 1$

$$(1 + z)(1 + z^2)(1 + z^4)(1 + z^8) \cdots = \frac{1}{1 - z}.$$

3. Prove that

$$\prod_1^\infty \left(1 + \frac{z}{n}\right) e^{-z/n}$$

converges absolutely and uniformly on every compact set.

4. Prove that the value of an absolutely convergent product does not change if the factors are reordered.

5. Show that the function

$$\theta(z) = \prod_1^\infty (1 + h^{2n-1}e^z)(1 + h^{2n-1}e^{-z})$$

where $|h| < 1$ is analytic in the whole plane and satisfies the functional equation

$$\theta(z + 2 \log h) = h^{-1}e^{-z}\,\theta(z).$$

2.3. *Canonical Products.* A function which is analytic in the whole plane is said to be *entire*, or *integral*. The simplest entire functions which are not polynomials are e^z, $\sin z$, and $\cos z$.

If $g(z)$ is an entire function, then $f(z) = e^{g(z)}$ is entire and $\neq 0$. Conversely, if $f(z)$ is any entire function which is never zero, let us show that $f(z)$ is of the form $e^{g(z)}$. To this end we observe that the function $f'(z)/f(z)$, being analytic in the whole plane, is the derivative of an entire function $g(z)$. From this fact we infer, by computation, that $f(z)e^{-g(z)}$ has the derivative zero, and hence $f(z)$ is a constant multiple of $e^{g(z)}$; the constant can be absorbed in $g(z)$.

By this method we can also find the most general entire function with a finite number of zeros. Assume that $f(z)$ has m zeros at the origin (m may be zero), and denote the other zeros by $a_1, a_2, \ldots, a_N$, multiple zeros being repeated. It is then plain that we can write

$$f(z) = z^m e^{g(z)} \prod_{1}^{N} \left(1 - \frac{z}{a_n}\right).$$

If there are infinitely many zeros, we can try to obtain a similar representation by means of an infinite product. The obvious generalization would be

$$f(z) = z^m e^{g(z)} \prod_{1}^{\infty} \left(1 - \frac{z}{a_n}\right). \tag{17}$$

This representation is valid if the infinite product converges uniformly on every compact set. In fact, if this is so the product represents an entire function with zeros at the same point (except for the origin) and with the same multiplicities as $f(z)$. It follows that the quotient can be written in the form $z^m e^{g(z)}$.

The product in (17) converges absolutely if and only if $\sum_{1}^{\infty} 1/|a_n|$ is convergent, and in this case the convergence is also uniform in every closed disk $|z| \leq R$. It is only under this special condition that we can obtain a representation of the form (17).

In the general case convergence-producing factors must be introduced. We consider an arbitrary sequence of complex numbers $a_n \neq 0$ with

$\lim_{n \to \infty} a_n = \infty$, and prove the existence of polynomials $p_n(z)$ such that

$$\prod_1^\infty \left(1 - \frac{z}{a_n}\right) e^{p_n(z)} \tag{18}$$

converges to an entire function. The product converges together with the series with the general term

$$r_n(z) = \log\left(1 - \frac{z}{a_n}\right) + p_n(z)$$

where the branch of the logarithm shall be chosen so that the imaginary part of $r_n(z)$ lies between $-\pi$ and π (inclusive).

For a given R we consider only the terms with $|a_n| > R$. In the disk $|z| \leqq R$ the principal branch of $\log(1 - z/a_n)$ can be developed in a Taylor series

$$\log\left(1 - \frac{z}{a_n}\right) = -\frac{z}{a_n} - \frac{1}{2}\left(\frac{z}{a_n}\right)^2 - \frac{1}{3}\left(\frac{z}{a_n}\right)^3 - \cdots.$$

We reverse the signs and choose $p_n(z)$ as a partial sum

$$p_n(z) = \frac{z}{a_n} + \frac{1}{2}\left(\frac{z}{a_n}\right)^2 + \cdots + \frac{1}{m_n}\left(\frac{z}{a_n}\right)^{m_n}.$$

Then $r_n(z)$ has the representation

$$r_n(z) = \frac{1}{m_n + 1}\left(\frac{z}{a_n}\right)^{m_n+1} + \frac{1}{m_n + 2}\left(\frac{z}{a_n}\right)^{m_n+2} + \cdots$$

and we obtain easily the estimate

$$|r_n(z)| \leqq \frac{1}{m_n + 1}\left(\frac{R}{|a_n|}\right)^{m_n+1}\left(1 - \frac{R}{|a_n|}\right)^{-1}. \tag{19}$$

Suppose now that the series

$$\sum_{n=1}^\infty \frac{1}{m_n + 1}\left(\frac{R}{|a_n|}\right)^{m_n+1} \tag{20}$$

converges. By the estimate (19) it follows first that $r_n(z) \to 0$, and hence $r_n(z)$ has an imaginary part between $-\pi$ and π as soon as n is sufficiently large. Moreover, the comparison shows that the series $\Sigma r_n(z)$ is absolutely and uniformly convergent for $|z| \leqq R$, and thus the product (18) represents an analytic function in $|z| < R$. For the sake of the reasoning we had to exclude the values $|a_n| \leqq R$, but it is clear that the uniform convergence of (18) is not affected when the corresponding factors are again taken into account.

It remains only to show that the series (20) can be made convergent for all R. But this is obvious, for if we take $m_n = n$, (20) becomes a power series with an infinite radius of convergence as seen either by use of the formula for the radius of convergence or by consideration of a majorant geometric series for any fixed value of R.

Theorem 7. *There exists an entire function with arbitrarily prescribed zeros a_n provided that, in the case of infinitely many zeros, $a_n \to \infty$. Every entire function with these and no other zeros can be written in the form*

$$f(z) = z^m e^{g(z)} \prod_{n=1}^{\infty} \left(1 - \frac{z}{a_n}\right) e^{\frac{z}{a_n} + \frac{1}{2}\left(\frac{z}{a_n}\right)^2 + \cdots + \frac{1}{m_n}\left(\frac{z}{a_n}\right)^{m_n}} \tag{21}$$

where the product is taken over all $a_n \neq 0$, the m_n are certain integers, and $g(z)$ is an entire function.

This theorem is due to Weierstrass. It has the following important corollary:

Corollary. *Every function which is meromorphic in the whole plane is the quotient of two entire functions.*

In fact, if $F(z)$ is meromorphic in the whole plane, we can find an entire function $g(z)$ with the poles of $F(z)$ for zeros. The product $F(z)g(z)$ is then an entire function $f(z)$, and we obtain $F(z) = f(z)/g(z)$.

The representation (21) becomes considerably more interesting if it is possible to choose all the m_n equal to each other. The preceding proof has shown that the product

$$\prod_{1}^{\infty} \left(1 - \frac{z}{a_n}\right) e^{\frac{z}{a_n} + \frac{1}{2}\left(\frac{z}{a_n}\right)^2 + \cdots + \frac{1}{h}\left(\frac{z}{a_n}\right)^{h}} \tag{22}$$

converges and represents an entire function provided that the series $\sum_{n=1}^{\infty} (R/|a_n|)^{h+1}/(h+1)$ converges for all R, that is to say provided that $\Sigma 1/|a_n|^{h+1} < \infty$. Assume that h is the smallest integer for which this series converges; the expression (22) is then called the *canonical product* associated with the sequence $\{a_n\}$, and h is the *genus* of the canonical product.

Whenever possible we use the canonical product in the representation (21), which is thereby uniquely determined. If in this representation $g(z)$ reduces to a polynomial, the function $f(z)$ is said to be of finite genus, and the genus of $f(z)$ is by definition equal to the degree of this polynomial or to the genus of the canonical product, whichever is the larger. For instance, an entire function of genus zero is of the form

$$Cz^m \prod_1^\infty \left(1 - \frac{z}{a_n}\right)$$

with $\Sigma 1/|a_n| < \infty$. The canonical representation of an entire function of genus 1 is either of the form

$$Cz^m e^{\alpha z} \prod_1^\infty \left(1 - \frac{z}{a_n}\right) e^{z/a_n}$$

with $\Sigma 1/|a_n|^2 < \infty$, $\Sigma 1/|a_n| = \infty$, or of the form

$$Cz^m e^{\alpha z} \prod_1^\infty \left(1 - \frac{z}{a_n}\right)$$

with $\Sigma 1/|a_n| < \infty$, $\alpha \neq 0$.

As an application we consider the product representation of $\sin \pi z$. The zeros are the integers $z = \pm n$. Since $\Sigma 1/n$ diverges and $\Sigma 1/n^2$ converges, we must take $h = 1$ and obtain a representation of the form

$$\sin \pi z = z e^{g(z)} \prod_{n \neq 0} \left(1 - \frac{z}{n}\right) e^{z/n}.$$

In order to determine $g(z)$ we form the logarithmic derivatives on both sides. We find

$$\pi \cot \pi z = \frac{1}{z} + g'(z) + \sum_{n \neq 0} \left(\frac{1}{z - n} + \frac{1}{n}\right)$$

where the procedure is easy to justify by uniform convergence on any compact set which does not contain the points $z = n$. By comparison with the previous formula (10) we conclude that $g'(z) = 0$. Hence $g(z)$ is a constant, and since $\lim_{z \to 0} \sin \pi z/z = \pi$ we must have $e^{g(z)} = \pi$, and thus

$$\sin \pi z = \pi z \prod_{n \neq 0} \left(1 - \frac{z}{n}\right) e^{z/n}. \tag{23}$$

In this representation the factors corresponding to n and $-n$ can be bracketed together, and we obtain the simple form

$$\sin \pi z = \pi z \prod_1^\infty \left(1 - \frac{z^2}{n^2}\right). \tag{24}$$

It follows from (23) that $\sin \pi z$ is an entire function of genus 1.

EXERCISES

1. Suppose that $a_n \to \infty$ and that the A_n are arbitrary complex numbers. Show that there exists an entire function $f(z)$ which satisfies $f(a_n) = A_n$.

Hint: Let $g(z)$ be a function with simple zeros at the a_n. Show that

$$\sum_1^\infty g(z) \frac{e^{\gamma_n(z-a_n)}}{z - a_n} \cdot \frac{A_n}{g'(a_n)}$$

converges for some choice of the numbers γ_n.

2. Prove that

$$\sin \pi(z + \alpha) = e^{\pi z \cot \pi\alpha} \prod_{-\infty}^{\infty} \left(1 + \frac{z}{n + \alpha}\right) e^{-z/(n+\alpha)}$$

whenever α is not an integer. *Hint:* Denote the factor in front of the canonical product by $g(z)$ and determine $g'(z)/g(z)$.

3. What is the genus of $\cos \sqrt{z}$?

4. If $f(z)$ is of genus h, how large and how small can the genus of $f(z^2)$ be?

5. Show that if $f(z)$ is of genus 0 or 1 with real zeros, and if $f(z)$ is real for real z, then all zeros of $f'(z)$ are real. *Hint:* Consider $\operatorname{Im} f'(z)/f(z)$.

2.4. The Gamma Function. The function $\sin \pi z$ has all the integers for zeros, and it is the simplest function with this property. We shall now introduce functions which have only the positive or only the negative integers for zeros. The simplest function with, for instance, the negative integers for zeros is the corresponding canonical product

$$G(z) = \prod_1^\infty \left(1 + \frac{z}{n}\right) e^{-z/n}. \tag{25}$$

It is evident that $G(-z)$ has then the positive integers for zeros, and by comparison with the product representation (23) of $\sin \pi z$ we find at once

$$zG(z)G(-z) = \frac{\sin \pi z}{\pi}. \tag{26}$$

Because of the manner in which $G(z)$ has been constructed, it is bound to have other simple properties. We observe that $G(z - 1)$ has the same zeros as $G(z)$, and in addition a zero at the origin. It is therefore clear that we can write

$$G(z - 1) = ze^{\gamma(z)}G(z),$$

where $\gamma(z)$ is an entire function. In order to determine $\gamma(z)$ we take the logarithmic derivatives on both sides. This gives the equation

$$(27)\qquad \sum_{n=1}^{\infty}\left(\frac{1}{z-1+n}-\frac{1}{n}\right)=\frac{1}{z}+\gamma'(z)+\sum_{n=1}^{\infty}\left(\frac{1}{z+n}-\frac{1}{n}\right).$$

In the series to the left we can replace n by $n+1$. By this change we obtain

$$\sum_{n=1}^{\infty}\left(\frac{1}{z-1+n}-\frac{1}{n}\right)=\frac{1}{z}-1+\sum_{n=1}^{\infty}\left(\frac{1}{z+n}-\frac{1}{n+1}\right)$$
$$=\frac{1}{z}-1+\sum_{n=1}^{\infty}\left(\frac{1}{z+n}-\frac{1}{n}\right)+\sum_{n=1}^{\infty}\left(\frac{1}{n}-\frac{1}{n+1}\right).$$

The last series has the sum 1, and hence equation (27) reduces to $\gamma'(z)=0$. Thus $\gamma(z)$ is a constant, which we denote by γ, and $G(z)$ has the reproductive property $G(z-1)=e^{\gamma}zG(z)$. It is somewhat simpler to consider the function $H(z)=G(z)e^{\gamma z}$ which evidently satisfies the functional equation $H(z-1)=zH(z)$.

The value of γ is easily determined. Taking $z=1$ we have

$$1=G(0)=e^{\gamma}G(1),$$

and hence

$$e^{-\gamma}=\prod_{n=1}^{\infty}\left(1+\frac{1}{n}\right)e^{-1/n}.$$

Here the nth partial product can be written in the form

$$(n+1)e^{-(1+\frac{1}{2}+\frac{1}{3}+\cdots+1/n)},$$

and we obtain

$$\gamma=\lim_{n\to\infty}\left(1+\frac{1}{2}+\frac{1}{3}+\cdots+\frac{1}{n}-\log n\right).$$

The constant γ is called Euler's constant; its approximate value is .57722.

If $H(z)$ satisfies $H(z-1)=zH(z)$, then $\Gamma(z)=1/[zH(z)]$ satisfies $\Gamma(z-1)=\Gamma(z)/(z-1)$, or

$$(28)\qquad \Gamma(z+1)=z\Gamma(z).$$

This is found to be a more useful relation, and for this reason it has become customary to implement the restricted stock of elementary functions by inclusion of $\Gamma(z)$ under the name of *Euler's gamma function*.

Our definition leads to the explicit representation

$$\Gamma(z) = \frac{e^{-\gamma z}}{z} \prod_{n=1}^{\infty} \left(1 + \frac{z}{n}\right)^{-1} e^{z/n}, \tag{29}$$

and the formula (26) takes the form

$$\Gamma(z)\Gamma(1 - z) = \frac{\pi}{\sin \pi z}. \tag{30}$$

We observe that $\Gamma(z)$ is a meromorphic function with poles at $z = 0, -1, -2, \ldots$ but *without zeros.*

We have $\Gamma(1) = 1$, and by the functional equation we find $\Gamma(2) = 1$, $\Gamma(3) = 1 \cdot 2$, $\Gamma(4) = 1 \cdot 2 \cdot 3$ and generally $\Gamma(n) = (n - 1)!$. The Γ-function can thus be considered as a generalization of the factorial. From (30) we conclude that $\Gamma(\frac{1}{2}) = \sqrt{\pi}$.

Other properties are most easily found by considering the second derivative of $\log \Gamma(z)$ for which we find, by (29), the very simple expression

$$\frac{d}{dz}\left(\frac{\Gamma'(z)}{\Gamma(z)}\right) = \sum_{n=0}^{\infty} \frac{1}{(z + n)^2}. \tag{31}$$

For instance, it is plain that $\Gamma(z)\,\Gamma(z + \frac{1}{2})$ and $\Gamma(2z)$ have the same poles, and by use of (31) we find indeed that

$$\frac{d}{dz}\left(\frac{\Gamma'(z)}{\Gamma(z)}\right) + \frac{d}{dz}\left(\frac{\Gamma'(z + \frac{1}{2})}{\Gamma(z + \frac{1}{2})}\right) = \sum_{n=0}^{\infty} \frac{1}{(z + n)^2} + \sum_{n=0}^{\infty} \frac{1}{(z + n + \frac{1}{2})^2}$$
$$= 4\left[\sum_{n=0}^{\infty} \frac{1}{(2z + 2n)^2} + \sum_{n=0}^{\infty} \frac{1}{(2z + 2n + 1)^2}\right] = 4 \sum_{m=0}^{\infty} \frac{1}{(2z + m)^2}$$
$$= 2\frac{d}{dz}\left(\frac{\Gamma'(2z)}{\Gamma(2z)}\right).$$

By integration we obtain

$$\Gamma(z)\Gamma(z + \tfrac{1}{2}) = e^{az+b}\Gamma(2z),$$

where the constants a and b have yet to be determined. Substituting $z = \frac{1}{2}$ and $z = 1$ we make use of the known values $\Gamma(\frac{1}{2}) = \sqrt{\pi}$, $\Gamma(1) = 1$, $\Gamma(1\frac{1}{2}) = \frac{1}{2}\Gamma(\frac{1}{2}) = \frac{1}{2}\sqrt{\pi}$, $\Gamma(2) = 1$ and are led to the relations

$$\tfrac{1}{2}a + b = \tfrac{1}{2}\log \pi, \qquad a + b = \tfrac{1}{2}\log \pi - \log 2.$$

It follows that

$$a = -2 \log 2 \qquad \text{and} \qquad b = \tfrac{1}{2} \log \pi + \log 2;$$

the final result is thus

$$\sqrt{\pi}\,\Gamma(2z) = 2^{2z-1}\Gamma(z)\Gamma(z + \tfrac{1}{2})$$

which is known as Legendre's duplication formula.

EXERCISES

1. Prove the formula of Gauss:

$$(2\pi)^{\frac{n-1}{2}}\,\Gamma(z) = n^{z-\frac{1}{2}}\,\Gamma\left(\frac{z}{n}\right)\Gamma\left(\frac{z+1}{n}\right)\cdots\Gamma\left(\frac{z+n-1}{n}\right).$$

2. Show that

$$\Gamma\left(\frac{1}{6}\right) = 2^{-\frac{1}{3}}\left(\frac{3}{\pi}\right)^{\frac{1}{2}}\Gamma\left(\frac{1}{3}\right)^2.$$

3. What are the residues of $\Gamma(z)$ at the poles $z = -n$?

2.5. Stirling's Formula. In most connections where the Γ function can be applied, it is of utmost importance to have some information on the behavior of $\Gamma(z)$ for very large values of z. Fortunately, it is possible to calculate $\Gamma(z)$ with great precision and very little effort by means of a classical formula which goes under the name of Stirling's formula. There are many proofs of this formula. We choose to derive it by use of the residue calculus, following mainly the presentation of Lindelöf in his classical book on the calculus of residues. This is a very simple and above all a very instructive proof inasmuch as it gives us an opportunity to use residues in less trivial cases than previously.

The starting point is the formula (31) for the second derivative of $\log \Gamma(z)$, and our immediate task is to express the partial sum

$$\frac{1}{z^2} + \frac{1}{(z+1)^2} + \frac{1}{(z+2)^2} + \cdots + \frac{1}{(z+n)^2}$$

as a convenient line integral. To this end we need a function with the residues $1/(z+\nu)^2$ at the integral points ν; a good choice is

$$\Phi(\zeta) = \frac{\pi \cot \pi\zeta}{(z+\zeta)^2}.$$

Here ζ is the variable while z enters only as a parameter, which in the first part of the derivation will be kept at a fixed value $z = x + iy$ with $x > 0$.

We apply the residue formula to the rectangle whose vertical sides lie on $\xi = 0$ and $\xi = n + \frac{1}{2}$ and with horizontal sides $\eta = \pm Y$, with the intention of letting first Y and then n tend to ∞. This contour, which we denote by K, passes through the pole at 0, but we know that the formula remains valid provided that we take the principal value of the integral and include one-half of the residue at the origin. Hence we obtain

$$\text{pr.v.}\ \frac{1}{2\pi i}\int_K \Phi(\zeta)\,d\zeta = -\frac{1}{2z^2} + \sum_{\nu=0}^{n} \frac{1}{(z+\nu)^2}.$$

On the horizontal sides of the rectangle $\cot \pi\zeta$ tends uniformly to $\pm i$ for $Y \to \infty$. Since the factor $1/(z+\zeta)^2$ tends to zero, the corresponding integrals have the limit zero. We are now left with two integrals over infinite vertical lines. On each line $\xi = n + \frac{1}{2}$, $\cot \pi\zeta$ is bounded, and because of the periodicity the bound is independent of n. The integral over the line $\xi = n + \frac{1}{2}$ is thus less than a constant times

$$\int_{\xi=n+\frac{1}{2}} \frac{d\eta}{|\zeta+z|^2}.$$

This integral can be evaluated, for on the line of integration

$$\bar{\zeta} = 2n + 1 - \zeta,$$

and we obtain by residues

$$\frac{1}{i}\int \frac{d\zeta}{|\zeta+z|^2} = \frac{1}{i}\int \frac{d\zeta}{(\zeta+z)(2n+1-\zeta+\bar{z})} = \frac{2\pi}{2n+1+2x}.$$

The limit for $n \to \infty$ is thus zero.

Finally, the principal value of the integral over the imaginary axis from $-i\infty$ to $+i\infty$ can be written in the form

$$\frac{1}{2}\int_0^\infty \cot \pi i\eta \left[\frac{1}{(i\eta - z)^2} - \frac{1}{(i\eta + z)^2}\right] d\eta = -\int_0^\infty \coth \pi\eta \cdot \frac{2\eta z}{(\eta^2+z^2)^2}\,d\eta.$$

The sign has to be reversed, and we obtain the formula

$$\frac{d}{dz}\left(\frac{\Gamma'(z)}{\Gamma(z)}\right) = \frac{1}{2z^2} + \int_0^\infty \coth \pi\eta \cdot \frac{2\eta z}{(\eta^2+z^2)^2}\,d\eta. \tag{32}$$

It is preferable to write

$$\coth \pi\eta = 1 + \frac{2}{e^{2\pi\eta}-1}$$

and observe that the integral obtained from the term 1 has the value $1/z$. We can thus rewrite (32) in the form

$$\frac{d}{dz}\left(\frac{\Gamma'(z)}{\Gamma(z)}\right) = \frac{1}{z} + \frac{1}{2z^2} + \int_0^\infty \frac{4\eta z}{(\eta^2+z^2)^2}\cdot\frac{d\eta}{e^{2\pi\eta}-1} \tag{33}$$

where the integral is now very strongly convergent.

For z restricted to the right half plane this formula can be integrated. We find

$$(34) \qquad \frac{\Gamma'(z)}{\Gamma(z)} = C + \log z - \frac{1}{2z} - \int_0^\infty \frac{2\eta}{\eta^2 + z^2} \cdot \frac{d\eta}{e^{2\pi\eta} - 1},$$

where $\log z$ is the principal branch and C is an integration constant. The integration of the last term needs some justification. We have to make sure that the integral in (34) can be differentiated under the sign of integration; this is so because the integral converges uniformly when z is restricted to any compact set in the half plane $x > 0$.

We wish to integrate (34) once more. This would obviously introduce arc tan (z/η) in the integral, and although a single-valued branch could be defined we prefer to avoid the use of multiple-valued functions. That is possible if we first transform the integral in (34) by partial integration. We obtain

$$\int_0^\infty \frac{2\eta}{\eta^2 + z^2} \cdot \frac{d\eta}{e^{2\pi\eta} - 1} = \frac{1}{\pi} \int_0^\infty \frac{z^2 - \eta^2}{(\eta^2 + z^2)^2} \log (1 - e^{-2\pi\eta})\, d\eta$$

where the logarithm is of course real. Now we can integrate with respect to z and obtain

$$(35) \quad \log \Gamma(z) = C' + Cz + \left(z - \frac{1}{2}\right) \log z + \frac{1}{\pi} \int_0^\infty \frac{z}{\eta^2 + z^2} \log \frac{1}{1 - e^{-2\pi\eta}}\, d\eta$$

where C' is a new integration constant and for convenience $C - 1$ has been replaced by C. The formula means that there exists, in the right half plane, a single-valued branch of $\log \Gamma(z)$ whose value is given by the right-hand member of the equation. By proper choice of C' we obtain the branch of $\log \Gamma(z)$ which is real for real z.

It remains to determine the constants C and C'. To this end we must first study the behavior of the integral in (35) which we denote by

$$(36) \qquad J(z) = \frac{1}{\pi} \int_0^\infty \frac{z}{\eta^2 + z^2} \log \frac{1}{1 - e^{-2\pi\eta}}\, d\eta.$$

It is practically evident that $J(z) \to 0$ for $z \to \infty$ provided that z keeps away from the imaginary axis. Suppose for instance that z is restricted to the half plane $x \geqq c > 0$. Breaking the integral into two parts we write

$$J(z) = \int_0^{\frac{|z|}{2}} + \int_{\frac{|z|}{2}}^\infty = J_1 + J_2.$$

In the first integral $|\eta^2 + z^2| \geqq |z|^2 - |z/2|^2 = 3|z|^2/4$, and hence

$$|J_1| \leqq \frac{4}{3\pi|z|} \int_0^\infty \log \frac{1}{1 - e^{-2\pi\eta}}\, d\eta.$$

In the second integral $|\eta^2 + z^2| = |z - i\eta| \cdot |z + i\eta| > c|z|$, and we find

$$|J_2| < \frac{1}{\pi c} \int_{\frac{|z|}{2}}^\infty \log \frac{1}{1 - e^{-2\pi\eta}}\, d\eta.$$

Since the integral of $\log (1 - e^{-2\pi\eta})$ is obviously convergent, we conclude that J_1 and J_2 tend to 0 as $z \to \infty$.

The value of C is found by substituting (35) in the functional equation $\Gamma(z + 1) = z\Gamma(z)$ or $\log \Gamma(z + 1) = \log z + \log \Gamma(z)$; if we restrict z to positive values, there is no hesitancy about the branch of the logarithm. The substitution yields

$$C' + Cz + C + (z + \tfrac{1}{2}) \log (z + 1) + J(z + 1) = C' + Cz + (z + \tfrac{1}{2}) \log z + J(z),$$

and this reduces to

$$C = -\left(z + \frac{1}{2}\right) \log\left(1 + \frac{1}{z}\right) + J(z) - J(z + 1).$$

Letting $z \to \infty$ we find that $C = -1$.

Next we apply (35) to the equation $\Gamma(z)\Gamma(1 - z) = \pi/\sin \pi z$, choosing $z = \frac{1}{2} + iy$. We obtain

$$2C' - 1 + iy \log (\tfrac{1}{2} + iy) - iy \log (\tfrac{1}{2} - iy) + J(\tfrac{1}{2} + iy) + J(\tfrac{1}{2} - iy) = \log \pi - \log \cosh \pi y.$$

This equation, in which the logarithms are to have their principal values, is so far proved only up to a constant multiple of $2\pi i$. But for $y = 0$ the equation is correct as it stands because (35) determines the real value of $\log \Gamma(\frac{1}{2})$; hence it holds for all y. As $y \to \infty$ we known that $J(\frac{1}{2} + iy)$ and $J(\frac{1}{2} - iy)$ tend to 0. Developing the logarithm in a Taylor series we find

$$iy \log \frac{\frac{1}{2} + iy}{\frac{1}{2} - iy} = iy \left(\pi i + \log \frac{1 + \dfrac{1}{2iy}}{1 - \dfrac{1}{2iy}} \right) = -\pi y + 1 + \varepsilon_1(y)$$

while in the right-hand member

$$\log \cosh \pi y = \pi y - \log 2 + \varepsilon_2(y)$$

with $\varepsilon_1(y)$ and $\varepsilon_2(y)$ tending to 0. These considerations yield the value $C' = \frac{1}{2} \log 2\pi$. We have thus proved Stirling's formula in the form

$$\log \Gamma(z) = \tfrac{1}{2} \log 2\pi - z + (z - \tfrac{1}{2}) \log z + J(z) \tag{37}$$

or equivalently

$$\Gamma(z) = \sqrt{2\pi}\, z^{z-\frac{1}{2}} e^{-z} e^{J(z)} \tag{38}$$

with the representation (36) of the remainder valid in the right half plane. We know that $J(z)$ tends to 0 when $z \to \infty$ in a half plane $x \geqq c > 0$.

In the expression for $J(z)$ we can develop the integrand in powers of $1/z$ and obtain

$$J(z) = \frac{C_1}{z} + \frac{C_2}{z^3} + \cdots + \frac{C_k}{z^{2k-1}} + J_k(z)$$

with

$$C_\nu = (-1)^\nu \frac{1}{\pi} \int_0^\infty \eta^{2\nu-2} \log \frac{1}{1 - e^{-2\pi\eta}}\, d\eta \tag{39}$$

and

$$J_k(z) = \frac{(-1)^k}{z^{2k+1}} \frac{1}{\pi} \int_0^\infty \frac{\eta^{2k}}{1 + (\eta/z)^2} \log \frac{1}{1 - e^{-2\pi\eta}}\, d\eta.$$

It can be proved (for instance by means of residues) that the coefficients C_ν are connected with the Bernoulli numbers (cf. Ex. 4, Sec. 1.3) by

$$C_\nu = (-1)^\nu \frac{1}{(2\nu - 1)2\nu} B_\nu. \tag{40}$$

Thus the development of $J(z)$ takes the form

$$J(z) = \frac{B_1}{1 \cdot 2} \frac{1}{z} - \frac{B_2}{3 \cdot 4} \cdot \frac{1}{z^3} + \cdots + (-1)^{k-1} \frac{B_k}{(2k - 1)2k} \frac{1}{z^{2k-1}} + J_k(z). \tag{41}$$

The reader is warned not to confuse this with a Laurent development. The function $J(z)$ is not defined in a neighborhood of ∞ and, therefore, does not have a Laurent development; moreover, if $k \to \infty$, the series obtained from (41) does not converge. What we can say is that for a fixed k the expression $J_k(z)z^{2k}$ tends to 0 for $z \to \infty$ (in a half plane $x \geqq c > 0$). This fact characterizes (41) as an *asymptotic development.* Such developments are very valuable when z is large in comparison with k, but for fixed z there is no advantage in letting k become very large.

Stirling's formula can be used to prove that

$$\Gamma(z) = \int_0^\infty e^{-t} t^{z-1}\, dt \tag{42}$$

whenever the integral converges, that is to say for $x > 0$. Until the identity has been proved, let the integral in (42) be denoted by $F(z)$. Integrating by parts we find at once that

$$F(z + 1) = \int_0^\infty e^{-t}t^z\,dt = z\int_0^\infty e^{-t}t^{z-1}\,dt = zF(z).$$

Hence $F(z)$ satisfies the same functional equation as $\Gamma(z)$, and we find that $F(z)/\Gamma(z) = F(z+1)/\Gamma(z+1)$. In other words $F(z)/\Gamma(z)$ is periodic with the period 1. This shows, incidentally, that $F(z)$ can be defined in the whole plane although the integral representation is valid only in a half plane.

In order to prove that $F(z)/\Gamma(z)$ is constant we have to estimate $|F/\Gamma|$ in a period strip, for instance in the strip $1 \leqq x \leqq 2$. In the first place we have by (42)

$$|F(z)| \leqq \int_0^\infty e^{-t}t^{x-1}\,dt = F(x),$$

and hence $F(z)$ is bounded in the strip. Next, we use Stirling's formula to find a lower bound of $|\Gamma(z)|$ for large y. From (37) we obtain

$$\log|\Gamma(z)| = \tfrac{1}{2}\log 2\pi - x + (x - \tfrac{1}{2})\log|z| - y\arg z + \operatorname{Re} J(z).$$

Only the term $-y \arg z$ becomes negatively infinite, being comparable to $-\pi|y|/2$. Thus $|F/T|$ does not grow much more rapidly than $e^{\pi|y|/2}$.

For an arbitrary function this would not suffice to conclude that the function must be constant, but for a function of period 1 it is more than enough. In fact, it is clear that F/Γ can be expressed as a single-valued function of the variable $\zeta = e^{2\pi i z}$; to every value of $\zeta \neq 0$ there correspond infinitely many values of z which differ by multiples of 1, and thus a single value of F/Γ. The function has isolated singularities at $\zeta = 0$ and $\zeta = \infty$, and our estimate shows that $|F/\Gamma|$ grows at most like $|\zeta|^{-\frac{1}{4}}$ for $\zeta \to 0$ and $|\zeta|^{\frac{1}{4}}$ for $\zeta \to \infty$. It follows that both singularities are removable, and hence F/Γ must reduce to a constant. Finally, the fact that $F(1) = \Gamma(1) = 1$ shows that $F(z) = \Gamma(z)$.

EXERCISES

1. Prove the development (41).

2. For real $x > 0$ prove that

$$\Gamma(x) = \sqrt{2\pi}\,x^{x-\frac{1}{2}}e^{-x}e^{\theta(x)/12x}$$

with $0 < \theta(x) < 1$.

3. The formula (42) permits us to evaluate the *probability integral*

$$\int_0^\infty e^{-t^2}\,dt = \tfrac{1}{2}\int_0^\infty e^{-x}x^{-\frac{1}{2}}\,dx = \tfrac{1}{2}\Gamma(\tfrac{1}{2}) = \tfrac{1}{2}\sqrt{\pi}.$$

Use this result together with Cauchy's theorem to compute the *Fresnel integrals*

$$\int_0^\infty \sin (x^2)\, dx, \qquad \int_0^\infty \cos (x^2)\, dx.$$

Answer: Both are equal to $\frac{1}{2}\sqrt{\pi/2}$.

3. ENTIRE FUNCTIONS

In Sec. 2.3 we have already considered the representation of entire functions as infinite products, and, in special cases, as canonical products. In this section we study the connection between the product representation and the rate of growth of the function. Such questions were first investigated by Hadamard who applied the results to his celebrated proof of the Prime Number Theorem. Space does not permit us to include this application, but the basic importance of Hadamard's factorization theorem will be quite evident.

3.1. Jensen's Formula. If $f(z)$ is an analytic function, then $\log |f(z)|$ is harmonic except at the zeros of $f(z)$. Therefore, if $f(z)$ is analytic and free from zeros in $|z| \leqq \rho$,

$$\log |f(0)| = \frac{1}{2\pi} \int_0^{2\pi} \log |f(\rho e^{i\theta})|\, d\theta, \tag{43}$$

and $\log |f(z)|$ can be expressed by Poisson's formula.

The equation (43) remains valid if $f(z)$ has zeros on the circle $|z| = \rho$. The simplest proof is by dividing $f(z)$ with one factor $z - \rho e^{i\theta_0}$ for each zero. It is sufficient to show that

$$\log \rho = \frac{1}{2\pi} \int^{2\pi} \log |\rho e^{i\theta} - \rho e^{i\theta_0}|\, d\theta$$

or

$$\int_0^{2\pi} \log |e^{i\theta} - e^{i\theta_0}|\, d\theta = 0.$$

This integral is evidently independent of θ_0, and we have only to show that

$$\int_0^{2\pi} \log |1 - e^{i\theta}|\, d\theta = 0.$$

But this is a consequence of the formula

$$\int_0^\pi \log \sin x\, dx = -\pi \log 2$$

proved in Chap. 4, Sec. 5.3 (cf. Chap. 4, Sec. 6.4, Ex. 5).

We will now investigate what becomes of (43) in the presence of zeros in the interior $|z| < \rho$. Denote these zeros by $a_1, a_2, \ldots, a_n$, multiple zeros being repeated, and assume first that $z = 0$ is not a zero. Then the function

$$F(z) = f(z) \prod_{i=1}^{n} \frac{\rho^2 - \bar{a}_i z}{\rho(z - a_i)}$$

is free from zeros in the disk, and $|F(z)| = |f(z)|$ on $|z| = \rho$. Consequently we obtain

$$\log |F(0)| = \frac{1}{2\pi} \int_0^{2\pi} \log |f(\rho e^{i\theta})| \, d\theta$$

and, substituting the value of $F(0)$,

$$\log |f(0)| = - \sum_{i=1}^{n} \log \left(\frac{\rho}{|a_i|} \right) + \frac{1}{2\pi} \int_0^{2\pi} \log |f(\rho e^{i\theta})| \, d\theta. \tag{44}$$

This is known as *Jensen's formula.* Its importance lies in the fact that it relates the modulus $|f(z)|$ on a circle to the moduli of the zeros.

If $f(0) = 0$, the formula is somewhat more complicated. Writing $f(z) = cz^h + \cdots$ we apply (44) to $f(z)(\rho/z)^h$ and find that the left-hand member must be replaced by $\log |c| + h \log \rho$.

There is a similar generalization of Poisson's formula. All that is needed is to apply the ordinary Poisson formula to $\log |F(z)|$. We obtain

$$\log |f(z)| = - \sum_{i=1}^{n} \log \left| \frac{\rho^2 - \bar{a}_i z}{\rho(z - \bar{a}_i)} \right| + \frac{1}{2\pi} \int_0^{2\pi} \operatorname{Re} \frac{\rho e^{i\theta} + z}{\rho e^{i\theta} - z} \log |f(\rho e^{i\theta})| \, d\theta, \tag{45}$$

provided that $f(z) \neq 0$. Equation (45) is frequently referred to as the *Poisson-Jensen formula.*

Strictly speaking the proof is valid only if $f \neq 0$ on $|z| = \rho$. But (44) shows that the integral on the right is a continuous function of ρ, and from there it is easy to infer that the integral in (45) is likewise continuous. In the general case (45) can therefore be derived by letting ρ approach a limit.

The Jensen and Poisson-Jensen formulas have important applications in the theory of entire functions.

3.2. Hadamard's Theorem. Let $f(z)$ be an entire function, and denote its zeros by a_n; for the sake of simplicity we will assume that $f(0) \neq 0$. We recall that the genus of an entire function (Sec. 2.3) is the smallest integer h such that $f(z)$ can be represented in the form

$$f(z) = e^{g(z)} \prod_n \left(1 - \frac{z}{a_n}\right) e^{z/a_n + \frac{1}{2}(z/a_n)^2 + \cdots + (1/h)(z/a_n)^h} \tag{46}$$

where $g(z)$ is a polynomial of degree $\leqq h$. If there is no such representation, the genus is infinite.

Denote by $M(r)$ the maximum of $|f(z)|$ on $|z| = r$. The *order* of the entire function $f(z)$ is defined by

$$\lambda = \overline{\lim_{r\to\infty}} \frac{\log \log M(r)}{\log r}.$$

According to this definition λ is the smallest number such that

$$M(r) \leqq e^{r^{\lambda+\epsilon}} \tag{47}$$

for any given $\varepsilon > 0$ as soon as r is sufficiently large.

The genus and the order are closely related, as seen by the following theorem:

Theorem 8. *The genus and the order of an entire function satisfy the double inequality* $h \leqq \lambda \leqq h + 1$.

Assume first that $f(z)$ is of finite genus h. The exponential factor in (46) is quite obviously of order $\leqq h$, and the order of a product cannot exceed the orders of both factors. Hence it is sufficient to show that the canonical product is of order $\leqq h + 1$. The convergence of the canonical product implies $\sum_n |a_n|^{-h-1} < \infty$; this is the essential hypothesis.

We denote the canonical product by $P(z)$ and write the individual factors as $E_h(z/a_n)$ where

$$E_h(u) = (1 - u)e^{u + \frac{1}{2}u^2 + \cdots + (1/h)u^h}$$

with the understanding that $E_0(u) = 1 - u$. We will show that

$$\log |E_h(u)| \leqq (2h + 1)|u|^{h+1} \tag{48}$$

for all u.

If $|u| < 1$ we have by power-series development

$$\log |E_h(u)| \leqq \frac{|u|^{h+1}}{h+1} + \frac{|u|^{h+2}}{h+2} + \cdots \leqq \frac{1}{h+1}\frac{|u|^{h+1}}{1-|u|}$$

and thus

$$(1 - |u|) \log |E_h(u)| \leqq |u|^{h+1}. \tag{49}$$

For arbitrary u and $h \geqq 1$,

$$\log |E_h(u)| \leqq \log |E_{h-1}(u)| + |u|^h. \tag{50}$$

If (50) is multiplied by $|u|$ and added to (49), we obtain

$$\log |E_h(u)| \leqq |u| \log |E_{h-1}(u)| + 2|u|^{h+1}, \tag{51}$$

valid for $|u| < 1$. But for $|u| \geqq 1$ (51) is a consequence of (50), provided that $|E_{h-1}(u)| \geqq 1$. If this condition is not satisfied, then $\log |E_h(u)| \leqq |u|^h < (2h + 1)|u|^{h+1}$ by (50), and (48) is fulfilled.

The truth of (48) follows now by induction. For $h = 0$ we have only to note that $\log |1 - u| \leqq \log (1 + |u|) \leqq |u|$. Assume that (48) holds with $h - 1$ in the place of h. Then, as just shown, either (48) or (51) holds. In the latter case the induction hypothesis yields

$$\log |E_h(u)| \leqq (2h - 1)|u|^{h+1} + 2|u|^{h+1} = (2h + 1)|u|^{h+1}$$

and (48) is proved.

The estimate (48) gives at once

$$\log |P(z)| = \sum_n \log \left| E_h\left(\frac{z}{a_n}\right)\right| \leqq (2h + 1)|z|^{h+1} \sum_n |a_n|^{-h-1}$$

and it follows that $P(z)$ is at most of order $h + 1$.

For the opposite inequality assume that $f(z)$ is of finite order λ and let h be the largest integer $\leqq \lambda$. Then $h + 1 > \lambda$, and we have to prove, first of all, that $\sum_n |a_n|^{-h-1}$ converges. It is for this proof that Jensen's formula is needed.

Let us denote by $\nu(\rho)$ the number of zeros a_n with $|a_n| \leqq \rho$. In order to find an upper bound for $\nu(\rho)$ we apply (44) with 2ρ in the place of ρ and omit the terms $\log (2\rho/|a_n|)$ with $|a_n| \geqq \rho$. We find

$$\nu(\rho) \log 2 \leqq \frac{1}{2\pi} \int_0^{2\pi} \log |f(2\rho e^{i\theta})| \, d\theta - \log |f(0)|. \tag{52}$$

In view of (47) it follows that $\lim_{\rho \to \infty} \nu(\rho)\rho^{-\lambda-\varepsilon} = 0$ for every $\varepsilon > 0$.

We assume now that the zeros a_n are ordered according to absolute values: $|a_1| \leqq |a_2| \leqq \cdots \leqq |a_n| \leqq \cdots$. Then it is clear that $n \leqq \nu(|a_n|)$, and from a certain n on we must have, for instance,

$$n \leqq \nu(|a_n|) < |a_n|^{\lambda+\varepsilon}.$$

According to this inequality the series $\sum_n |a_n|^{-h-1}$ has the majorant

$$\sum_n n^{-\frac{h+1}{\lambda+\varepsilon}},$$

and if we choose ε so that $\lambda + \varepsilon < h + 1$ the majorant converges. We have thus proved that $f(z)$ can be written in the form (46) where so far $g(z)$ is only known to be entire.

It remains to prove that $g(z)$ is a polynomial of degree $\leqq h$. For this purpose it is easiest to use the Poisson-Jensen formula. If the operation $(\partial/\partial x) - i(\partial/\partial y)$ is applied to both sides of the identity (45), we obtain

$$\frac{f'(z)}{f(z)} = \sum_{1}^{\nu(\rho)} (z - a_n)^{-1} + \sum_{1}^{\nu(\rho)} \bar{a}_n(\rho^2 - \bar{a}_n z)^{-1} + \frac{1}{2\pi}\int_0^{2\pi} 2\rho e^{i\theta}(\rho e^{i\theta} - z)^{-2} \log |f(\rho e^{i\theta})|\, d\theta.$$

On differentiating h times with respect to z this yields

$$(53) \qquad D^{(h)}\frac{f'(z)}{f(z)} = -h!\sum_{1}^{\nu(\rho)} (a_n - z)^{-h-1} + h!\sum_{1}^{\nu(\rho)} \bar{a}_n^{h+1}(\rho^2 - \bar{a}_n z)^{-h-1} + (h+1)!\,\frac{1}{2\pi}\int_0^{2\pi} 2\rho e^{i\theta}(\rho e^{i\theta} - z)^{-h-2} \log |f(\rho e^{i\theta})|\, d\theta.$$

It is our intention to let ρ tend to ∞. In order to estimate the integral in (53) we observe first that

$$\int_0^{2\pi} \rho e^{i\theta}(\rho e^{i\theta} - z)^{-h-2}\, d\theta = 0.$$

Therefore nothing changes if we subtract $\log M(\rho)$ from $\log |f|$. If $\rho > 2|z|$ it follows that the last term in (53) has a modulus at most equal to

$$(h+1)!2^{h+3}\rho^{-h-1}\frac{1}{2\pi}\int_0^{2\pi} \log \frac{M(\rho)}{|f(\rho e^{i\theta})|}\, d\theta,$$

for $\log M(\rho)/|f(\rho e^{i\theta})| \geqq 0$. But

$$\frac{1}{2\pi}\int_0^{2\pi} \log |f|\, d\theta \geqq \log |f(0)|$$

by Jensen's formula, and $\rho^{-h-1} \log M(\rho) \to 0$ since $\lambda < h + 1$. We conclude that the integral in (53) tends to 0.

As for the second sum in (53), the same preliminary inequality $\rho > 2|z|$ together with $|a_n| \leqq \rho$ makes each term absolutely less than $(2/\rho)^{h+1}$, and the whole sum has modulus at most $2^{h+1}\nu(\rho)\rho^{-h-1}$. We have already proved that this tends to 0. Therefore we obtain

$$(54) \qquad D^{(h)}\frac{f'(z)}{f(z)} = -h!\sum_{n=1}^{\infty} (a_n - z)^{-h-1}.$$

Writing $f(z) = e^{g(z)}P(z)$ we find

$$g^{(h+1)}(z) = D^{(h)}\frac{f'}{f} - D^{(h)}\frac{P'}{P}.$$

However, by Weierstrass's theorem the quantity $D^{(h)}(P'/P)$ can be found by separate differentiation of each factor, and in this way we obtain precisely the right-hand member of (54). Consequently, $g^{(h+1)}(z)$ is identically zero, and $g(z)$ must be a polynomial of degree $\leq h$. We have proved Theorem 8.

The theorem is a factorization theorem for entire functions of finite order λ. If λ is not an integer, the genus h, and thereby the form of the product, is uniquely determined. If the order is not integral, there is an ambiguity.

The following impressive corollary shows the strength of Hadamard's theorem:

Corollary. *An entire function of fractional order assumes every finite value infinitely many times.*

It is clear that f and $f - a$ have the same order for any constant a. Therefore we need only show that f has infinitely many zeros. If f has only a finite number of zeros we can divide by a polynomial and obtain a function of the same order without zeros. By the theorem it must be of the form e^g where g is a polynomial. But it is evident that the order of e^g is exactly the degree of g, and hence an integer. The contradiction proves the corollary.

4. NORMAL FAMILIES

In Chap. 3, Sec. 1 we have already familiarized the reader with the idea of regarding a function as a point in a space. In principle there is thus no difference between a set of points and a set of functions. In order to make a clear distinction we shall nevertheless prefer to speak of *families* of functions, and usually we assume that all functions in a family are defined on the same set.

We are primarily interested in families of analytic functions, defined in a fixed region. Important examples are the families of bounded analytic functions, of functions which do not take the same value twice, etc. The aim is to study convergence properties within such families.

4.1. Equicontinuity. Although analytic functions are our main concern, it is expedient to choose a more general starting point. It turns out that our basic theorems are valid, and equally easy to prove, for families of functions with values in any complete metric space.

As a basic assumption we shall let $\mathfrak{F}$ denote a family of functions f, defined in a fixed region Ω of the complex plane, and with values in a *complete metric space* S. As in Chap. 3, Sec. 1 the distance function in S will be denoted by d.

We are interested in the convergence of sequences $\{f_n\}$ formed by functions in $\mathfrak{F}$. There is no particular reason to expect a sequence $\{f_n\}$ to be convergent; on the contrary, it is perhaps more likely that we run into the opposite extreme of a sequence that does not possess a single convergent subsequence. In many situations the latter possibility is a serious disadvantage, and the purpose of the considerations that follow is to find conditions which rule out this kind of behavior.

Let us review the definition of continuity of a function f with values in a metric space. By definition, f is continuous at z_0 if to every $\varepsilon > 0$ there exists a $\delta > 0$ such that $d(f(z),f(z_0)) < \varepsilon$ as soon as $|z - z_0| < \varepsilon$. We recall that f is said to be uniformly continuous if we can choose δ independent of z_0. But in the case of a family of functions there is another relevant kind of uniformity, namely, whether we can choose δ independent of f. We choose to require both, and are thus led to the following definition:

Definition 1. *The functions in a family $\mathfrak{F}$ are said to be equicontinuous on a set $E \subset \Omega$ if and only if, for each $\varepsilon > 0$, there exists a $\delta > 0$ such that $d(f(z),f(z_0)) < \varepsilon$ whenever $|z - z_0| < \delta$ and $z_0,z \in E$, simultaneously for all functions $f \in \mathfrak{F}$.*

Observe that, with this definition, each f in an equicontinuous family is itself uniformly continuous on E.

We return now to the question of convergent subsequences. Our second definition serves to characterize functions with a regular behavior:

Definition 2. *A family $\mathfrak{F}$ is said to be normal in Ω if every sequence $\{f_n\}$ of functions $f_n \in \mathfrak{F}$ contains a subsequence which converges uniformly on every compact subset of Ω.*

This definition does *not* require the limit functions of the convergent subsequences to be members of $\mathfrak{F}$.

4.2. Normality and Compactness. The reader cannot fail to have noticed the close similarity between normality and the Bolzano-Weierstrass property (Chap. 3, Theorem 7). To make it more than a similarity we need to define a distance on the space of functions on Ω with values in S, and convergence with respect to this distance function should mean precisely the same as uniform convergence on compact sets.

For this purpose we need, first of all, an *exhaustion* of Ω by an increasing sequence of compact sets $E_k \subset \Omega$. By this we mean that every compact subset E of Ω shall be contained in an E_k. The construction is possible in many ways: To be specific, let E_k consist of all points in Ω at distance $\leqq k$ from the origin, and at distance $\geqq 1/k$ from the boundary $\partial\Omega$. It is clear that each E_k is bounded and closed, hence compact. Any compact set $E \subset \Omega$ is bounded and at positive distance from $\partial\Omega$; therefore it is contained in an E_k.

Let f and g be any two functions on Ω with values in S. We shall define a distance $\rho(f,g)$ between these *functions*, not to be confused with the distances $d(f(z),g(z))$ between their values. To do so we first replace d by the distance function

$$\delta(a,b) = \frac{d(a,b)}{1 + d(a,b)}$$

which also satisfies the triangle inequality and has the advantage of being bounded (Chap. 3, Sec. 1.2, Ex. 1). Next, we set

$$\delta_k(f,g) = \sup_{z \in E_k} \delta(f(z),g(z))$$

which may be described as the distance between f and g on E_k. Finally, we agree on the definition

$$\rho(f,g) = \sum_{k=1}^{\infty} \delta_k(f,g)2^{-k}. \tag{55}$$

It is trivial to verify that $\rho(f,g)$ is finite and satisfies all the conditions for a distance function (Chap. 3, Sec. 1.2).

The distance $\rho(f,g)$ has the property we were looking for. Suppose first that $f_n \to f$ in the sense of the ρ-distance. For large n we have then $\rho(f_n,f) < \varepsilon$ and consequently, by (55), $\delta_k(f_n,f) < 2^k\varepsilon$. But this implies that $f_n \to f$ uniformly on E_k, first with respect to the δ-metric, but hence also with respect to the d-metric. Since every compact E is contained in an E_k it follows that the convergence is uniform on E.

Conversely, suppose that f_n converges uniformly to f on every compact set. Then $\delta_k(f_n,f) \to 0$ for every k, and because the series $\Sigma\delta_k(f_n,f)2^{-k}$ has a convergent majorant with terms independent of n it follows readily (as in Weierstrass's M test) that $\rho(f_n,f) \to 0$.

We have shown that convergence with respect to the distance ρ is equivalent to convergence on compact sets. An even simpler reasoning, which we leave to the reader, shows that the space of all functions with values in S is complete as a metric space with the distance ρ.

It can be said with some justification that the metric we have introduced is arbitrary and artificial. However, from what we have proved it follows that the open sets are independent of the choices involved in the construction. In other words, the *topology* has an intrinsic meaning, tailored to the needs of the theory of analytic functions.

We now recall the Bolzano-Weierstrass theorem, according to which a metric space is compact if and only if every infinite sequence has a convergent subsequence (Chap. 3, Theorem 7). The theorem is applied to the set $\mathfrak{F}$, equipped with the distance ρ, and we conclude that $\mathfrak{F}$ is compact if and only if $\mathfrak{F}$ is normal, *and* if the limit functions are themselves in $\mathfrak{F}$. On the other hand, if $\mathfrak{F}$ is normal, so is its closure $\mathfrak{F}^-$. Therefore we obtain the following characterization of normal families:

Theorem 9. *A family $\mathfrak{F}$ is normal if and only if its closure $\mathfrak{F}^-$ with respect to the distance function* (55) *is compact.*

It is also customary to say that $\mathfrak{F}$ is *precompact* (or *relatively compact*) if $\mathfrak{F}^-$ is compact. Thus, normal and precompact families are the same.

Finally, let us also characterize normality in terms of total boundedness. According to Chap. 3, Theorem 6, the set $\mathfrak{F}^-$ is compact if and only if it is complete and totally bounded. But as a closed subset of a complete space $\mathfrak{F}^-$ is automatically complete (this is where we use the completeness of S). It is clear that $\mathfrak{F}^-$ is totally bounded if and only if $\mathfrak{F}$ is totally bounded, and this is so if to every $\varepsilon > 0$ we can find a finite number of functions $f_1, \ldots, f_n \in \mathfrak{F}$ such that every $f \in \mathfrak{F}$ satisfies $\rho(f,f_j) < \varepsilon$ for some f_j. By (55) this implies $\delta_k(f,g) < 2^k\varepsilon$, or $\delta(f,f_j) < 2^k\varepsilon$ on E_k. If we fix k beforehand, we can thus make $\delta(f,f_j)$ arbitrarily small on E_k, and the same is true of $d(f,f_j)$. This proves one part of the following theorem:

Theorem 10. *The family $\mathfrak{F}$ is normal if and only if to every compact set $E \subset \Omega$ and every $\varepsilon > 0$ it is possible to find $f_1, \ldots, f_n \in \mathfrak{F}$ such that every $f \in \mathfrak{F}$ satisfies $d(f,f_j) < \varepsilon$ on E for some f_j.*

For the proof of the converse part, determine k_0 so that $2^{-k_0} < \varepsilon/2$. By assumption we can find $f_1, \ldots, f_n$ such that, for any $f \in \mathfrak{F}$, one of the inequalities $\delta(f,f_j) \leqq d(f,f_j) < \varepsilon/2k_0$ holds on C_{k_0}. It follows that $\delta_k(f,f_j) < \varepsilon/2k_0$ for $k \leqq k_0$, while trivially $\delta_k(f,f_j) < 1$ for $k > k_0$. From (55) we obtain

$$\rho(f,f_j) < k_0 \frac{\varepsilon}{2k_0} + (2^{-k_0-1} + 2^{-k_0-2} + \cdots) = \frac{\varepsilon}{2} + 2^{-k_0} < \varepsilon,$$

which is precisely what we wanted to prove.

4.3. Arzela's Theorem. We shall now study the relationship between Definition 1 and Definition 2. The connection is established by a famous and extremely useful theorem known as *Arzela's theorem* (or the Arzela-Ascoli theorem).

Theorem 11. *A family $\mathfrak{F}$ of continuous functions with values in a metric space S is normal in the region Ω of the complex plane if and only if*

(i) *$\mathfrak{F}$ is equicontinuous on every compact set $E \subset \Omega$;*

(ii) *for any $z \in \Omega$ the values $f(z)$, $f \in \mathfrak{F}$, lie in a compact subset of S.*

We give two proofs of the necessity of (i). Assume that $\mathfrak{F}$ is normal and determine $f_1, \ldots, f_n$ as in Theorem 10. Because each of these functions is uniformly continuous on E we can find a $\delta > 0$ such that $d(f_j(z),f_j(z_0)) < \varepsilon$ for $z,z_0 \in E$, $|z - z_0| < \delta$, $j = 1, \ldots, n$. For any given $f \in \mathfrak{F}$ and corresponding f_j we obtain

$$d(f(z),f(z_0)) \leqq d(f(z),f_j(z)) + d(f_j(z),f_j(z_0)) + d(f_j(z_0),f(z_0)) < 3\varepsilon$$

and (i) is proved.

Less elegantly, but without use of Theorem 10, a proof can be given as follows: If $\mathfrak{F}$ fails to be equicontinuous on E there exists an $\varepsilon > 0$, sequences of points $z_n,z'_n \in E$, and functions $f_n \in \mathfrak{F}$ such that $|z_n - z'_n| \to 0$ while $d(f_n(z_n),f_n(z'_n)) \geqq \varepsilon$ for all n. Because E is compact we can choose subsequences of $\{z_n\}$ and $\{z'_n\}$ which converge to a common limit $z'' \in E$, and because $\mathfrak{F}$ is normal there exists a subsequence of $\{f_n\}$ which converges uniformly on E. It is clear that we may choose all three subsequences to have the same subscripts n_k. The limit function f of $\{f_{n_k}\}$ is uniformly continuous on E. Hence we can find k such that the distances from $f_{n_k}(z_{n_k})$ to $f(z_{n_k})$, from $f(z_{n_k})$ to $f(z'_{n_k})$, and from $f(z'_{n_k})$ to $f_{n_k}(z'_{n_k})$ are all $< \varepsilon/3$. It follows that $d(f_{n_k}(z_{n_k}),f_{n_k}(z'_{n_k})) < \varepsilon$, contrary to the assumption that $d(f_n(z_n),f_n(z'_n)) \geqq \varepsilon$ for all n.

To prove the necessity of (ii) we show that the closure of the set formed by the values $f(z)$, $f \in \mathfrak{F}$, is compact. Let $\{w_n\}$ be a sequence in this closure. To each w_n we determine $f_n \in \mathfrak{F}$ so that $d(f_n(z),w_n) < 1/n$. By normality there exists a convergent subsequence $\{f_{n_k}(z)\}$, and the sequence $\{w_{n_k}\}$ converges to the same value.

The sufficiency of (i) together with (ii) is proved by Cantor's famous diagonal process. We observe first that there exists an everywhere dense sequence of points ζ_k in Ω, for instance the points with rational coordinates. From the sequence $\{f_n\}$ we are going to extract a subsequence which converges at all points ζ_k. To find a subsequence which converges at one given point is always possible because of condition (ii). We can therefore find an array of subscripts

$$
\begin{array}{ll}
& n_{11} < n_{12} < \cdots < n_{1j} < \cdots \\
& n_{21} < n_{22} < \cdots < n_{2j} < \cdots \\
(56) & \cdots\cdots\cdots\cdots\cdots\cdots \\
& n_{k1} < n_{k2} < \cdots < n_{kj} < \cdots \\
& \cdots\cdots\cdots\cdots\cdots\cdots
\end{array}
$$

such that each row is contained in the preceding one, and such that $\lim_{j\to\infty} f_{n_{kj}}(\zeta_k)$ exists for all k. The diagonal sequence $\{n_{jj}\}$ is strictly increasing, and it is ultimately a subsequence of each row in (56). Hence $\{f_{n_{jj}}\}$ is a subsequence of $\{f_n\}$ which converges at all points ζ_k. For convenience we replace the notation n_{jj} by n_j.

Consider now a compact set $E \subset \Omega$ and assume that $\mathfrak{F}$ is equicontinuous on E. We shall show that $\{f_{n_j}\}$ converges uniformly on E. Given $\varepsilon > 0$ we choose $\delta > 0$ such that, for $z,z' \in E$ and $f \in \mathfrak{F}$, $|z - z'| < \delta$ implies $d(f(z),f(z')) < \varepsilon/3$. Because E is compact, it can be covered by a finite number of $\delta/2$-neighborhoods. We select a point ζ_k from each of these neighborhoods. There exists an i_0 such that $i,j > i_0$ implies $d(f_{n_i}(\zeta_k),f_{n_j}(\zeta_k)) < \varepsilon/3$ for all these ζ_k. For each $z \in E$ one of the ζ_k is within distance δ from z; hence $d(f_{n_i}(z),f_{n_i}(\zeta_k)) < \varepsilon/3$, $d(f_{n_j}(z), f_{n_j}(\zeta_k)) < \varepsilon/3$. The three inequalities yield $d(f_{n_i}(z),f_{n_j}(z)) < \varepsilon$. Because all values $f(z)$ belong to a compact and consequently complete subset of S it follows that $\{f_{n_j}\}$ is uniformly convergent on E.

4.4. Families of Analytic Functions. Analytic functions have their values in **C**, the finite complex plane. In order to apply the preceding considerations to families of analytic functions it is therefore natural to choose $S = \mathbf{C}$ with the usual euclidean distance.

The compact subsets of **C** are the bounded and closed sets. For this reason condition (ii) in Arzela's theorem is fulfilled if and only if the values $f(z)$ are bounded for each $z \in \Omega$, with a bound that may depend on z. Suppose now that condition (i) is also satisfied. For a given $z_0 \in \Omega$ determine ρ so that the closed disk $|z - z_0| \leqq \rho$ is contained in Ω. Then $\mathfrak{F}$, the given family of functions, is equicontinuous on the closed disk. If in the definition of equicontinuity $\delta(< \rho)$ corresponds to ε, and if $|f(z_0)| \leqq M$ for all $f \in \mathfrak{F}$, then $|f(z)| \leqq M + \varepsilon$ in $|z - z_0| < \delta$. Because any compact set can be covered by a finite number of neighborhoods with this property, it follows that the functions are uniformly bounded on every compact set, the bound depending on the set. According to Arzela's theorem this is true for all normal families of complex-valued functions.

For analytic functions this condition is also sufficient.

Theorem 12. *A family $\mathfrak{F}$ of analytic functions is normal with respect to* **C** *if and only if the functions in $\mathfrak{F}$ are uniformly bounded on every compact set.*

To prove the sufficiency we prove equicontinuity. Let C be the boundary of a closed disk in Ω, of radius r. If z, z_0 are inside C we obtain by Cauchy's integral theorem

$$f(z) - f(z_0) = \frac{1}{2\pi i}\int_C \left(\frac{1}{\zeta - z} - \frac{1}{\zeta - z_0}\right) f(\zeta)\, d\zeta$$
$$= \frac{z - z_0}{2\pi i}\int_C \frac{f(\zeta)\, d\zeta}{(\zeta - z)(\zeta - z_0)}.$$

If $|f| \leqq M$ on C, and if we restrict z and z_0 to the smaller concentric disk of radius $r/2$, it follows that

$$|f(z) - f(z_0)| \leqq \frac{4M|z - z_0|}{r}. \tag{57}$$

This proves equicontinuity on the smaller disk.

Let E be a compact set in Ω. Each point of E is the center of a disk with radius r, as above. The open disks of radius $r/4$ form an open covering of E. We select a finite subcovering and denote the corresponding centers, radii, and bounds by ζ_k, r_k, M_k; let r be the smallest of the r_k and M the largest of the M_k. For a given $\varepsilon > 0$ let δ be the smaller of $r/4$ and $\varepsilon r^2/4M$. If $|z - z_0| < \delta$ and $|z_0 - \zeta_k| < r_k/4$ it follows that $|z - \zeta_k| < \delta + r_k/4 \leqq r_k/2$. Hence (57) is applicable and we find $|f(z) - f(z_0)| \leqq 4M_k\delta/r_k \leqq 4M\delta/r \leqq \varepsilon$ as desired.

In view of Theorem 12 we may abandon the term "normal with respect to **C**" which has no historic justification. If a family has the property of the theorem, we say instead that it is *locally bounded.* Indeed, if the family is bounded in a neighborhood of each point, then it is obviously bounded on every compact set. The theorem tells us that every sequence has a subsequence which converges uniformly on compact sets if and only if it is locally bounded.

An interesting feature is that local boundedness is inherited by the derivatives.

Theorem 13. *A locally bounded family of analytic functions has locally bounded derivatives.*

This follows at once by the Cauchy representation of the derivative. If C is the boundary of a closed disk in Ω, of radius r, then

$$f'(z) = \frac{1}{2\pi i}\int_C \frac{f(\zeta)\, d\zeta}{(\zeta - z)^2}.$$

Hence $|f'(z)| \leqq 4M/r$ in the concentric disk of radius $r/2$ (M is the bound of $|f|$ on C). We see that the f' are indeed locally bounded.

What is true of the first derivatives is of course also true of higher derivatives.

4.5. The Classical Definition. If a sequence tends to ∞ there is no great scattering of values, and it may well be argued that for the purposes of normal families such a sequence should be regarded as convergent. This is the classical point of view, and we shall restyle our definition to conform with traditional usage.

Definition 3. *A family of analytic functions in a region Ω is said to be normal if every sequence contains either a subsequence that converges uniformly on every compact set $E \subset \infty$, or a subsequence that tends uniformly to ∞ on every compact set.*

We shall show that this definition agrees with Definition 2 if we take S to be the Riemann sphere. If that is what we do, then we can also allow ∞ as a possible value, which means that we may consider families of meromorphic functions. There is no need to rephrase the definition so that it covers normal families of meromorphic functions, for Definition 2 applies without change.

It is necessary, however, to prove a lemma which extends Weierstrass's and Hurwitz's theorems to meromorphic functions (Theorems 1 and 2).

Lemma. *If a sequence of meromorphic functions converges in the sense of spherical distance, uniformly on every compact set, then the limit function is meromorphic or identically equal to ∞.*

If a sequence of analytic functions converges in the same sense, then the limit function is either analytic or identically equal to ∞.

Suppose $f(z) = \lim_{n\to\infty} f_n(z)$ in the sense of the lemma. We know that $f(z)$ is continuous in the spherical metric. If $f(z_0) \neq \infty$, then $f(z)$ is bounded in a neighborhood of z_0, and for large n the functions f_n are $\neq \infty$ in the same neighborhood. It follows by the ordinary form of Weierstrass's theorem that $f(z)$ is analytic in a neighborhood of z_0. If $f(z_0) = \infty$ we consider the reciprocal $1/f(z)$ which is the limit of $1/f_n(z)$ in the spherical sense. We conclude that $1/f(z)$ is analytic near z_0, and hence $f(z)$ is meromorphic. If the f_n are analytic and the second case occurs, then $1/f$ must be identically zero by virtue of Hurwitz's theorem, and f is identically ∞.

The lemma makes it clear that Definition 3 is nothing other than Definition 2 applied to the spherical metric.

It is *not* true that the derivatives of a normal family form a normal family. For instance, consider the family formed by the functions $f_n = n(z^2 - n)$ in the whole plane. This family is normal, for it is clear that $f_n \to \infty$ uniformly on every compact set. Nevertheless, the derivatives $f'_n = 2nz$ do not form a normal family, for $f'_n(z)$ tends to ∞ for $z \neq 0$ and to 0 for $z = 0$.

By Arzela's theorem a family of meromorphic functions is normal if and only if it is equicontinuous on compact sets, for condition (ii) is now trivially fulfilled. The equicontinuity can be replaced by a boundedness condition. We have indeed:

Theorem 14. *A family of analytic or meromorphic functions f is normal in the classical sense if and only if the expressions*

$$\rho(f) = \frac{2|f'(z)|}{1 + |f(z)|^2} \tag{58}$$

are locally bounded.

The geometric meaning of the quantity $\rho(f)$ is rather evident. Indeed, by use of the formula in Chap. 1, Sec. 2.4

$$d(f(z_1),f(z_2)) = \frac{2|f(z_1) - f(z_2)|}{[(1 + |f(z_1)|^2)(1 + |f(z_2)|^2)]^{\frac{1}{2}}}$$

it is readily seen that f followed by stereographic projection maps an arc γ on an image with length

$$\int_\gamma \rho(f(z))|dz|.$$

If $\rho(f) \leqq M$ on the line segment between z_1 and z_2 we conclude that $d(f(z_1),f(z_2)) \leqq M|z_1 - z_2|$, and this immediately proves the equicontinuity when $\rho(f)$ is locally bounded (we challenge the reader to give an analytic proof).

To prove the necessity we remark first that $\rho(f) = \rho(1/f)$ as a simple calculation shows. Assume that the family $\mathfrak{F}$ of meromorphic functions is normal, but that the $\rho(f)$ fail to be bounded on a compact set E. Consider a sequence of $f_n \in \mathfrak{F}$ such that the maximum of $\rho(f_n)$ on E tends to ∞. Let f denote the limit function of a convergent subsequence $\{f_{n_k}\}$. Around each point of E we can find a small closed disk, contained in Ω, on which either f or $1/f$ is analytic. If f is analytic it is bounded on the closed disk, and it follows by the spherical convergence that $\{f_{n_k}\}$ has no poles in the disk as soon as k is sufficiently large. We can then use Weierstrass's theorem (Theorem 1) to conclude that $\rho(f_{n_k}) \to \rho(f)$, uniformly on a slightly smaller disk. Since $\rho(f)$ is continuous it follows that $\rho(f_{n_k})$ is bounded on the smaller disk. If $1/f$ is analytic the same proof applies to $\rho(1/f_{n_k})$, which is the same as $\rho(f_{n_k})$. In conclusion, since E is compact it can be covered by a finite number of the smaller disks, and we find that the $\rho(f_{n_k})$ are bounded on E, contrary to assumption. The contradiction completes the proof of the theorem.

EXERCISES

1. Prove that in any region Ω the family of analytic functions with positive real part is normal. Under what added condition is it locally bounded? *Hint:* Consider the functions e^f.

2. Show that the functions z^n, n a nonnegative integer, form a normal family in $|z| < 1$, also in $|z| > 1$, but not in any region that contains a point on the unit circle.

3. If $f(z)$ is analytic in the whole plane, show that the family formed by all functions $f(kz)$ with constant k is normal in the annulus $r_1 < |z| < r_2$ if and only if f is a polynomial.

4. If the family $\mathfrak{F}$ of analytic (or meromorphic) functions is not normal in Ω, show that there exists a point z_0 such that $\mathfrak{F}$ is not normal in any neighborhood of z_0. *Hint:* A compactness argument.

6 CONFORMAL MAPPING. DIRICHLET'S PROBLEM

In the geometrically oriented part of the theory of analytic functions the problem of conformal mapping plays a dominating role. Existence and uniqueness theorems permit us to define important analytic functions without resorting to analytic expressions, and geometric properties of the regions that are being mapped lead to analytic properties of the mapping function.

The Riemann mapping theorem deals with the mapping of one simply connected region onto another. We shall give a proof that leans on the theory of normal families. To handle the more difficult case of multiply connected regions we shall have to solve the Dirichlet problem, which is the boundary-value problem for the Laplace equation.

1. THE RIEMANN MAPPING THEOREM

We shall prove that the unit disk can be mapped conformally onto any simply connected region in the plane, other than the plane itself. This will imply that any two such regions can be mapped conformally onto each other, for we can use the unit disk as an intermediary step. The theorem is applied to polygonal regions, and in this case an explicit form for the mapping function is derived.

1.1. Statement and Proof. Although the mapping theorem was formulated by Riemann, its first successful proof was due to

P. Koebe.† The proof we shall present is a shorter variant of the original proof.

Theorem 1. *Given any simply connected region Ω which is not the whole plane, and a point $z_0 \in \Omega$, there exists a unique analytic function $f(z)$ in Ω, normalized by the conditions $f(z_0) = 0$, $f'(z_0) > 0$, such that $f(z)$ defines a one-to-one mapping of Ω onto the disk $|w| < 1$.*

The uniqueness is easily proved, for if f_1 and f_2 are two such functions, then $f_1[f_2^{-1}(w)]$ defines a one-to-one mapping of $|w| < 1$ onto itself. We know that such a mapping is given by a linear transformation S (Chap. 4, Sec. 3.4, Ex. 5). The conditions $S(0) = 0$, $S'(0) > 0$ imply $S(w) = w$; hence $f_1 = f_2$.

An analytic function $g(z)$ in Ω is said to be *univalent* if $g(z_1) = g(z_2)$ only for $z_1 = z_2$, in other words, if the mapping by g is one to one (the German word *schlicht*, which lacks an adequate translation, is also in common use). For the existence proof we consider the family $\mathfrak{F}$ formed by all functions g with the following properties: (i) g is analytic and univalent in Ω, (ii) $|g(z)| \leqq 1$ in Ω, (iii) $g(z_0) = 0$ and $g'(z_0) > 0$. We contend that f is the function in $\mathfrak{F}$ for which the derivative $f'(z_0)$ is a maximum. The proof will consist of three parts: (1) it is shown that the family $\mathfrak{F}$ is not empty; (2) there exists an f with maximal derivative; (3) this f has the desired properties.

To prove that $\mathfrak{F}$ is not empty we note that there exists, by assumption, a point $a \neq \infty$ not in Ω. Since Ω is simply connected, it is possible to define a single-valued branch of $\sqrt{z - a}$ in Ω; denote it by $h(z)$. This function does not take the same value twice, nor does it take opposite values. The image of Ω under the mapping h covers a disk $|w - h(z_0)| < \rho$, and therefore it does not meet the disk $|w + h(z_0)| < \rho$. In other words, $|h(z) + h(z_0)| \geqq \rho$ for $z \in \Omega$, and in particular $2|h(z_0)| \geqq \rho$. It can now be verified that the function

$$g_0(z) = \frac{\rho}{4} \frac{|h'(z_0)|}{|h(z_0)|^2} \cdot \frac{h(z_0)}{h'(z_0)} \cdot \frac{h(z) - h(z_0)}{h(z) + h(z_0)}$$

belongs to the family $\mathfrak{F}$. Indeed, because it is obtained from the univalent function h by means of a linear transformation, it is itself univalent. Moreover, $g_0(z_0) = 0$ and $g_0'(z_0) = (\rho/8)|h'(z_0)|/|h(z_0)|^2 > 0$. Finally, the estimate

$$\left| \frac{h(z) - h(z_0)}{h(z) + h(z_0)} \right| = |h(z_0)| \cdot \left| \frac{1}{h(z_0)} - \frac{2}{h(z) + h(z_0)} \right| \leqq \frac{4|h(z_0)|}{\rho}$$

shows that $|g_0(z)| \leqq 1$ in Ω.

† A related theorem from which the mapping theorem can be derived had been proved earlier by W. F. Osgood, but did not attract the attention it deserves.

The derivatives $g'(z_0)$, $g \in \mathfrak{F}$, have a least upper bound B which a priori could be infinite. There is a sequence of functions $g_n \in \mathfrak{F}$ such that $g_n'(z_0) \to B$. By Chap. 5, Theorem 12 the family $\mathfrak{F}$ is normal. Hence there exists a subsequence $\{g_{n_k}\}$ which tends to an analytic limit function f, uniformly on compact sets. It is clear that $|f(z)| \leqq 1$ in Ω, $f(z_0) = 0$ and $f'(z_0) = B$ (this proves that $B < +\infty$). If we can show that f is univalent, it will follow that f is in $\mathfrak{F}$ and has a maximal derivative at z_0.

In the first place f is not a constant, for $f'(z_0) = B > 0$. Choose a point $z_1 \in \Omega$, and consider the functions $g_1(z) = g(z) - g(z_1)$, $g \in \mathfrak{F}$. They are all $\neq 0$ in the region obtained by omitting z_1 from Ω. By Hurwitz's theorem (Chap. 5, Theorem 2) every limit function is either identically zero or never zero. But $f(z) - f(z_1)$ is a limit function, and it is not identically zero. Hence $f(z) \neq f(z_1)$ for $z \neq z_1$, and since z_1 was arbitrary we have proved that f is univalent.

It remains to show that f takes every value w with $|w| < 1$. Suppose it were true that $f(z) \neq w_0$ for some w_0, $|w_0| < 1$. Then, since Ω is simply connected, it is possible to define a single-valued branch of

$$F(z) = \sqrt{\frac{f(z) - w_0}{1 - \bar{w}_0 f(z)}} \tag{1}$$

(Recall that all closed curves in a simply connected region are homologous to 0. If $\varphi(z) \neq 0$ in Ω we can define $\log \varphi(z)$ by integration of $\varphi'(z)/\varphi(z)$, and $\sqrt{\varphi(z)} = \exp\left(\frac{1}{2}\log \varphi(z)\right)$.)

It is clear that F is univalent and that $|F| \leqq 1$. To normalize it we form

$$G(z) = \frac{|F'(z_0)|}{F'(z_0)} \cdot \frac{F(z) - F(z_0)}{1 - \overline{F(z_0)}F(z)} \tag{2}$$

which vanishes and has a positive derivative at z_0. For its value we find, after brief computation,

$$G'(z_0) = \frac{|F'(z_0)|}{1 - |F(z_0)|^2} = \frac{1 + |w_0|}{2\sqrt{|w_0|}} B > B.$$

This is a contradiction, and we conclude that $f(z)$ assumes all values w, $|w| < 1$. The proof is now complete.

At first glance it may seem like pure luck that our computation yields $G'(z_0) > f'(z_0)$. This is not quite so, for the formulas (1) and (2) permit us to express $f(z)$ as a single-valued analytic function of $W = G(z)$ which maps $|W| < 1$ into itself. The inequality $|f'(z_0)| < |G'(z_0)|$ is therefore a consequence of Schwarz's lemma.

The purely topological content of Theorem 1 is important by itself. We know now that any simply connected region can be mapped topologically onto a disk (for the whole plane a very simple mapping can be constructed), and hence any two simply connected regions are topologically equivalent.

EXERCISES

1. If z_0 is real and Ω is symmetric with respect to the real axis, prove by the uniqueness that f satisfies the symmetry relation $f(\bar{z}) = \overline{f(z)}$.

2. What is the corresponding conclusion if Ω is symmetric with respect to the point z_0?

1.2. Boundary Behavior. We are assuming that $f(z)$ defines a conformal mapping of a region Ω onto another region Ω'. What happens when z approaches the boundary? There are cases where the boundary behavior can be foretold with great precision. For instance, if Ω and Ω' are Jordan regions,† then f can be extended to a topological mapping of the closure of Ω onto the closure of Ω'. Unfortunately, considerations of space do not permit us to include a proof of this important theorem (the proof would require a considerable amount of preparation).

What we can and shall prove is a very modest theorem of purely topological content. Let us first make it clear what we mean when we say that z approaches the boundary of Ω. There are two cases: we may consider a sequence $\{z_n\}$ of points in Ω, or we may consider an arc $z(t)$, $0 \leqq t < 1$, such that all $z(t)$ are in Ω. We shall say that the sequence or the arc tends to the boundary if the points z_n or $z(t)$ will ultimately stay away from any point in Ω. In other words, if $z \in \Omega$ there shall exist an $\varepsilon > 0$ and an n_0 or a t_0 such that $|z_n - z| \geqq \varepsilon$ for $n > n_0$, or such that $|z(t) - z| \geqq \varepsilon$ for all $t > t_0$.

In this situation, the disks of center z and radius ε (which may depend on z) form an open covering of Ω. It follows that any compact subset $K \subset \Omega$ is covered by a finite number of these disks. If we consider the largest of the corresponding n_0 or t_0 we find that z_n or $z(t)$ cannot belong to K for $n > n_0$ or $t > t_0$. Colloquially speaking, for any compact set $K \subset \Omega$ there exists a tail end of the sequence or of the arc which does not meet K. Conversely, this implies the original condition, for if $z \in \Omega$ is given we may choose K to be a closed disk with center z that is contained in Ω. If the radius of the disk is ρ the original statement holds for any $\varepsilon < \rho$.

After these preliminary considerations the theorem we shall prove is almost trivial:

† It is known, although not so easy to prove, that a Jordan curve (Chap. 3 Sec. 2.1) divides the plane into exactly two regions, one bounded and one unbounded. The bounded region is called a Jordan region.

Theorem 2. *Let f be a topological mapping of a region Ω onto a region Ω'. If $\{z_n\}$ or $z(t)$ tends to the boundary of Ω, then $\{f(z_n)\}$ or $f(z(t))$ tends to the boundary of Ω'.*

Indeed, let K be a compact set in Ω'. Then $f^{-1}(K)$ is a compact set in Ω, and there exists n_0 (or t_0) such that z_n (or $z(t)$) is not in $f^{-1}(K)$ for $n > n_0$ (or $t > t_0$). But then $f(z_n)$ [or $f(z(t))$] is not in K.

Although the theorem is topological, it is the application to conformal mappings that is of greatest interest to us.

1.3. Use of the Reflection Principle. Stronger statements become possible if we have more information. We are mainly interested in simply connected regions and may therefore assume that one of the regions is a disk. With the same notation as in Sec. 1.1, let $f(z)$ define a conformal mapping of the region Ω onto the unit disk with the normalization $f(z_0) = 0$ (the normalization by the derivative is irrelevant). We shall derive additional information by use of the reflection principle (Chap. 4, Theorem 26).

Let us assume that the boundary of Ω contains a segment γ of a straight line. Because rotations are unimportant we may as well suppose that γ lies on the real axis; let it be the interval $a < x < b$. The assumption involves a significant simplification only if the rest of the boundary stays away from γ. For this reason we shall strengthen the hypothesis and require that every point of γ has a neighborhood whose intersection with the whole boundary $\partial\Omega$ is the same as its intersection with γ. We say then that γ is a *free boundary arc.*

By this assumption every point on γ is the center of a disk whose intersection with $\partial\Omega$ is its real diameter. It is clear that each of the half disks determined by this diameter is entirely in or entirely outside of Ω, and at least one must be inside. If only one is inside we call the point a one-sided boundary point, and if both are inside it is a two-sided boundary point. Because γ is connected all its points will be of the same kind, and we speak of a one-sided or a two-sided boundary arc.

Theorem 3. *Suppose that the boundary of a simply connected region Ω contains a line segment γ as a one-sided free boundary arc. Then the function $f(z)$ which maps Ω onto the unit disk can be extended to a function which is analytic and one to one on $\Omega \cup \gamma$. The image of γ is an arc γ' on the unit circle.*

For two-sided arcs the same will be true with obvious modifications.

For the proof we consider a disk around $x_0 \in \gamma$ which is so small that the half disk in Ω does not contain the point z_0 with $f(z_0) = 0$. Then

$\log f(z)$ has a single-valued branch in the half disk, and its real part tends to 0 as z approaches the diameter, for we know by Theorem 2 that $|f(z)|$ tends to 1. It follows by the reflection principle that $\log f(z)$ has an analytic extension to the whole disk. Therefore $\log f(z)$, and consequently $f(z)$, is analytic at x_0. The extensions to overlapping disks must coincide and define a function which is analytic on $\Omega \cup \gamma$.

We note further that $f'(z) \neq 0$ on γ. Indeed, $f'(x_0) = 0$ would imply that $f(x_0)$ were a multiple value, and the two real radii from x_0 would be mapped on arcs that form an angle $< \pi$; this is clearly impossible. If, for instance, the upper half disks are in Ω, then

$$\partial \log |f|/\partial y = -\partial \arg f/\partial x < 0$$

on γ, and $\arg f$ moves constantly in the same direction. This proves that the mapping is one to one on γ.

The theorem can be generalized to regions with free boundary arcs on a circle.

1.4. Analytic Arcs. A real or complex function $\varphi(t)$ of a real variable t, defined on an interval $a < t < b$, is said to be *real analytic* (or analytic in the real sense) if, for every t_0 in the interval, the Taylor development $\varphi(t) = \varphi(t_0) + \varphi'(t_0)(t - t_0) + \frac{1}{2}\varphi'(t_0)(t - t_0)^2 + \cdots$ converges in some interval $(t_0 - \rho, t_0 + \rho)$, $\rho > 0$. But if this is so we know by Abel's theorem that the series is also convergent for complex values of t, as long as $|t - t_0| < \rho$, and that it represents an analytic function in that disk. In overlapping disks the functions are the same, for they coincide on a segment of the real axis. We conclude that $f(t)$ can be defined as an analytic function in a region Δ, symmetric to the real axis, which contains the segment (a,b).

In these circumstances we say that $\varphi(t)$ determines an *analytic arc*. It is *regular* if $\varphi'(t) \neq 0$, and it is a simple arc if $\varphi(t_1) = \varphi(t_2)$ only when $t_1 = t_2$.

We shall assume that the boundary of Ω contains a regular, simple, analytic arc γ, and that it is a free one-sided arc. The definition could be modeled on the previous one, but to avoid long explanations we shall assume offhand that there exists a region Δ, symmetric to the interval (a,b), with the property that $\varphi(t) \in \Omega$ when t lies in the upper half of Δ, and that $\varphi(t)$ lies outside Ω for t in the lower half.

If $f(z)$ is the mapping function with $f(z_0) = 0$, and if we take care that $\varphi(t) \neq z_0$ in Δ, then the reflection principle tells us that $\log f(\varphi(t))$, and hence $f(\varphi(t))$, has an analytic extension from the upper to the lower half of Δ. For a real $t_0 \in (a,b)$ we know further that $\varphi'(t_0) \neq 0$. Therefore φ has an analytic inverse φ^{-1} in a neighborhood of $\varphi(t_0)$, and it follows by composition that $f(z)$ is analytic in that neighborhood.

Theorem 4. *If the boundary of Ω contains a free one-sided analytic arc γ, then the mapping function has an analytic extension to $\Omega \cup \gamma$, and γ is mapped on an arc of the unit circle.*

We trust the reader to make the last statement more precise and to complete the proof.

2. CONFORMAL MAPPING OF POLYGONS

When Ω is a polygon, the mapping problem has an almost explicit solution. Indeed, we shall find that the mapping function can be expressed through a formula in which only certain parameters have values that depend on the specific shape of the polygon.

2.1. The Behavior at an Angle. We assume that Ω is a bounded simply connected region whose boundary is a closed polygonal line without self-intersections. Let the consecutive vertices be $z_1, \ldots, z_n$ in positive cyclic order (we set $z_{n+1} = z_1$). The *angle* at z_k is given by the value of $\arg (z_{k-1} - z_k)/(z_{k+1} - z_k)$ between 0 and 2π. We shall denote it by $\alpha_k\pi$, $0 < \alpha_k < 2$. It is also convenient to introduce the *outer angles* $\beta_k\pi = (1 - \alpha_k)\pi$, $-1 < \beta_k < 1$. Observe that $\beta_1 + \cdots + \beta_n = 2$. The polygon is convex if and only if all $\beta_k > 0$.

We know by Theorem 3 that the mapping function $f(z)$ can be extended by continuity to any side of the polygon (that is, to the open line segment between two consecutive vertices), and that each side is mapped in a one-to-one way onto an arc of the unit circle. We wish to show that these arcs are disjoint and leave no gap between them.

To see this we consider a circular sector S_k which is the intersection of Ω with a sufficiently small disk about z_k. A single-valued branch of $\zeta = (z - z_k)^{1/\alpha_k}$ maps S_k onto a half disk S_k'. A suitable branch of $z_k + \zeta^{\alpha_k}$ has its values in Ω, and we may consider the function $g(\zeta) = f(z_k + \zeta^{\alpha_k})$ in S_k'. It follows by Theorem 2 that $|g(\zeta)| \to 1$ as ζ approaches the diameter. The reflection principle applies, and we conclude that $g(\zeta)$ has an analytic continuation to the whole disk. In particular, this implies that $f(z)$ has a limit $w_k = e^{i\theta_k}$ as $z \to z_k$, and we find that the arcs that correspond to the sides meeting at z_k do indeed have a common end point. Since $\arg f(z)$ must increase as z traces the boundary in positive direction, the arcs do not overlap, at least not in a neighborhood of w_k. If we take into account that f maps the boundary

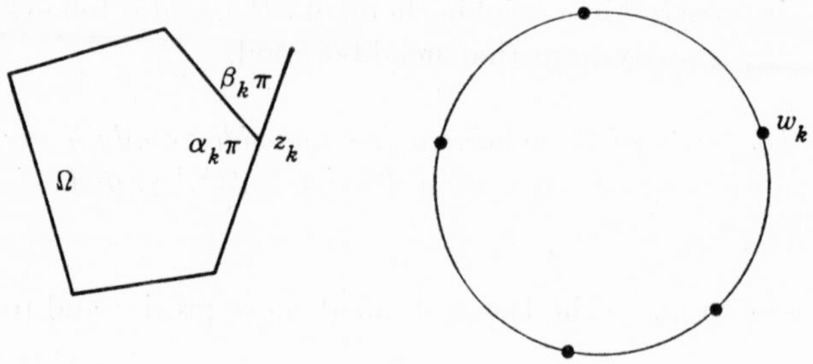

FIG. 29. Conformal mapping of a polygon.

on a curve with winding number 1 about the origin, it can easily be concluded that all the arcs are mutually disjoint. In other words, f can be extended to a homeomorphic map of Ω^- onto the closed unit disk, the vertices z_k go into points w_k, and the sides correspond to the arcs between these points (Fig. 29).

2.2. The Schwarz-Christoffel Formula. The formula we are looking for refers not to the function f, but to its inverse function, which we shall denote by F.

Theorem 5. *The functions $z = F(w)$ which map $|w| < 1$ conformally onto polygons with angles $\alpha_k\pi (k = 1, \ldots, n)$ are of the form*

$$F(w) = C \int_0^w \prod_{k=1}^n (w - w_k)^{-\beta_k}\, dw + C' \tag{3}$$

where $\beta_k = 1 - \alpha_k$, the w_k are points on the unit circle, and C, C' are complex constants.

Because the function $g(\zeta) = f(z_k + \zeta^{\alpha_k})$ considered in the last paragraph of 2.1 is analytic at the origin, it has a Taylor development

$$f(z_k + \zeta^{\alpha_k}) = w_k + \sum_{m=1}^{\infty} a_m \zeta^m.$$

Here $a_1 \neq 0$, for otherwise the image of the half disk S'_k could not be contained in the unit disk. Therefore the series can be inverted, and on setting $w = f(z_k + \zeta^{\alpha_k})$ we obtain

$$\zeta = \sum_{m=1}^{\infty} b_m (w - w_k)^m$$

with $b_1 \neq 0$, the development being valid in a neighborhood of w_k. We raise to the power α_k and find, in terms of the inverse function F,

$$F(w) - z_k = (w - w_k)^{\alpha_k} G_k(w)$$

where G_k is analytic and $\neq 0$ near w_k. It follows by differentiation that $F'(w)(w - w_k)^{\beta_k}$ is analytic and $\neq 0$ at w_k, and therefore the product

$$H(w) = F'(w) \prod_{k=1}^{n} (w - w_k)^{\beta_k} \tag{4}$$

is analytic and $\neq 0$ in the closed unit disk.

We claim that $H(w)$ is, in actual fact, a constant. For this purpose we examine its argument when $w = e^{i\theta}$ lies on the unit circle between $w_k = e^{i\theta_k}$ and $w_{k+1} = e^{i\theta_{k+1}}$. We know that $\arg F'(e^{i\theta})$ equals the angle between the tangent to the unit circle at $e^{i\theta}$ and the tangent to its image at $F(e^{i\theta})$; with an abbreviated notation we express this by $\arg F' = \arg dF - \arg dw$. But $\arg dF$ is constant because F describes a straight line, and $\arg dw = \theta + \pi/2$. The factor $w - w_k$ can be written $e^{i\theta} - e^{i\theta_k} = 2ie^{i(\theta+\theta_k)/2} \sin \frac{1}{2}(\theta - \theta_k)$, and hence its argument is $\theta/2$ plus a constant (this is also evident geometrically). When we add the arguments of all factors on the right-hand side of (4) we find that $\arg H(w)$ differs by a constant from $-\theta + \left(\sum_1^n \beta_k\right) \cdot \theta/2 = 0$. Thus we conclude that $\arg H(w)$ is constant between w_k and w_{k+1}, and since it is continuous it must be constant on the whole unit circle. The maximum principle permits us to conclude that $\arg H(w) = \operatorname{Im} \log H(w)$ is constant inside the unit circle, and so is consequently $H(w)$.

We have now proved that

$$F'(w) = C \prod_{k=1}^{n} (w - w_k)^{-\beta_k},$$

and formula (3) follows by integration.

We remark that a linear transformation of the unit circle permits us to place three of the points w_k, for instance, w_1, w_2, w_3, in prescribed positions. For $n = 3$ we see that the mapping function depends only on the angles, except for trivial variable transformations; this reflects the fact that triangles with the same angles are similar. For $n > 3$ the remaining constants $w_4, \ldots, w_n$, or their arguments θ_k, are called the *accessory parameters* of the problem. It is only in rare cases that they can be determined other than by numerical computation.

If we give arbitrary values to the θ_k it is quite easy to verify that a function of the form (3) maps the unit circle on a closed polygonal line, but usually we are unable to tell whether it will intersect itself or not. If it does not, it is not difficult to show that $F(w)$, as given by (3), yields a one-to-one mapping onto the inside of the polygonal line (the precise proof makes use of the argument principle).

Formula (3) is known as the *Schwarz-Christoffel formula.* Another version of the same formula serves to map the upper half plane onto the inside of a polygon. The mapping function, from $\operatorname{Im} w > 0$ to Ω, can now be written in the form

$$F(w) = C \int_0^w \prod_{k=1}^{n-1} (w - \xi_k)^{-\beta_k} \, dw + C' \tag{5}$$

where the ξ_k are real. The last exponent β_n does not appear explicitly in the formula, but it is determined by $\beta_n = 2 - (\beta_1 + \cdots + \beta_{n-1})$, and like the other exponents it is subject to the condition $-1 < \beta_n < 1$. It then follows that the integral (5) converges for $w = \infty$, and the point at ∞ will correspond to a vertex with angle $\alpha_n \pi$, $\alpha_n = 1 - \beta_n$. If $\beta_n = 0$ the vertex is only apparent, and the polygon reduces to one with $n - 1$ sides.

EXERCISES

1. Show that the β_k in (3) may be allowed to become $= -1$. What is the geometric interpretation?

2. If a vertex of the polygon is allowed to be at ∞, what modification does the formula undergo? If in this context $\beta_k = 1$, what is the polygon like?

3. Show that the mappings of a disk onto a parallel strip, or onto a half strip with two right angles, can be obtained as special cases of the Schwarz-Christoffel formula.

4. Derive formula (5), either directly or with the help of (3).

5. Show that

$$F(w) = \int_0^w (1 - w^n)^{-2/n} \, dw$$

maps $|w| < 1$ onto the interior of a regular polygon with n sides.

2.3. Mapping on a Rectangle. In case Ω is a rectangle we may choose $x_1 = 0$, $x_2 = 1$, $x_3 = \rho > 1$ in (5). The mapping function will thus be given by

$$F(w) = \int_0^w \frac{dw}{\sqrt{w(w-1)(w-\rho)}}$$

which is an *elliptic integral.* To be unambiguous we decide that the values of $\sqrt{w}$, $\sqrt{w-1}$, and $\sqrt{w-\rho}$ shall lie in the first quadrant. For a detailed study of the mapping, let us follow $F(w)$ as w traces the real axis. When w is real, each of the square roots is either positive or purely imaginary with a positive imaginary part (save for the point where the square root is 0). As $0 < w < 1$ there are one real and two imaginary square roots. Therefore $F(w)$ decreases from 0 to a value $-K$ where

$$K = \int_0^1 \frac{dt}{\sqrt{t(1-t)(\rho-t)}}. \tag{6}$$

For $1 < w < \rho$ there is only one imaginary square root. It follows that the integral from 1 to w is purely imaginary with a negative imaginary part. Hence $F(w)$ will follow a vertical segment from $-K$ to $-K - iK'$,

$$K' = \int_1^\rho \frac{dt}{\sqrt{t(t-1)(\rho-t)}}.$$

For $w > \rho$ the integrand is positive, and $F(w)$ will trace a horizontal segment in the positive direction. How far does it extend? Since the image is to be a rectangle, it must end at the point $-iK'$, but we prefer a direct verification. One way is to express the length of the segment by the integral

$$\int_\rho^\infty \frac{dt}{\sqrt{t(t-1)(t-\rho)}}$$

and to show by the change of integration variable $t = (\rho - u)/(1 - u)$ that the integral transforms to (6). It is easier, however, to observe that Cauchy's theorem yields

$$\int_{-\infty}^\infty \frac{dt}{\sqrt{t(t-1)(t-\rho)}} = 0,$$

for the integral over a semicircle with radius R tends to 0 as $R \to \infty$. The vanishing of the real part implies the equality of the horizontal segments, and from the vanishing of the imaginary part we deduce that $-\infty < w < 0$ is mapped on the segment from $-iK'$ to 0. The rectangle is completed.

It is often preferable to use a formula which reflects the double symmetry of the rectangle. The vertices can be made to correspond to points ± 1 and $\pm 1/k$. Since a constant factor does not matter we can choose the mapping to be given by

$$F(w) = \int_0^w \frac{dw}{\sqrt{(1-w^2)(1-k^2w^2)}}, \tag{7}$$

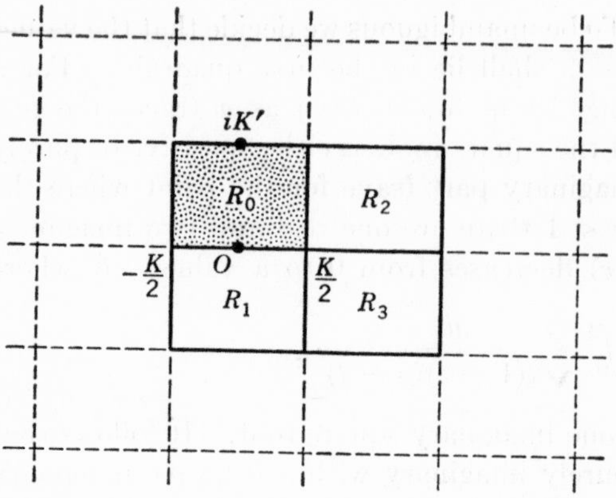

FIG. 30.

and this time we agree that $\sqrt{1 - w^2}$ and $\sqrt{1 - k^2w^2}$ shall have positive real parts. It is seen that the rectangle will have vertices at $-\frac{K}{2}, \frac{K}{2}, \frac{K}{2} + iK', -\frac{K}{2} + iK'$ where

$$K = \int_0^1 \frac{dt}{\sqrt{(1 - t^2)(1 - k^2t^2)}}$$

$$K' = \int_1^{1/k} \frac{dt}{\sqrt{(t^2 - 1)(1 - k^2t^2)}}.$$

The image of the upper half plane is the shaded rectangle R_0 in Fig. 30. We denote the inverse function of F by $w = f(z)$; it is defined in R_0 and can be extended by continuity to a one-to-one mapping of the closed rectangle onto the closed half plane (with the topology of the Riemann sphere). Observe that $z = iK'$ corresponds to ∞.

The reflection principle allows us to extend the definition of f to the adjacent rectangles R_1 and R_2, namely by setting $f(z) = \overline{f(\bar{z})}$ for $z \in R_1$ and $f(z) = \overline{f(K - \bar{z})}$ for $z \in R_2$. Similarly we can pass to R_3 either from R_1 or R_2; the extension is given by $f(z) = f(K - z)$. The process of reflection can obviously be continued until $f(z)$ is defined as a meromorphic function in the whole plane. It is perhaps even more convenient to define the extension by periodicity, for we find that the extended function must satisfy $f(z + 2K) = f(z), f(z + 2iK') = f(z)$.

We have shown that the inverse function of the elliptic integral (7) is a meromorphic function with periods $2K$ and $2iK'$. Such functions are known as *elliptic functions.* The connection between elliptic integrals and elliptic functions was discovered, but not published, by Gauss; it was rediscovered by Abel and Jacobi.

EXERCISES

1. Prove that formula (7) gives $F(\infty) = iK'$.
2. Show that $K = K'$ if and only if $k = (\sqrt{2} - 1)^2$.
3. Show that $f(z)$, $f(z + K)$, and $f(z + iK')$ are even functions.

2.4. The Triangle Functions of Schwarz. The upper half plane is mapped on a triangle with angles $\alpha_1\pi$, $\alpha_2\pi$, $\alpha_3\pi$ by

$$F(w) = \int_0^w w^{\alpha_1-1}(w-1)^{\alpha_2-1}\,dw.$$

There are no accessory parameters, as we have already noted.

The inverse function $f(z)$ can again be extended to neighboring triangles by reflection over the sides. This process is particularly interesting when it leads, as in the case of a rectangle, to a meromorphic function. In order that this be so it is necessary that repeated reflections across sides with a common end point should ultimately lead back to the original triangle in an even number of steps. In other words, the angles must be of the form π/n_1, π/n_2, π/n_3 with integral denominators. Elementary reasoning shows that the condition

$$\frac{1}{n_1} + \frac{1}{n_2} + \frac{1}{n_3} = 1$$

is fulfilled only by the triples (3,3,3), (2,4,4), and (2,3,6). They correspond to an equilateral triangle, an isosceles right triangle, and half an equilateral triangle.

In each case it is easy to verify that the reflected images of the triangle fill out the plane, without overlapping and without gaps. This shows that the mapping functions are indeed restrictions of meromorphic functions, known as the *Schwarz triangle functions.*

The reader is urged to draw a picture of the triangle net in each of the three cases. He will then observe that each triangle function has a pair of periods with nonreal ratio, and is thus an elliptic function. As an exercise, the reader should determine how many triangles there are in a parallelogram spanned by the periods.

3. A CLOSER LOOK AT HARMONIC FUNCTIONS

We have already discussed the basic properties of harmonic functions in Chap. 4, Sec. 6. At that time it was expedient to use a rather crude definition, namely one that requires all second-order derivatives to be continuous. This was sufficient to prove the mean-value property from which we could in turn derive the Poisson representation and the reflection principle. We shall now show that a more satisfactory theory is obtained if we make the mean-value property rather than the Laplace equation our starting point.

In this connection we shall also derive an important theorem on monotone sequences of harmonic functions, usually referred to as *Harnack's principle.*

3.1. Functions with the Mean-value Property. Let $u(z)$ be a real-valued continuous function in a region Ω. We say that u satisfies the mean-value property if

$$u(z_0) = \frac{1}{2\pi}\int_0^{2\pi} u(z_0 + re^{i\theta})\,d\theta \tag{8}$$

when the disk $|z - z_0| \leqq r$ is contained in Ω. We showed in Chap. 4 that the mean-value property implies the maximum principle. Actually, closer examination of the proof shows that it is sufficient to assume that (8) holds for sufficiently small r, $r < r_0$, where we may even allow r_0 to depend on z_0. We repeat the conclusion: a continuous function with this property cannot have a relative maximum (or minimum) without reducing to a constant.

We have shown earlier that every harmonic function satisfies the mean-value condition, and we shall now prove the following converse:

Theorem 6. *A continuous function $u(z)$ which satisfies condition* (8) *is necessarily harmonic.*

Again, the condition need be satisfied only for sufficiently small r. If u satisfies (8), so does the difference between u and any harmonic function. Suppose that the disk $|z - z_0| \leqq \rho$ is contained in Ω, the region where u is defined. By use of Poisson's formula (Chap. 4, Sec. 6.3) we can construct a function $v(z)$ which is harmonic for $|z - z_0| < \rho$, continuous and equal to $u(z)$ on $|z - z_0| = \rho$. The maximum and minimum principle, applied to $u - v$, implies that $u(z) = v(z)$ in the whole disk, and consequently $u(z)$ is harmonic.

The implication of Theorem 6 is that we may, if we choose, define a harmonic function to be a continuous function with the mean-value property. Such a function has automatically continuous derivatives of all orders, and it satisfies Laplace's equation.

An analogous reasoning shows that even without the condition (8) the assumptions about the derivatives can be relaxed to a considerable degree. Suppose merely that $u(z)$ is continuous and that the derivatives $\partial^2 u/\partial x^2$, $\partial^2 u/\partial y^2$ exist and satisfy $\Delta u = 0$. With the same notations as above we show that the function

$$V = u - v + \varepsilon(x - x_0)^2,$$

$\varepsilon > 0$, must obey the maximum principle. Indeed, if V had a maximum the rules of the calculus would yield $\partial^2 V/\partial x^2 \leqq 0$, $\partial^2 V/\partial y^2 \leqq 0$, and hence $\Delta V \leqq 0$ at that point. On the other hand,

$$\Delta V = \Delta u - \Delta v + 2\varepsilon = 2\varepsilon > 0.$$

The contradiction shows that the maximum principle obtains. We can thus conclude that $u - v + \varepsilon(x - x_0)^2 \leqq \varepsilon\rho^2$ in the disk $|z - z_0| \leqq \rho$. Letting ε tend to zero we find $u \leqq v$, and the opposite inequality can be proved in the same way. Hence u is harmonic.†

3.2. Harnack's Principle. We recall that Poisson's formula (Chap. 4, Sec. 6.3) permits us to express a harmonic function through its values on a circle. To fit our present needs we write it in the form

$$u(z) = \frac{1}{2\pi}\int_0^{2\pi} \frac{\rho^2 - r^2}{|\rho e^{i\theta} - z|^2}\, u(\rho e^{i\theta})\, d\theta \tag{9}$$

where $|z| = r < \rho$ and u is assumed to be harmonic in $|z| \leqq \rho$ (or harmonic for $|z| < \rho$, continuous for $|z| \leqq \rho$). Together with the second of the elementary inequalities

$$\frac{\rho - r}{\rho + r} \leqq \frac{\rho^2 - r^2}{|\rho e^{i\theta} - z|^2} \leqq \frac{\rho + r}{\rho - r} \tag{10}$$

formula (9) yields the estimate

$$|u(z)| \leqq \frac{1}{2\pi}\frac{\rho + r}{\rho - r}\int_0^{2\pi} |u(\rho e^{i\theta})|\, d\theta.$$

If it is known that $u(\rho e^{i\theta}) \geqq 0$ we can use the first inequality (10) as well, and obtain a double estimate

$$\frac{1}{2\pi}\frac{\rho - r}{\rho + r}\int_0^{2\pi} u\, d\theta \leqq u(z) \leqq \frac{1}{2\pi}\frac{\rho + r}{\rho - r}\int_0^{2\pi} u\, d\theta.$$

But the arithmetic mean of $u(\rho e^{i\theta})$ equals $u(0)$, and we end up with the following upper and lower bounds:

$$\frac{\rho - r}{\rho + r}\, u(0) \leqq u(z) \leqq \frac{\rho + r}{\rho - r}\, u(0). \tag{11}$$

† This proof is due to C. Carathéodory.

This is *Harnack's inequality;* we emphasize that it is valid only for positive harmonic functions.

The main application of (11) is to series with positive terms or, equivalently, increasing sequences of harmonic functions. It leads to a powerful and simple theorem known as *Harnack's principle:*

Theorem 7. *Consider a sequence of functions $u_n(z)$, each defined and harmonic in a certain region Ω_n. Let Ω be a region such that every point in Ω has a neighborhood contained in all but a finite number of the Ω_n, and assume moreover that in this neighborhood $u_n(z) \leqq u_{n+1}(z)$ as soon as n is sufficiently large. Then there are only two possibilities: either $u_n(z)$ tends uniformly to $+\infty$ on every compact subset of Ω, or $u_n(z)$ tends to a harmonic limit function $u(z)$ in Ω, uniformly on compact sets.*

The simplest situation occurs when the functions $u_n(z)$ are harmonic and form a nondecreasing sequence in Ω. There are, however, applications for which this case is not sufficiently general.

For the proof, suppose first that $\lim_{n\to\infty} u_n(z_0) = \infty$ for at least one point $z_0 \in \Omega$. By assumption there exist r and m such that the functions $u_n(z)$ are harmonic and form a nondecreasing sequence for $|z - z_0| < r$ and $n \geqq m$. If the left-hand inequality (11) is applied to the nonnegative functions $u_n - u_m$, it follows that $u_n(z)$ tends uniformly to ∞ in the disk $|z - z_0| \leqq r/2$. On the other hand, if $\lim_{n\to\infty} u_n(z_0) < \infty$, application of the right-hand inequality shows in the same way that $u_n(z)$ is bounded on $|z - z_0| \leqq r/2$. Therefore the sets on which $\lim u_n(z)$ is, respectively, finite or infinite are both open, and since Ω is connected, one of the sets must be empty. As soon as the limit is infinite at a single point, it is hence identically infinite. The uniformity follows by the usual compactness argument.

In the opposite case the limit function $u(z)$ is finite everywhere. With the same notations as above $u_{n+p}(z) - u_n(z) \leqq 3(u_{n+p}(z_0) - u_n(z_0))$ for $|z - z_0| \leqq r/2$ and $n + p \geqq n \geqq m$. Hence convergence at z_0 implies uniform convergence in a neighborhood of z_0, and use of the Heine-Borel property shows that the convergence is uniform on every compact set. The harmonicity of the limit function can be inferred from the fact that $u(z)$ can be represented by Poisson's formula.

EXERCISES

1. If E is a compact set in a region Ω, prove that there exists a constant M, depending only on E and Ω, such that every positive harmonic function $u(z)$ in Ω satisfies $u(z_2) \leqq Mu(z_1)$ for any two points $z_1, z_2 \in E$.

2. For a fixed region, prove that the analytic functions with positive real part form a normal family.

3. With E and Ω as in Ex. 1, show that the oscillation on E of any harmonic function in Ω is less than a fixed constant times the oscillation on Ω.

4. THE DIRICHLET PROBLEM

The most important problem in the theory of harmonic functions is that of finding a harmonic function with given boundary values; it is known as the *Dirichlet problem.* Poisson's formula solves the problem for a disk, but the case of an arbitrary region is much more difficult. Many methods of solution are known, but none as simple and as suitable for presentation in an elementary text as the method of O. Perron, which is based on the use of *subharmonic functions.*

4.1. Subharmonic Functions. Laplace's equation in one dimension would have the form $d^2u/dx^2 = 0$. The harmonic functions of one variable would thus be the linear functions $u = ax + b$. A function $v(x)$ is said to be *convex* if, in any interval, it is at most equal to the linear function $u(x)$ with the same values as $v(x)$ at the end points of the interval.

If this situation is generalized to two dimensions, we are led to the class of *subharmonic functions.* Linear functions correspond to harmonic functions, intervals correspond to regions, and the end points of an interval correspond to the boundary of the region. Accordingly, a function $v(z)$ of one complex or two real variables will be called subharmonic if in any region $v(z)$ is less than or equal to the harmonic function $u(z)$ which coincides with $v(z)$ on the boundary of the region. Since this formulation requires that we can solve the Dirichlet problem it is preferable to replace the condition by the simpler requirement that $v(z) \leqq u(z)$ on the boundary of the region implies $v(z) \leqq u(z)$ in the region.

An equivalent but in some respects simpler formulation is the following:

Definition 1. *A continuous real-valued function $v(z)$, defined in a region Ω, is said to be subharmonic in Ω if for any harmonic function $u(z)$ in a region $\Omega' \subset \Omega$ the difference $v - u$ satisfies the maximum principle in Ω'.*

The condition means that $v - u$ cannot have a maximum in Ω' without being identically constant. In particular, v itself can have no maximum in Ω. It is important to note that the definition has local character: if v is subharmonic in a neighborhood of each point $z \in \Omega$, then it is subharmonic in Ω. The proof is immediate. A function is said to be subharmonic at a point z_0 if it is subharmonic in a neighborhood of z_0. Hence a function is subharmonic in a region if and only if it is subharmonic at all points of the region.

A harmonic function is trivially subharmonic.

A sufficient condition for subharmonicity is that v has a positive Laplacian. In fact, if $v - u$ has a maximum it follows by elementary calculus that $\partial^2/\partial x^2(v - u) \leqq 0$, $\partial^2/\partial y^2(v - u) \leqq 0$ at that point; this would imply $\Delta v = \Delta(v - u) \leqq 0$. The condition is not necessary, and as a matter of fact a subharmonic function need not have partial derivatives. If the function has continuous derivatives of the first and second order, it can be shown that the condition $\Delta v \geqq 0$ is necessary and sufficient. Since we shall not need this property, its proof will be relegated to the exercise section. The condition yields a simple way to ascertain whether a given elementary function of x and y is subharmonic.

We show now that subharmonic functions can be characterized by an inequality which generalizes the mean-value property of harmonic functions:

Theorem 8. *A continuous function $v(z)$ is subharmonic in Ω if and only if it satisfies the inequality*

$$v(z_0) \leqq \frac{1}{2\pi} \int_0^{2\pi} v(z_0 + re^{i\theta})\, d\theta \tag{12}$$

for every disk $|z - z_0| \leqq r$ contained in Ω.

The sufficiency follows by the fact that (12), rather than the mean-value property, is what is actually needed in order to show that v cannot have a maximum without being constant. Since $v - u$ satisfies the same inequality, it follows that v is subharmonic.

In order to prove the necessity we form the Poisson integral $P_v(z)$ in the disk $|z - z_0| < r$ with the values of v taken on the circumference $|z - z_0| = r$. If v is subharmonic, the function $v - P_v$ can have no maximum in the disk unless it is constant. By Schwarz's theorem (Chap. 4, Theorem 25) $v - P_v$ tends to 0 as z approaches a point on the circumference. Hence $v - P_v$ has a maximum in the closed disk. If the maximum were positive it would be taken at an interior point, and the function could not be constant. This is a contradiction, and we conclude that $v \leqq P_v$. For $z = z_0$ we obtain $v(z_0) \leqq P_v(z_0)$, and this is the inequality (12).

We list now a number of elementary properties of subharmonic functions:

1. *If v is subharmonic, so is kv for any constant $k \geqq 0$.*

2. *If v_1 and v_2 are subharmonic, so is $v_1 + v_2$.*

These are immediate consequences of Theorem 8. The next property follows most easily from the original definition.

3. *If v_1 and v_2 are subharmonic in Ω, then $v = \max(v_1,v_2)$ is likewise subharmonic in Ω.*

The notation is to be understood in the sense that $v(z)$ is at each point equal to the greater of the values $v_1(z)$ and $v_2(z)$. The continuity of v is obvious. Suppose now that $v - u$ has a maximum at $z_0 \in \Omega'$ where u is defined and harmonic in Ω'. We may assume that $v(z_0) = v_1(z_0)$. Then

$$v_1(z) - u(z) \leqq v(z) - u(z) \leqq v(z_0) - u(z_0) = v_1(z_0) - u(z_0)$$

for $z \in \Omega'$. Hence $v_1 - u$ is constant, and by the same inequality $v - u$ must also be constant. It is proved that v is subharmonic.

Let Δ be a disk whose closure is contained in Ω, and denote by P_v the Poisson integral formed with the values of v on its circumference. Then the following is true:

4. *If v is subharmonic, then the function v' defined as P_v in Δ and as v outside of Δ is also subharmonic.*

The continuity of v' follows by the theorem of Schwarz. We have proved that $v \leqq P_v$ in Δ, and hence $v \leqq v'$ throughout Ω. It is clear that v' is subharmonic in the interior and exterior of Δ. Suppose now that $v' - u$ had a maximum at a point z_0 on the circumference of Δ. It follows at once that $v - u$ would also have a maximum at z_0. Hence $v - u$ would be constant, and the inequality

$$v - u \leqq v' - u \leqq v'(z_0) - u(z_0) = v(z_0) - u(z_0)$$

shows that $v' - u$ is likewise constant. We conclude that v' is subharmonic.

EXERCISES

1. Show that the functions $|x|$, $|z|^\alpha (\alpha \geqq 0)$, $\log(1 + |z|^2)$ are subharmonic.

2. If $f(z)$ is analytic, prove that $|f(z)|^\alpha (\alpha \geqq 0)$ and $\log(1 + |f(z)|^2)$ are subharmonic.

3. If v is continuous together with its partial derivatives up to the second order, prove that v is subharmonic if and only if $\Delta v \geqq 0$. *Hint:* For the sufficiency, prove first that $v + \varepsilon x^2$, $\varepsilon > 0$, is subharmonic. For the necessity, show that if $\Delta v < 0$ the mean value over a circle would be a decreasing function of the radius.

4. Prove that a subharmonic function remains subharmonic if the independent variable is subjected to a conformal mapping.

5. Formulate and prove a theorem to the effect that a uniform limit of subharmonic functions is subharmonic.

4.2. Solution of Dirichlet's Problem. The first to use subharmonic functions for the study of Dirichlet's problem was O. Perron. His method is characterized by extreme generality, and it is completely elementary.

We consider a bounded region Ω and a real-valued function $f(\zeta)$ defined on its boundary Γ (for clarity, boundary points will be denoted by ζ). To begin with, $f(\zeta)$ need not even be continuous, but for the sake of simplicity we assume that it is bounded, $|f(\zeta)| \leqq M$. With each f we associate a harmonic function $u(z)$ in Ω, defined by a simple process which will be detailed below. If f is continuous, and if Ω satisfies certain mild conditions, the corresponding function u will solve the Dirichlet problem for Ω with the boundary values f.

We define the class $\mathfrak{B}(f)$ of functions v with the following properties:

(*a*) v is subharmonic in Ω;

(*b*) $\overline{\lim}_{z \to \zeta} v(z) \leqq f(\zeta)$ for all $\zeta \in \Gamma$.

The precise meaning of (*b*) is this: given $\varepsilon > 0$ and a point $\zeta \in \Gamma$ there exists a neighborhood Δ of ζ such that $v(z) < f(\zeta) + \varepsilon$ in $\Delta \cap \Omega$. The class $\mathfrak{B}(f)$ is not empty, for it contains all constants $\leqq -M$. We prove:

Lemma 1. *The function u, defined as $u(z) =$ l.u.b. $v(z)$ for $v \in \mathfrak{B}(f)$, is harmonic in Ω.*

In the first place, each v is $\leqq M$ in Ω. This is a simple enough consequence of the maximum principle, but because of its importance we want to explain this point in some detail. For a given $\varepsilon > 0$, let E be the set of points $z \in \Omega$ for which $v(z) \geqq M + \varepsilon$. The points z in the complement $\sim E$ are of three kinds: (1) points in the exterior of Ω, (2) points on Γ, (3) points in Ω with $v(z) < M + \varepsilon$. In case (1) z has a neighborhood contained in the exterior, in case (2) there is a neighborhood Δ with $v < M + \varepsilon$ in $\Delta \cap \Omega$, by property (*b*), and in case (3) there exists, by continuity, a neighborhood in Ω with $v < M + \varepsilon$. Hence $\sim E$ is open, and E is closed. Moreover, since Ω is bounded, E is compact. If E were not void, v would have a maximum on E, and this would also be a maximum in Ω. This is impossible, for because of (*b*) v cannot be a constant $> M$. Hence E is void for every ε, and it follows that $v \leqq M$ in Ω.

Consider a disk Δ whose closure is contained in Ω, and a point $z_0 \in \Delta$.

There exists a sequence of functions $v_n \in \mathfrak{B}(f)$ such that $\lim_{n\to\infty} v_n(z_0) = u(z_0)$. Set $V_n = \max(v_1,v_2, \ldots ,v_n)$. Then the V_n form a nondecreasing sequence of functions in $\mathfrak{B}(f)$. We construct V'_n equal to V_n outside of Δ and equal to the Poisson integral of V_n in Δ. By property (4) of the preceding section the V'_n are still in $\mathfrak{B}(f)$. They form a nondecreasing sequence, and the inequality $v_n(z_0) \leqq V_n(z_0) \leqq V'_n(z_0) \leqq u(z_0)$ shows that $\lim_{n\to\infty} V'_n(z_0) = u(z_0)$. By Harnack's principle the sequence $\{V'_n\}$ converges to a harmonic limit function U in Δ which satisfies $U \leqq u$ and $U(z_0) = u(z_0)$.

Suppose now that we start the same process from another point $z_1 \in \Delta$. We select $w_n \in \mathfrak{B}(f)$ so that $\lim_{n\to\infty} w_n(z_1) = u(z_1)$, but this time, before proceeding with the construction, we replace w_n by $\bar{w}_n = \max(v_n,w_n)$. Setting $W_n = \max(\bar{w}_1, \ldots ,\bar{w}_n)$ we construct the corresponding sequence $\{W'_n\}$ with the aid of the Poisson integral and are led to a harmonic limit function U_1 which satisfies $U \leqq U_1 \leqq u$ and $U_1(z_1) = u(z_1)$. It follows that $U - U_1$ has the maximum zero at z_0. Therefore U is identically equal to U_1, and we have proved that $u(z_1) = U(z_1)$ for arbitrary $z_1 \in \Delta$. It follows that u is harmonic in any disk Δ and, consequently, in all of Ω.

We will now investigate the circumstances under which u solves the Dirichlet problem for continuous f. We note first that the Dirichlet problem does not always have a solution. For instance, if Ω is the punctured disk $0 < |z| < 1$, consider the boundary values $f(0) = 1$ and $f(\zeta) = 0$ for $|\zeta| = 1$. A harmonic function with these boundary values would be bounded and would, hence, present a removable singularity at the origin. But then the maximum principle would imply that the function vanishes identically and thus could not have the boundary value 1 at the origin. It follows that no solution can exist.

It is also easy to see that a solution, if it exists, must be identical with u. In fact, if U is a solution it is first of all clear that $U \in \mathfrak{B}(f)$, and hence $u \geqq U$. The opposite inequality $u \leqq U$ follows by the maximum principle which implies $v \leqq U$ for all $v \in \mathfrak{B}(f)$.

The existence of a solution can be asserted for a wide class of regions. Generally speaking, the solution exists if the complement of Ω is not too "thin" in the neighborhood of any boundary point. We begin by proving a lemma which, on the surface, seems to have little to do with the notion of thinness.

Lemma 2. *Suppose that there exists a harmonic function $w(z)$ in Ω whose continuous boundary values $\omega(\zeta)$ are strictly positive except at one point ζ_0 where $\omega(\zeta_0) = 0$. Then, if $f(\zeta)$ is continuous at ζ_0, the corresponding function u determined by Perron's method satisfies* $\lim_{z\to\zeta_0} u(z) = f(\zeta_0)$.

The lemma will be proved if we show that $\overline{\lim}_{z\to\zeta_0} u(z) \leqq f(\zeta_0) + \varepsilon$ and $\underline{\lim}_{z\to\zeta_0} u(z) \geqq f(\zeta_0) - \varepsilon$ for all $\varepsilon > 0$. We are still assuming that Ω is bounded and $|f(\zeta)| \leqq M$.

Determine a neighborhood Δ of ζ_0 such that $|f(\zeta) - f(\zeta_0)| < \varepsilon$ for $\zeta \in \Delta$. In $\Omega - \Delta \cap \Omega$ the function $\omega(z)$ has a positive minimum ω_0. We consider the boundary values of the harmonic function

$$W(z) = f(\zeta_0) + \varepsilon + \frac{\omega(z)}{\omega_0}(M - f(\zeta_0)).$$

For $\zeta \in \Delta$ we have $W(\zeta) \geqq f(\zeta_0) + \varepsilon > f(\zeta)$, and for ζ outside of Δ we obtain $W(\zeta) \geqq M + \varepsilon > f(\zeta)$. By the maximum principle any function $v \in \mathfrak{B}(f)$ must hence satisfy $v(z) < W(z)$. It follows that $u(z) \leqq W(z)$ and consequently $\overline{\lim}_{z\to\zeta_0} u(z) \leqq W(\zeta_0) = f(\zeta_0) + \varepsilon$, which is the first inequality we set out to prove.

For the second inequality we need only show that the function

$$V(z) = f(\zeta_0) - \varepsilon - \frac{\omega(z)}{\omega_0}(M + f(\zeta_0))$$

is in $\mathfrak{B}(f)$. For $\zeta \in \Delta$ we have $V(\zeta) \leqq f(\zeta_0) - \varepsilon < f(\zeta)$, and at all other boundary points $V(\zeta) \leqq -M - \varepsilon < f(\zeta)$. Since V is harmonic it belongs to $\mathfrak{B}(f)$ and we obtain $u(z) \geqq V(z)$, $\underline{\lim}_{z\to\zeta_0} u(z) \geqq V(\zeta_0) = f(\zeta_0) - \varepsilon$. This completes the proof.

The function $\omega(z)$ of Lemma 2 is sometimes called a *barrier* at the point ζ_0. Clearly, we can now say that the Dirichlet problem is solvable provided that there is a barrier at each boundary point. It remains to formulate geometric conditions which imply the existence of a barrier. Actually, necessary and sufficient conditions of a purely geometric character are not known, but it is relatively easy to find sufficient conditions with a wide range of applicability.

To begin with the simplest case, suppose that $\Omega \cup \Gamma$ is contained in an open half plane, except for a point ζ_0 which lies on the boundary line. If the direction of this line is α (with the half plane to the left), then $\omega(z) = \operatorname{Im} e^{-i\alpha}(z - \zeta_0)$ is a barrier at ζ_0.

More generally, suppose that ζ_0 is the end point of a line segment all of whose points, except ζ_0, lie in the exterior of Ω. If the other end point is denoted by ζ_1, we know that a single-valued branch of

$$\sqrt{\frac{z - \zeta_0}{z - \zeta_1}}$$

can be defined outside of the segment. With a proper determination of the angle α the function

$$\operatorname{Im}\left[e^{-i\alpha}\sqrt{\frac{z-\zeta_0}{z-\zeta_1}}\right]$$

is easily seen to be a barrier at ζ_0.

This is not the strongest result that can be obtained by these methods, but it is sufficient for most applications. We shall therefore be content with the following statement:

Theorem 9. *The Dirichlet problem can be solved for any region Ω such that each boundary point is the end point of a line segment whose other points are exterior to Ω.*

The hypothesis is fulfilled if Ω and its complement have a common boundary consisting of a finite number of simple closed curves with a tangent at each point. Corners and certain types of cusps are also permissible.†

5. CANONICAL MAPPINGS OF MULTIPLY CONNECTED REGIONS

Riemann's mapping theorem permits us to conclude that any two simply connected regions, with the exception of the whole plane, can be mapped conformally onto each other, or that they are *conformally equivalent.* For multiply connected regions of the same connectivity this is no longer true. Instead we must try to find a system of *canonical regions* with the property that each multiply connected region is conformally equivalent to one and only one canonical region. The choice of canonical regions is to a certain extent arbitrary, and there are several types with equally simple properties.

In order to stay on an elementary level we will limit ourselves to the study of regions of finite connectivity. We shall find that the basic step toward the construction of canonical mappings is the introduction of certain harmonic functions with a particularly simple behavior on the boundary. Of these the *harmonic measures* are related only to the region and one of its contours, while the *Green's function* is related to the region and an interior point.

† The best result that can be proved by essentially the same method is the following: *The Dirichlet problem can be solved for any region whose complement is such that no component reduces to a point.* From this proposition an independent proof of the Riemann mapping theorem can easily be derived.

5.1. Harmonic Measures. When studying the conformal mappings of a region Ω we can of course replace Ω by any region known to be conformally equivalent to Ω, that is to say, we can perform preliminary conformal mappings at will. Because of this freedom in the choice of the original region it turns out that it is never necessary to deal with the difficulties which may arise from a complicated structure of the boundary.

In the following Ω denotes a plane region of connectivity $n > 1$. The components of the complement are denoted by $E_1, E_2, \ldots, E_n$, and we take E_n to be the unbounded component. Without loss of generality we can and will assume that no E_k reduces to a point, for it is clear that a point component is a removable singularity of any mapping function, and consequently the mappings remain the same if this isolated boundary point is added to the region.

The complement of E_n is a simply connected region Ω'. By Riemann's theorem, Ω' can be mapped conformally onto the disk $|z| < 1$; under this mapping Ω is transformed into a new region, and the images of $E_1, \ldots, E_{n-1}$ are the bounded components of its complement. For the sake of convenience we agree to use the same notations as before the mapping; in particular, E_n is now the set $|z| \geqq 1$. The unit circle $|z| = 1$, traced in the positive direction, will be denoted by C_n and is called the *outer contour* of the new region Ω.

Consider now the complement of E_1 with respect to the extended plane. This is again a simply connected region, and we map it onto the *outside* of the unit circle with ∞ corresponding to itself. The image of C_n is a directed closed analytic curve which we continue to denote by C_n, just as we keep all the other notations. In addition we define the *inner contour* C_1 to be the unit circle in the new plane, traced in the negative direction.

The process can evidently be repeated until we end up with a region Ω bounded by an outer contour C_n and $n - 1$ inner contours $C_1, \ldots, C_{n-1}$ (Fig. 31). It is important to note that the index of a contour with respect to an arbitrary point in the plane can be readily computed. For instance, at the stage where C_k, $k < n$, is the unit circle, the index of C_k is -1 with respect to interior points of E_k and 0 with respect to all other points not on C_k. The subsequent mappings will not change this state of affairs. The fact is clear, and a formal proof based on the argument principle can easily be given. One shows in the same way that the outer contour C_n has the index 0 with respect to interior points of E_n and the index 1 with respect to all other points not on C_n. It follows that the cycle $C = C_1 + C_2 + \cdots + C_n$ bounds Ω in the sense of Chap. 4, Sec. 5.1, Definition 4. The distinction between outer and inner contours is coin-

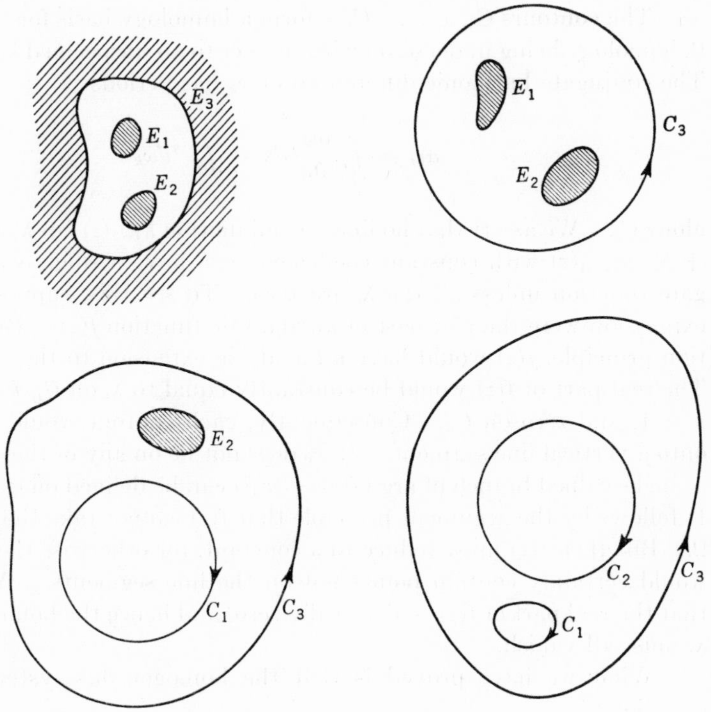

FIG. 31. Transformations of a multiply connected region.

cidental, for evidently an inversion with respect to an interior point of E_k will make C_k the outer contour.

It is clear that Theorem 9 applies to Ω. As a matter of fact the existence of a barrier is completely obvious since any contour can be transformed into a circle.

Suppose now that we solve the Dirichlet problem in Ω with the boundary values 1 on C_k and 0 on the other contours. The solution is denoted by $\omega_k(z)$, and it is called the *harmonic measure* of C_k with respect to the region Ω. We have clearly $0 < \omega_k(z) < 1$ in Ω and

$$\omega_1(z) + \omega_2(z) + \cdots + \omega_n(z) \equiv 1.$$

If we map Ω so that C_i becomes a circle, then ω_k can be continued across C_i according to the reflection principle. We conclude that ω_k is harmonic in the closed region Ω in the sense that it can be extended to a larger region.

The contours $C_1, \ldots, C_{n-1}$ form a homology basis for the cycles in Ω, homology being understood with respect to an unspecified larger region. The conjugate harmonic differential of ω_k has periods

$$\alpha_{kj} = \int_{C_j} \frac{\partial \omega_k}{\partial n}\, ds = \int_{C_j} {}^*d\omega_k$$

along C_j. We assert that no linear combination $\lambda_1\omega_1(z) + \lambda_2\omega_2(z) + \cdots + \lambda_{n-1}\omega_{n-1}(z)$ with constant coefficients can have a single-valued conjugate function unless all the λ_i are zero. To see this, suppose that this expression were the real part of an analytic function $f(z)$. By the reflection principle, $f(z)$ would have an analytic extension to the closure of Ω. The real part of $f(z)$ would be constantly equal to λ_i on C_i, $i = 1, \ldots, n-1$, and zero on C_n. Consequently, each contour would be mapped onto a vertical line segment. If w_0 does not lie on any of these segments, a single-valued branch of $\arg(f(z) - w_0)$ can be defined on each contour. It follows by the argument principle that $f(z)$ cannot take the value w_0 in Ω. But then $f(z)$ must reduce to a constant, for otherwise the image of Ω would certainly contain points not on the line segments. We conclude that the real part of $f(z)$ is identically zero, and hence the boundary values λ_i must all vanish.

What we have proved is that the homogeneous system of linear equations

$$(13)\quad \lambda_1\alpha_{1j} + \lambda_2\alpha_{2j} + \cdots + \lambda_{n-1}\alpha_{n-1,j} = 0 \quad (j = 1, \ldots, n-1)$$

has only the trivial solution $\lambda_i = 0$, for these are the conditions under which $\lambda_1\omega_1 + \cdots + \lambda_{n-1}\omega_{n-1}$ has a single-valued conjugate. By the theory of linear equations any inhomogeneous system of equations with the same coefficients as (13) must have a solution. In particular, we conclude that it is possible to solve the system

$$(14)\quad \begin{aligned} \lambda_1\alpha_{11} + \lambda_2\alpha_{21} + \cdots + \lambda_{n-1}\alpha_{n-1,1} &= 2\pi \\ \lambda_1\alpha_{12} + \lambda_2\alpha_{22} + \cdots + \lambda_{n-1}\alpha_{n-1,2} &= 0 \\ \cdots\cdots\cdots\cdots\cdots\cdots\cdots\cdots \\ \lambda_1\alpha_{1,n-1} + \lambda_2\alpha_{2,n-1} + \cdots + \lambda_{n-1}\alpha_{n-1,n-1} &= 0 \\ \lambda_1\alpha_{1n} + \lambda_2\alpha_{2n} + \cdots + \lambda_{n-1}\alpha_{n-1,n} &= -2\pi \end{aligned}$$

where the last equation is a consequence of the $n-1$ first (because $\alpha_{k1} + \alpha_{k2} + \cdots + \alpha_{kn} = 0$). In other words, we can find a multiple-valued integral $f(z)$ with periods $\pm 2\pi i$ along C_1 and C_n and all other periods equal to zero, the real part being constantly equal to λ_k on C_k (we set $\lambda_n = 0$). The function $F(z) = e^{f(z)}$ is then single-valued. We prove:

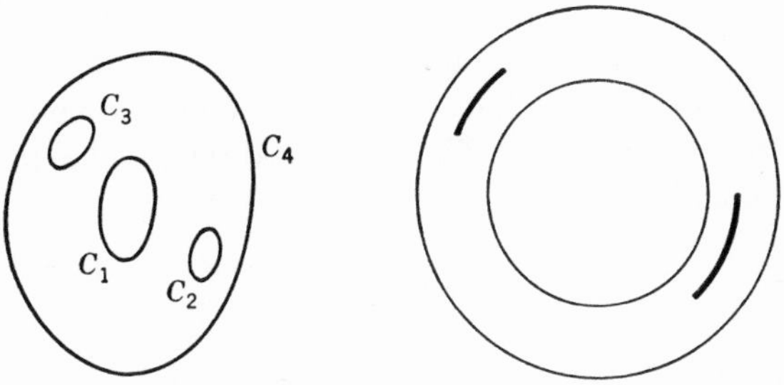

FIG. 32. Concentric slit region.

Theorem 10. *The function $F(z)$ effects a one-to-one conformal mapping of Ω onto the annulus $1 < |w| < e^{\lambda_1}$ minus $n - 2$ concentric arcs situated on the circles $|w| = e^{\lambda_i}$, $i = 2, \ldots, n - 1$.*

The mapping is illustrated in Fig. 32. The contours C_1 and C_n are in one-to-one correspondence with the full circles, while the other contours are flattened into circular slits. It should be imagined that each slit has two edges which together with the end points form a closed contour.

The proof is by use of the argument principle. We know that $F(z)$ is analytic with a constant modulus on each contour. The number of roots of the equation $F(z) = w_0$ is given by

$$(15)\quad \frac{1}{2\pi i}\int_{C_1}\frac{F'(z)\,dz}{F(z) - w_0} + \frac{1}{2\pi i}\int_{C_2}\frac{F'(z)\,dz}{F(z) - w_0} + \cdots + \frac{1}{2\pi i}\int_{C_n}\frac{F'(z)\,dz}{F(z) - w_0},$$

at any rate if w_0 is not taken on the boundary. For $w_0 = 0$ the terms in (15) are known, being equal to $1, 0, \ldots, 0, -1$, respectively. The integral over C_1 remains constantly equal to 1 for $|w_0| < e^{\lambda_1}$, and it vanishes for $|w_0| > e^{\lambda_1}$; similarly, the last integral is -1 for $|w_0| < 1$ and 0 for $|w_0| > 1$. The integrals over C_k, $1 < k < n$, vanish for all w_0 with $|w_0| \neq e^{\lambda_k}$. Suppose now that the value w_0 is actually taken by $F(z)$; inasmuch as Ω must be mapped onto an open set, we can choose $|w_0| \neq$ all e^{λ_i}. For this w_0 the expression (15) must be positive. But that is possible only if $1 < |w_0| < e^{\lambda_1}$. Thus $\lambda_1 > 0$ and, by continuity, $0 \leqq \lambda_i \leqq \lambda_1$.

From here on the proof could be completed by means of a purely topological argument. It is more instructive, however, and in fact simpler, to draw the conclusion from the argument principle. When there are simple poles on the boundary, the residue theorem continues to hold provided that the contour integral is replaced by its Cauchy principal value, and provided that the sum of the residues includes one-half of the residues on the boundary.† In the present situation the second convention means that a value taken on the boundary is counted with half its multiplicity. The computation of the principal values causes no difficulty. If $|w_0| = e^{\lambda_k}$, we find that

$$\text{pr.v.} \int_{C_k} \frac{F'(z)\,dz}{F(z) - w_0} = \frac{1}{2} \int_{C_k} \frac{F'(z)\,dz}{F(z)},$$

for by elementary geometry (or direct computation)

$$d \arg\,(F(z) - w_0) = \tfrac{1}{2}\, d \arg F(z).$$

Consequently, the principal values in (15) are $\frac{1}{2}$ for $k = 1$, 0 for $2 \leq k \leq n - 1$, $-\frac{1}{2}$ for $k = n$.

We conclude now that each value on the circle $|w_0| = 1$ or $|w_0| = e^{\lambda_1}$ is taken one-half time, that is to say once on the boundary; this proves that C_1 and C_n are mapped in a one-to-one manner and that $0 < \lambda_i < \lambda_1$, $i \neq 1, n$. Next, if $1 < |w_0| < e^{\lambda_1}$, it follows that w_0 is taken either once in the interior, twice on the boundary, or once on the boundary with the multiplicity 2. On each contour $C_2, \ldots, C_{n-1}$ a single-valued branch of $\arg F(z)$ can be defined, and the values of multiplicity 2 correspond to relative maxima and minima of $\arg F(z)$. There is at least one maximum and one minimum, and there cannot be more or else $F(z)$ would pass more than twice through the same values. Furthermore, the difference between the maximum and the minimum must be $<2\pi$, which shows that each contour is mapped onto a proper arc. Finally, the arcs which correspond to different contours must be disjoint.

We have proved the complete Theorem 10, and in addition we have been able to describe the correspondence of the boundaries. The significance of the theorem is that we can map Ω onto a canonical region bounded by two circles and $n - 2$ concentric circular slits; by way of normalization the radius of the inner circle is chosen equal to 1. For a given choice of C_1 and C_n the canonical mapping is uniquely determined up to a rotation. This follows from the fact that the system (15) has only one solution.

The shape of a canonical region of connectivity n depends on $3n - 6$ real constants. In fact, the position and size of each slit is determined

† In Chap. 4, Sec. 5.3, the Cauchy principal value was introduced in the case of an integral over a straight line. In the case of an arbitrary analytic arc it is simplest to define the principal value by means of an auxiliary conformal mapping which transforms a subarc into a line segment. The stated generalization of the residue theorem follows quite easily and proves that the principal value is independent of the auxiliary conformal mapping.

by three numbers, a total of $3n - 6$; the thickness of the annulus gives one additional parameter, but another parameter must be discounted to allow for the arbitrary rotation.

EXERCISES

1. Prove directly that two circular annuli are conformally equivalent if and only if the ratios of their radii are equal.

2. Prove that $\alpha_{ij} = \alpha_{ji}$. *Hint:* Apply Theorem 21, Chap. 4.

5.2. Green's Function. We suppose again that Ω is a region of finite connectivity, and inasmuch as preliminary conformal mappings will be permissible we can assume that Ω is bounded by analytic contours $C_1, \ldots, C_n$; this time the case $n = 1$ will be included.

We consider a point $z_0 \in \Omega$ and solve the Dirichlet problem in Ω with the boundary values $\log |\zeta - z_0|$. The solution is denoted by $G(z)$, but the main interest is attached to the function $g(z) = G(z) - \log |z - z_0|$, known as the *Green's function* of Ω with pole at z_0. When the dependence on z_0 is emphasized, it is denoted by $g(z,z_0)$.

The Green's function is harmonic in Ω except at z_0, and it vanishes on the boundary. In a neighborhood of z_0 it differs from $-\log |z - z_0|$ by a harmonic function. By these properties $g(z)$ is uniquely determined. In fact, if $g_1(z)$ has the same properties, then $g - g_1$ is harmonic throughout Ω and vanishes on the boundary. By the maximum principle it follows that g_1 is identically equal to g.

If two regions are conformally equivalent, then the Green's functions with corresponding poles are equal at points which correspond to each other. To be more explicit, let $z = z(\zeta)$ define a one-to-one conformal mapping of a region Ω' in the ζ-plane onto a region Ω in the z-plane. Choose a point $\zeta_0 \in \Omega'$ and denote by $g(z,z_0)$ the Green's function of Ω with pole at $z_0 = z(\zeta_0)$. It is claimed that $g(z(\zeta),z_0)$ is the Green's function of Ω'. To begin with, if ζ tends to a boundary point, then $z(\zeta)$ approaches the boundary of Ω, and hence $g(z(\zeta),z_0)$ has the boundary values zero. As to the behavior at ζ_0 we know that $g(z(\zeta),z_0)$ differs from $-\log |z(\zeta) - z(\zeta_0)|$ by a harmonic function of $z(\zeta)$, and hence by a harmonic function of ζ. But the difference $\log |z(\zeta) - z(\zeta_0)| - \log |\zeta - \zeta_0|$ is also harmonic, and it follows that $g(z(\zeta),z_0)$ has the desired behavior at ζ_0. We have proved that the Green's function is *invariant* under conformal mappings, and it is in view of this invariance that preliminary conformal mappings can be performed at will.

In the case of a simply connected region there is a simple connection between Green's function and the Riemann mapping function. For the unit disk $|w| < 1$ the Green's function with respect to the origin is evidently $-\log |w|$. Therefore, if $w = f(z)$ maps Ω onto the unit disk with z_0 going into the origin, we find by the invariance that

$$g(z,z_0) = -\log |f(z)|.$$

Conversely, if $g(z,z_0)$ is known, the mapping function can be determined.

The Green's function has an important symmetry property. Given two points $z_1, z_2 \in \Omega$, we write for short $g(z,z_1) = g_1$, $g(z,z_2) = g_2$. By Theorem 21, Chap. 4, the differential $g_1 \, {}^*dg_2 - g_2 \, {}^*dg_1$ is locally exact in the region obtained by omitting the points z_1 and z_2 from Ω. If c_1 and c_2 are small circles about z_1 and z_2, described in the positive sense, the cycle $C - c_1 - c_2$ is homologous to zero (as before, $C = C_1 + \cdots + C_n$). Since g_1 and g_2 vanish on C, we conclude that

$$\int_{c_1+c_2} g_1 \, {}^*dg_2 - g_2 \, {}^*dg_1 = 0.$$

Introducing $G_1 = g_1 + \log |z - z_1|$ we have ${}^*dg_1 = {}^*dG_1 - d \arg (z - z_1)$ and find

$$\int_{c_1} g_1 \, {}^*dg_2 - g_2 \, {}^*dg_1 = \int_{c_1} G_1 \, {}^*dg_2 - g_2 \, {}^*dG_1 - \int_{c_1} \log |z - z_1| \, {}^*dg_2 + \int_{c_1} g_2 d \arg (z - z_1).$$

On the right-hand side the first integral vanishes because G_1 and g_2 are harmonic inside c_1, and the second integral vanishes because $|z - z_1|$ is constant on c_1 and ${}^*dg_2$ is an exact differential in a neighborhood of z_1. The last integral equals $2\pi g_2(z_1)$ by the mean-value property of harmonic functions. In a symmetric way the integral over c_2 must equal $-2\pi g_1(z_2)$, and it is proved that $g_2(z_1) - g_1(z_2) = 0$ or

$$g(z_1,z_2) = g(z_2,z_1).$$

Because of this symmetry property the Green's function $g(z,z_0)$ is harmonic also in the second variable.

The conjugate function of $g(z,z_0)$, denoted by $h(z,z_0)$, is of course multiple-valued. It has above all the period 2π along a small circle c about z_0. In addition, it has the periods

$$P_k(z_0) = \int_{C_k} dh \, (z,z_0) = \int_{C_k} {}^*dg \, (z,z_0) \qquad (k = 1, \ldots, n).$$

Lemma 3. *The period $P_k(z_0)$ equals the harmonic measure $\omega_k(z_0)$ multiplied by 2π.*

The proof is another application of Theorem 21, Chap. 4. We express the fact that the integral of $\omega_k \, {}^*dg - g \, {}^*d\omega_k$ over $C - c$ must vanish. The integral over C reduces to $P_k(z_0)$, and by the same computation as above the integral over c equals $2\pi\omega_k(c_0)$. Hence $P_k(z_0) = 2\pi\omega_k(z_0)$.

5.3. Parallel Slit Regions. A little more explicitly than before, let us write

$$g(z,z_0) = G(z,z_0) - \log|z - z_0| \tag{16}$$

with $z_0 = x_0 + iy_0 \in \Omega$. We know that $G(z,z_0)$ is symmetric, and harmonic in each variable; as a function of z it has the boundary values $\log|\zeta - z_0|$.

Consider the difference quotient $Q(z,h) = (G(z,z_0 + h) - G(z,z_0))/h$ where we choose h real and so small that $z_0 + h$ is still in Ω. This is a harmonic function of z with boundary values $(\log|\zeta - z_0 - h| - \log|\zeta - z_0|)/h$. As $h \to 0$ these boundary values tend uniformly to $\partial/\partial x_0 \log|\zeta - z_0| = \text{Re}\, 1/(\zeta - z_0)$. It follows by the maximum-minimum principle that $Q(z,h)$ tends to its limit $(\partial/\partial x_0)G(z,z_0)$ uniformly, not only on compact sets, but on all of Ω. If we include the boundary values, we have thus uniform convergence on the closure Ω^-, which is a compact set. The conclusion is that $(\partial/\partial x_0)G(z,z_0)$ is harmonic in Ω, as a function of z, and that it has the boundary values $\text{Re}\, 1/(\zeta - z_0)$. If we compare with (16) it follows that $u_1(z) = (\partial/\partial x_0)g(z,z_0)$ is harmonic for $z \neq z_0$, continuously zero on the boundary, and differs from $\text{Re}\, 1/(z - z_0)$ by a harmonic function.

The conjugate differential of $u_1(z)$ has certain periods A_k along the contours C_k. But it is easy to construct a linear combination of $u_1(z)$ and the harmonic measures $\omega_j(z)$ whose conjugate differential is free from periods. Indeed, $u_1 + \lambda_1\omega_1 + \cdots + \lambda_{n-1}\omega_{n-1}$ has this property provided that

$$\lambda_1\alpha_{1k} + \lambda_2\alpha_{2k} + \cdots \lambda_{n-1}\alpha_{n-1,k} = -A_k \qquad (k = 1, \ldots, n-1).$$

We know already that this inhomogeneous system of equations always has a solution. We have thus established the existence of a function $p(z)$ which is single-valued and analytic in Ω, except for a simple pole with the residue 1 at z_0, and whose real part is constant on each contour. By these requirements $p(z)$ is uniquely determined up to an additive constant.

By differentiation with respect to y_0 we conclude quite similarly that $v_2(z) = -(\partial/\partial y_0)g(z,z_0)$ vanishes on the boundary and has the same singularity as $\text{Im}\, 1/(z - z_0)$. If a suitable linear combination of harmonic measures is added, the conjugate function becomes single-valued.

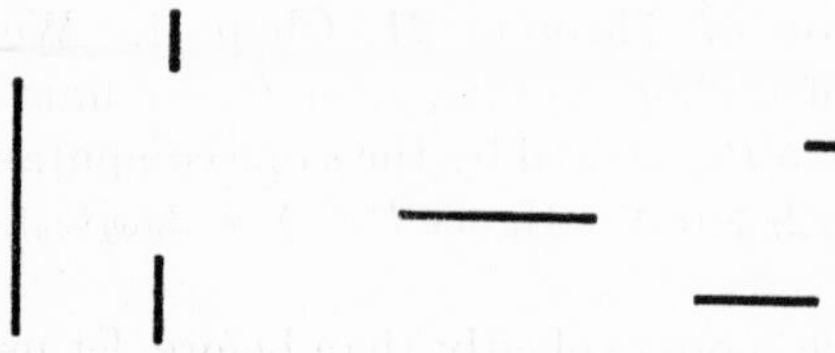

(a) (b) **FIG. 33.** Parallel slit regions.

Hence there exists a single-valued analytic function $q(z)$ with the singular part $1/(z - z_0)$ whose imaginary part is constant on each contour.

The functions $p(z)$ and $q(z)$ lead to simple canonical mappings.

Theorem 11. *The mappings determined by $p(z)$ and $q(z)$ are one to one, and the image of Ω is a slit region whose complement consists of n vertical or horizontal segments, respectively* (Fig. 33a, b).

The proof is quite similar to that of Theorem 10. This time the expression

$$\sum_{k=1}^{n} \frac{1}{2\pi i} \int_{C_k} \frac{p'(z)\,dz}{p(z) - w_0} \tag{17}$$

represents the number of zeros of $p(z) - w_0$ minus the number of poles. But it is easy to see that (17) vanishes for all w_0, including boundary values. In the latter case the principal value must be formed, but if w_0 is taken on C_k the imaginary part of $p'\,dz/(p - w_0)$ vanishes along C_k and there is no difficulty whatsoever. Since there is exactly one pole we conclude that $p(z)$ takes every value once in the interior of Ω, twice on the boundary, or once on the boundary with the multiplicity 2. The rest of the proof is an exact duplication of the earlier reasoning. The proof remains valid for $q(z)$ without change.

Parallel slit regions may be thought of as canonical regions, but they are not all conformally inequivalent, even if it is required that the point at ∞ should correspond to itself. For instance, the mappings by $p(z)$ and $iq(z)$ lead to vertical slit regions which are different, but conformally equivalent. It is only for mappings with the same residue at z_0 that the slit mappings are uniquely determined, except for a parallel translation.

EXERCISES

1. Prove that $g(z,z_0)$ is simultaneously continuous in both variables, for $z \neq z_0$. *Hint:* Apply the maximum-minimum principle to $G(z,z_0)$.

2. Show that the function $e^{-i\alpha}(q \cos \alpha + ip \sin \alpha)$ maps Ω onto a region bounded by inclined slits.

***3.** Using Ex. 2, show that $p + q$ maps Ω in a one-to-one manner onto a region bounded by convex contours. *Comments:*

(i) A closed curve is said to be convex if it intersects every straight line at most twice.

(ii) To prove that the image of C_k under $p + q$ is convex we need only show that for every α the function Re $(p + q)e^{i\alpha}$ takes no value more than twice on C_k. But Re $(p + q)e^{i\alpha}$ differs from Re $(q \cos \alpha + ip \sin \alpha)$ only by a constant, and the desired conclusion follows by the properties of the mapping function in Ex. 2.

(iii) Finally, the argument principle can be used to show that the images of the contours C_k have winding number 0 with respect to all values of $p + q$. This implies, in particular, that the convex curves lie outside of each other.

7 ELLIPTIC FUNCTIONS

1. SIMPLY PERIODIC FUNCTIONS

A function $f(z)$ is said to be *periodic* with period $\omega \neq 0$ if

$$f(z + \omega) = f(z)$$

for all z. For instance, e^z has the period $2\pi i$, and $\sin z$ and $\cos z$ have the period 2π. To be more precise, we are interested only in analytic or meromorphic functions $f(z)$, and they shall be considered in a region Ω which is mapped onto itself by the translation $z \to z + \omega$.

If ω is a period, so are all integral multiples $n\omega$. There may be other periods as well, but for the present we focus our attention exclusively on the periods $n\omega$. From this point of view we shall call $f(z)$ a *simply periodic function* with period ω. In particular, it is irrelevant whether ω is itself a multiple of another period.

1.1. Representation by Exponentials. The simplest function with period ω is the exponential $e^{2\pi iz/\omega}$. It is a fundamental fact that any function with period ω can be expressed in terms of this particular function.

Let Ω be a region with the property that $z \in \Omega$ implies $z + \omega \in \Omega$ and $z - \omega \in \Omega$. We define Ω' in the ζ-plane to be the image of Ω under the mapping $\zeta = e^{2\pi iz/\omega}$; it is obviously a region. For instance, if Ω is the whole plane, then Ω' is the plane punctured at 0. If Ω is a parallel strip, defined by $a < \operatorname{Im}(2\pi z/\omega) < b$, then Ω' is the annulus $e^{-b} < |\zeta| < e^{-a}$.

Suppose that $f(z)$ is meromorphic in Ω and has the period ω. Then there exists a unique function F in Ω' such that

$$f(z) = F(e^{2\pi iz/\omega}). \tag{1}$$

Indeed, to determine $F(\zeta)$ we write $\zeta = e^{2\pi iz/\omega}$; z is unique up to an additive multiple of ω, and this multiple does not influence the value $f(z)$. It is evident that F is meromorphic. Conversely, if F is meromorphic in Ω', then (1) defines a meromorphic function f with period ω.

1.2. The Fourier Development. Assume that Ω' contains an annulus $r_1 < |\zeta| < r_2$ in which F has no poles. In this annulus F has a Laurent development

$$F(\zeta) = \sum_{n=-\infty}^{\infty} c_n\zeta^n,$$

and we obtain

$$f(z) = \sum_{-\infty}^{\infty} c_n e^{2\pi inz/\omega}.$$

This is the complex Fourier development of $f(z)$, valid in the parallel strip that corresponds to the given annulus.

The coefficients (cf. Chap. 5, Sec. 1.3) are given by

$$c_n = \frac{1}{2\pi i}\int_{|\zeta|=r} F(\zeta)\zeta^{-n-1}\,d\zeta, \qquad (r_1 < r < r_2),$$

and by change of variable this becomes

$$c_n = \frac{1}{\omega}\int_a^{a+\omega} f(z)e^{-2\pi inz/\omega}\,dz.$$

Here a is an arbitrary point in the parallel strip, and the integration is along any path from a to $a + \omega$ which remains within the strip. If $f(z)$ is analytic in the whole plane, the same Fourier development is valid everywhere.

1.3. Functions of Finite Order. When Ω is the whole plane $F(\zeta)$ has isolated singularities at $\zeta = 0$ and $\zeta = \infty$. If both these singularities are inessential, that is, either removable singularities or poles, then F is a rational function. We say in this case that f has finite order, equal to the order of F.

We recall that a rational function assumes every complex value, including ∞, the same number of times, provided that we observe the usual multiplicity convention. We obtain a similar result for simply periodic functions of finite order if we agree not to distinguish between z

and $z + \omega$. For convenient terminology, let us say that $z + n\omega$ is equivalent to z. If f is of order m we find that every complex value $c \neq F(0)$ and $F(\infty)$ is assumed at m inequivalent points, with due count of multiplicities. We observe further that $f(z) \to F(0)$ when $\text{Im}\,(z/\omega) \to +\infty$ and $f(z) \to F(\infty)$ when $\text{Im}\,(z/\omega) \to \infty$. If we are willing to agree that these values are also "assumed" (with proper multiplicity), we can maintain that all complex values are assumed exactly m times.

For another interpretation we may consider the period strip, defined by $0 \leqq \text{Im}\,(z/\omega) < 2\pi$. Since this strip contains only one representative from each equivalence class we find that $f(z)$ assumes each complex value m times in the period strip, except that the values $F(0)$ and $F(\infty)$ require a special convention.

2. DOUBLY PERIODIC FUNCTIONS

The terms *elliptic function* and *doubly periodic function* are interchangeable; we have already met examples of such functions in connection with the conformal mapping of rectangles and certain triangles (Chap. 6, Sec. 2). Elliptic functions have been the object of very extensive study, partly because of their function theoretic properties and partly because of their importance in algebra and number theory. Our introduction to the topic covers only the most elementary aspects.

2.1. The Period Module. Let $f(z)$ be meromorphic in the whole plane. We shall examine the set M of all its periods. If ω is a period, so are all integral multiples $n\omega$, and if ω_1 and ω_2 belong to M, so does $\omega_1 + \omega_2$; as a consequence, all linear combinations $n_1\omega_1 + n_2\omega_2$ are in M. In algebra, a set with these properties is called a module (more precisely: a module over the integers), and we shall call M the *period module* of f.

Apart from the trivial case of a constant function, M has also a topological property: all its points are isolated. In fact, since $f(\omega) = f(0)$ for all $\omega \in M$ the existence of a finite accumulation point would immediately imply that f is constant. A module with isolated points is said to be *discrete.*

Our first step is to determine all discrete modules.

Theorem 1. *A discrete module consists either of zero alone, of the integral multiples $n\omega$ of a single complex number $\omega \neq 0$, or of all linear combinations $n_1\omega + n_2\omega_2$ with integral coefficients of two numbers ω_1, ω_2 with nonreal ratio ω_2/ω_1.*

As soon as M contains a number $\omega \neq 0$ it also contains one, call it ω_1, whose absolute value is a minimum. Indeed, if r is large enough the disk $|z| \leqq r$ contains a point from M, other than 0. Because the points are isolated there are only a finite number of such points, and we choose ω_1 to be one closest to the origin (the reader may show that there are always 2, 4, or 6 closest points). The multiples $n\omega_1$ are also in M, and these may be all.

Suppose now that there exists an $\omega \in M$ which is not an integral multiple of ω_1. Among all such there is one, ω_2, whose absolute value is smallest. We claim that ω_2/ω_1 is not real. If it were, there would exist an integer n such that $n < \omega_2/\omega_1 < n + 1$. This would give $0 < |n\omega_1 - \omega_2| < |\omega_1|$, an obvious contradiction.

It can now be concluded that all numbers in M are of the form $n_1\omega_1 + n_2\omega_2$. First of all, because ω_2/ω_1 is nonreal any complex number ω can be written in the form $\lambda_1\omega_1 + \lambda_2\omega_2$ with real λ_1 and λ_2. To see this we need only solve the equations

$$\omega = \lambda_1\omega_1 + \lambda_2\omega_2$$
$$\bar{\omega} = \lambda_1\bar{\omega}_1 + \lambda_2\bar{\omega}_2.$$

Since the determinant $\omega_1\bar{\omega}_2 - \omega_2\bar{\omega}_1$ is $\neq 0$ the system has a unique solution (λ_1,λ_2); but $(\bar{\lambda}_1,\bar{\lambda}_2)$ is also a solution, and we conclude that λ_1 and λ_2 are real. To continue the proof, there exist integers m_1, m_2 such that $|\lambda_1 - m_1| \leqq \frac{1}{2}$, $|\lambda_2 - m_2| \leqq \frac{1}{2}$. If ω belongs to M, so does

$$\omega' = \omega - m_1\omega_1 - m_2\omega_2.$$

We have $|\omega'| < \frac{1}{2}|\omega_1| + \frac{1}{2}|\omega_2| \leqq |\omega_2|$ where the first inequality is strict because ω_2 is not a real multiple of ω_1. By the way ω_2 was chosen it follows that ω' must an integral multiple of ω_1, and hence ω has the asserted form.

2.2. Unimodular Transformations. We assume henceforth that it is the third alternative in Theorem 1 that occurs. The pair (ω_1,ω_2) has the property that any $\omega \in M$ has a unique representation of the form $\omega = n_1\omega_1 + n_2\omega_2$. Any pair with this property will be called a *basis* of M (even if it is not determined by the construction in the proof of Theorem 1).

We investigate the relation between two bases (ω_1,ω_2) and (ω_1',ω_2'). Because (ω_1,ω_2) is a basis there exist integers a, b, c, d such that

$$\begin{aligned} \omega_2' &= a\omega_2 + b\omega_1 \\ \omega_1' &= c\omega_2 + d\omega_1. \end{aligned} \tag{2}$$

We prefer to write these equations in matrix form

$$\begin{pmatrix} \omega_2' \\ \omega_1' \end{pmatrix} = \begin{pmatrix} a & b \\ c & d \end{pmatrix} \begin{pmatrix} \omega_2 \\ \omega_1 \end{pmatrix}.$$

The same relation is valid for the complex conjugates, and we have thus

$$(3) \qquad \begin{pmatrix} \omega_2' & \bar{\omega}_2' \\ \omega_1' & \bar{\omega}_1' \end{pmatrix} = \begin{pmatrix} a & b \\ c & d \end{pmatrix} \begin{pmatrix} \omega_2 & \bar{\omega}_2 \\ \omega_1 & \bar{\omega}_1 \end{pmatrix}.$$

Since (ω_1',ω_2') is also a basis we have similarly

$$(4) \qquad \begin{pmatrix} \omega_2 & \bar{\omega}_2 \\ \omega_1 & \bar{\omega}_1 \end{pmatrix} = \begin{pmatrix} a' & b' \\ c' & d' \end{pmatrix} \begin{pmatrix} \omega_2' & \bar{\omega}_2' \\ \omega_2' & \bar{\omega}_1' \end{pmatrix}$$

with integral a', b', c', d'.

From (3) and (4) we obtain

$$(5) \qquad \begin{pmatrix} \omega_2 & \bar{\omega}_2 \\ \omega_1 & \bar{\omega}_1 \end{pmatrix} = \begin{pmatrix} a' & b' \\ c' & d' \end{pmatrix} \begin{pmatrix} a & b \\ c & d \end{pmatrix} \begin{pmatrix} \omega_2 & \bar{\omega}_2 \\ \omega_1 & \bar{\omega}_1 \end{pmatrix}.$$

Here the determinant $\omega_2\bar{\omega}_1 - \omega_1\bar{\omega}_2$ is $\neq 0$, for otherwise any two numbers in the module would have a real ratio, contrary to assumption. A matrix with determinant $\neq 0$ has an inverse matrix, and if we multiply (5) by the inverse of $\begin{pmatrix} \omega_2 & \bar{\omega}_2 \\ \omega_1 & \bar{\omega}_1 \end{pmatrix}$ we obtain

$$\begin{pmatrix} a' & b' \\ c' & d' \end{pmatrix} \begin{pmatrix} a & b \\ c & d \end{pmatrix} = \begin{pmatrix} 1 & 0 \\ 0 & 1 \end{pmatrix}.$$

The matrices $\begin{pmatrix} a & b \\ c & d \end{pmatrix}$ and $\begin{pmatrix} a' & b' \\ c' & d' \end{pmatrix}$ are inverse to each other. In particular, their determinants must satisfy

$$\begin{vmatrix} a' & b' \\ c' & d' \end{vmatrix} \cdot \begin{vmatrix} a & b \\ c & d \end{vmatrix} = 1,$$

and since both are integers we must have

$$\begin{vmatrix} a & b \\ c & d \end{vmatrix} = \begin{vmatrix} a' & b' \\ c' & d' \end{vmatrix} = \pm 1.$$

Linear transformations of the form (2) with integral coefficients and determinant ± 1 are said to be *unimodular*. We have proved:

Any two bases of the same module are connected by a unimodular transformation.

Geometrically, it is natural to consider the parallelogram spanned by a basis (ω_1,ω_2) in its relation to the lattice formed by all numbers in the module. Figure 34 shows two bases of the same module. Observe that the parallelograms have equal area.

We note here that the unimodular matrices, or the corresponding linear transformations, form a group, the *modular group*.

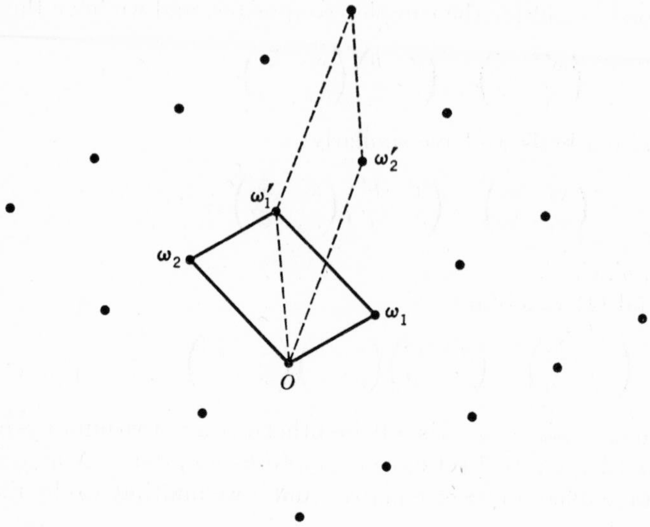

FIG. 34. Period module.

2.3. The Canonical Basis. Among all possible bases of M it is possible to single out one, almost uniquely, to be called the canonical basis. It will not always be necessary , or even desirable, to use such a special basis, but it is important to know that one exists. Except for minor adjustments it will be the basis introduced in the course of the proof of Theorem 1.

Theorem 2. *There exists a basis* (ω_1,ω_2) *such that the ratio* $\tau = \omega_2/\omega_1$ *satisfies the following conditions:* (i) $\text{Im } \tau > 0$, (ii) $-\frac{1}{2} < \text{Re } \tau \leqq \frac{1}{2}$, (iii) $|\tau| \geqq 1$, (iv) $\text{Re } \tau \geqq 0$ if $|\tau| = 1$. *The ratio* τ *is uniquely determined by these conditions, and there is a choice of two, four, or six corresponding bases.*

Proof. If we select ω_1 and ω_2 as in the proof of Theorem 1, then $|\omega_1| \leqq |\omega_2|$, $|\omega_2| \leqq |\omega_1 + \omega_2|$, and $|\omega_2| \leqq |\omega_1 - \omega_2|$. In terms of τ these conditions are equivalent to $|\tau| \geqq 1$ and $|\text{Re } \tau| \leqq \frac{1}{2}$. If $\text{Im } \tau < 0$ we replace (ω_1,ω_2) by $(-\omega_1,\omega_2)$; this makes $\text{Im } \tau > 0$ without changing the condition on $\text{Re } \tau$. If $\text{Re } \tau = -\frac{1}{2}$ we replace the basis by $(\omega_1,\omega_1 + \omega_2)$, and if $|\tau| = 1$, $\text{Re } \tau < 0$ we replace it by $(-\omega_2,\omega_1)$. After these minor changes all the conditions are satisfied.

We have seen that the most general change of basis is by a unimodular transformation. If the new ratio is τ' we obtain

(6) $$\tau' = \frac{a\tau + b}{c\tau + d}$$

with $ad - bc = \pm 1$. Simple computation gives

$$\operatorname{Im} \tau' = \frac{\pm \operatorname{Im} \tau}{|c\tau + d|^2} \tag{7}$$

where the sign is the same as that of $ad - bc$.

Suppose that both τ and τ' satisfy conditions (i) to (iv). We shall show that they must then be equal. Our first remark is that by condition (i) it is the upper sign that is valid in (7), and hence $ad - bc = 1$. Second, because τ and τ' play symmetric roles we are free to assume that $\operatorname{Im} \tau' \leqq \operatorname{Im} \tau$. It then follows from (7) that $|c\tau + d| \leqq 1$. Because c and d are integers there are very few possibilities for this inequality to hold.

One such possibility is to have $c = 0$, $d = \pm 1$. The relation $ad - bc = 1$ reduces to $ad = 1$, and because a and d are integers we have either $a = d = 1$ or $a = d = -1$. Equation (6) becomes $\tau' = \tau \pm b$, and by use of condition (ii) it follows that $|b| = |\operatorname{Re} \tau' - \operatorname{Re} \tau| < 1$. Therefore, and because b is an integer, $b = 0$ and $\tau' = \tau$.

A second possibility is to have $d = 0$. Then $bc = -1$ so that either $b = 1, c = -1$ or $b = -1, c = 1$. The inequality $|c\tau + d| \leqq 1$ becomes $|\tau| \leqq 1$, and according to condition (iii) we have thus $|\tau| = 1$. Equation (6) reads $\tau' = \pm a - 1/\tau$, which we may write as $\tau' = \pm a - \bar{\tau}$. It follows by (ii) that $|a| = |\operatorname{Re} \tau' + \operatorname{Re} \tau| < 1$, except when $\tau = \tau' = e^{\pi i/3}$. Save for this exception we have thus $a = 0$, $\tau' = -\bar{\tau}$. But by condition (iv) this can hold only if $\tau = \tau' = i$.

There remains only the possibility that c and d are both $\neq 0$, in which case $|cd| \geqq 1$. We conclude by use of (ii) and (iii) that

$$\begin{aligned} |c\tau + d|^2 = c^2|\tau|^2 + d^2 + 2cd \operatorname{Re} \tau &\geqq c^2 + d^2 - |cd| \\ &= (|c| - |d|)^2 + |cd| \geqq 1. \end{aligned}$$

Because of the opposite inequality $|c\tau + d| \leqq 1$ the equality sign must hold in all places. This is possible only if $|\tau| = 1$ and $\operatorname{Re} \tau = \frac{1}{2}$, that is for $\tau = e^{\pi i/3}$. However, under the restrictions (i) to (iv) this value corresponds to a strict minimum of $\operatorname{Im} \tau$. Therefore the assumption $\operatorname{Im} \tau' \leqq \operatorname{Im} \tau$ gives again $\tau' = \tau$.

We have proved that τ is unique, and Fig. 35 shows the part of the plane to which a canonical τ must belong. The canonical basis (ω_1, ω_2) can always be replaced by $(-\omega_1, -\omega_2)$. There are other bases with the same τ if and only if τ is a fixpoint of a unimodular transformation (6). This happens only for $\tau = i$ and $\tau = e^{\pi i/3}$; the former is a fixpoint of $-1/\tau$, the latter of $-(\tau + 1)/\tau$ and of $-1/(\tau + 1)$. These are the multiple choices referred to in the theorem.

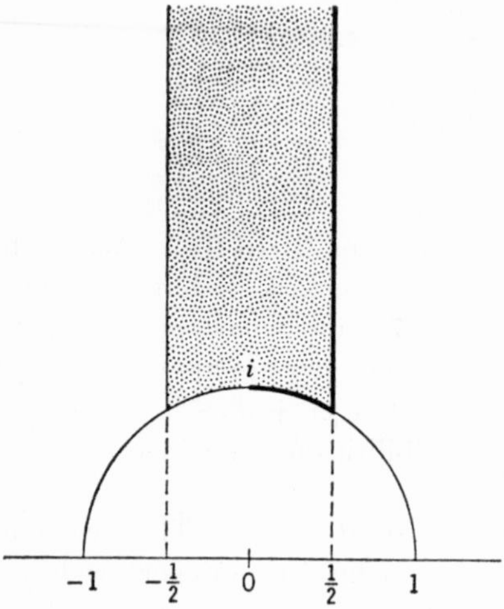

FIG. 35. τ-plane.

2.4. General Properties of Elliptic Functions. In the following $f(z)$ will denote a meromorphic function which admits all numbers in the module M with basis (ω_1,ω_2) as periods. We shall not assume that the basis is canonical, and it will not be required that M comprise all the periods.

It is convenient to say that z_1 is congruent to z_2, $z_1 \equiv z_2 \pmod{M}$, if the difference $z_1 - z_2$ belongs to M, i.e., $z_1 = z_2 + n_1\omega_1 + n_2\omega_2$. The function f takes the same values at congruent points, and may thus be regarded as a function on the congruence classes. A concrete way to make use of this property is to restrict the function to a parallelogram P_a with vertices a, $a + \omega_1$, $a + \omega_2$, $a + \omega_1 + \omega_2$. By including part of the boundary we may represent each congruence class by exactly one point in P_a, and then f is completely determined by its values on P_a. The choice of a is irrelevant, and we leave it free in order to attain, for instance, that f has no poles on the boundary of P_a.

Theorem 3. *An elliptic function without poles is a constant.*

If $f(z)$ has no poles, it is bounded on the closure of P_a, and hence in the whole plane. By Liouville's theorem (Chap. 4, Sec. 2.3) it must reduce to a constant.

Because the poles have no accumulation point there are only finitely many poles in P_a. When we speak of *the* poles of an elliptic function we mean a full set of mutually incongruent poles. Multiplicities are counted in the usual manner.

Theorem 4. *The sum of the residues of an elliptic function is zero.*

We may choose a so that none of the poles fall on the boundary of P_a. If the boundary ∂P_a is traced in the positive sense, the sum of the residues at the poles in P_a equals

$$\frac{1}{2\pi i}\int_{\partial P_a} f(z)\,dz.$$

Because f has periods ω_1, ω_2 the integral vanishes, for the integrals over opposite sides of the parallelogram cancel against each other.

As a consequence of the theorem there does not exist an elliptic function with a single simple pole.

Theorem 5. *A nonconstant elliptic function has equally many poles as it has zeros.*

The poles and zeros of f are simple poles of f'/f, which is itself an elliptic function. The multiplicities are the residues of f'/f, counted positive for zeros and negative for poles. The theorem now follows from Theorem 4.

If c is any constant, $f(z) - c$ has the same poles as $f(z)$. Therefore, all values are assumed equally many times. The number of incongruent roots of the equations $f(z) = c$ is called the *order* of the elliptic function.

Theorem 6. *The zeros $a_1, \ldots, a_n$ and poles $b_1, \ldots, b_n$ of an elliptic function satisfy $a_1 + \cdots + a_n \equiv b_1 + \cdots + b_n \pmod M$.*

This is proved by considering the integral

$$\frac{1}{2\pi i}\int_{\partial P_a} \frac{zf'(z)}{f(z)}\,dz \tag{8}$$

where we may again assume that there are no zeros or poles on the boundary. By the calculus of residues the integral equals $a_1 + \cdots + a_n - b_1 - \cdots - b_n$ provided that we choose the representative zeros and poles inside P_a. Consider the sides from a to $a + \omega_1$ and from $a + \omega_2$ to $a + \omega_1 + \omega_2$. The corresponding part of the integral may be written

$$\frac{1}{2\pi i}\left(\int_a^{a+\omega_1} - \int_{a+\omega_2}^{a+\omega_1+\omega_2}\right)\frac{zf'(z)}{f(z)}\,dz = -\frac{\omega_2}{2\pi i}\int_a^{a+\omega_1}\frac{f'(z)}{f(z)}\,dz.$$

Except for the factor $-\omega_2$ the right-hand member represents the winding number around the origin of the closed curve described by $f(z)$ when z

varies from a to $a + \omega_1$. It is consequently an integer. The same applies to the other pair of opposite sides. Therefore the value of (8) is of the form $n_1\omega_1 + n_2\omega_2$, and the theorem is proved.

3. THE WEIERSTRASS THEORY

The simplest elliptic functions are of order 2, and such functions have either a double pole with residue zero, or two simple poles with opposite residues. We shall follow the classical example of Weierstrass, who chose a function with a double pole as the starting point of a systematic theory.

3.1. The Weierstrass $\wp$-function. We may as well place the pole at the origin, and since multiplication with a constant factor is clearly irrelevant, we may require that the singular part is z^{-2}. If f is elliptic and has only this singularity at the origin and its congruent points, it is easy to see that f must be an even function. Indeed, $f(z) - f(-z)$ has the same periods and no singularity. Therefore it must reduce to a constant, and on setting $z = \omega_1/2$ we conclude that the constant is zero.

A constant can be added at will, and we can therefore choose the constant term in the Laurent development about the origin to be zero. With this additional normalization $f(z)$ is uniquely determined, and it is traditionally denoted by a special typographical symbol $\wp(z)$. The Laurent development has the form

$$\wp(z) = z^{-2} + a_1z^2 + a_2z^4 + \cdots .$$

So far all this is hypothetical, for we have not yet shown the existence of an elliptic function with this development. We shall follow the usual procedure in such cases, namely to postulate the existence and derive an explicit expression. The clue is to develop in partial fractions by the method in Chap. 5, Sec. 2. Our aim is to prove the formula

$$\wp(z) = \frac{1}{z^2} + \sum_{\omega \neq 0} \left(\frac{1}{(z-\omega)^2} - \frac{1}{\omega^2} \right) \tag{9}$$

where the sum ranges over all $\omega = n_1\omega_1 + n_2\omega_2$ except 0. Observe that $(z - \omega)^{-2}$ is the singular part at ω, and that we have subtracted ω^{-2} in order to produce convergence.

Our first task is to verify that the series converges. If $|\omega| > 2|z|$, say, an immediate estimate gives

$$\left| \frac{1}{(z-\omega)^2} - \frac{1}{\omega^2} \right| = \left| \frac{z(2\omega - z)}{\omega^2(z-\omega)^2} \right| \leq \frac{10|z|}{|\omega|^3}.$$

Therefore the series (9) converges, uniformly on every compact set, provided that

$$\sum_{\omega\neq 0} \frac{1}{|\omega|^3} < \infty.$$

This is indeed the case. Because ω_2/ω_1 is nonreal, there exists a $k > 0$ such that $|n_1\omega_1 + n_2\omega_2| \geqq k(|n_1| + |n_2|)$ for all real pairs (n_1,n_2). If we consider only integers there are $4n$ pairs (n_1,n_2) with $|n_1| + |n_2| = n$. This gives

$$\sum_{\omega\neq 0} |\omega|^{-3} \leqq 4k^{-3} \sum_{1}^{\infty} n^{-2} < \infty.$$

The next step is to prove that the right-hand side of (9) has periods ω_1 and ω_2. Direct verification is relatively cumbersome. Instead we write, temporarily,

$$f(z) = \frac{1}{z^2} + \sum_{\omega\neq 0} \left(\frac{1}{(z-\omega)^2} - \frac{1}{\omega^2}\right) \tag{10}$$

and obtain by termwise differentiation

$$f'(z) = -\frac{2}{z^3} - \sum_{\omega\neq 0} \frac{2}{(z-\omega)^3} = -2\sum_{\omega} \frac{1}{(z-\omega)^3}.$$

The last sum is obviously doubly periodic. Therefore $f(z + \omega_1) - f(z)$ and $f(z + \omega_2) - f(z)$ are constants. Because $f(z)$ is even (as seen from (10)), it suffices to choose $z = -\omega_1/2$ and $z = -\omega_2/2$ to conclude that the constants are zero. We have thus proved that f has the asserted periods.

It follows now that $\wp(z) - f(z)$ is a constant, and by the form of the development at the origin the constant is zero. We have thereby proved the existence of $\wp(z)$, and also that it can be represented by the series (9). For convenient reference we display the important formula

$$\wp'(z) = -2\sum_{\omega} \frac{1}{(z-\omega)^3}. \tag{11}$$

3.2. The Functions $\zeta(z)$ and $\sigma(z)$. Because $\wp(z)$ has zero residues, it is the derivative of a single-valued function. It is traditional to denote the antiderivative of $\wp(z)$ by $-\zeta(z)$, and to normalize it so that it is odd. By use of (9) we are led to the explicit expression

$$\zeta(z) = \frac{1}{z} + \sum_{\omega\neq 0} \left(\frac{1}{z-\omega} + \frac{1}{\omega} + \frac{z}{\omega^2}\right). \tag{12}$$

The convergence is obvious, for apart from the term $1/z$ we obtain the new series by integration from 0 to z along any path that does not pass through the poles.

It is clear that $\zeta(z)$ satisfies conditions $\zeta(z + \omega_1) = \zeta(z) + \eta_1$, $\zeta(z + \omega_2) = \zeta(z) + \eta_2$, where η_1 and η_2 are constants. They are connected with ω_1, ω_2 by a very simple relation. To derive it we choose any $a \neq 0$ and observe that

$$\frac{1}{2\pi i} \int_{\partial P_a} \zeta(z)\, dz = 1,$$

by the residue theorem. The integral is easy to evaluate by adding the contributions from opposite sides of the parallelogram, and we obtain the equation

$$\eta_1\omega_2 - \eta_2\omega_1 = 2\pi i,$$

known as *Legendre's relation.*

The integration can be carried one step further provided that we use an exponential to eliminate the multiple-valuedness. Just as easily we can verify directly that the product

$$\sigma(z) = z \prod_{\omega \neq 0} \left(1 - \frac{z}{\omega}\right) e^{z/\omega + \frac{1}{2}(z/\omega)^2} \tag{13}$$

converges and represents an entire function which satisfies

$$\sigma'(z)/\sigma(z) = \zeta(z).$$

The formula (13) is a canonical product representation of $\sigma(z)$.

How does $\sigma(z)$ change when z is replaced by $z + \omega_1$ or $z + \omega_2$? From

$$\frac{\sigma'(z + \omega_1)}{\sigma(z + \omega_1)} = \frac{\sigma'(z)}{\sigma(z)} + \eta_1$$

it follows at once that

$$\sigma(z + \omega_1) = C_1\sigma(z)e^{\eta_1 z}$$

with constant C_1. To determine the constant we observe that $\sigma(z)$ is an odd function. On setting $z = -\omega_1/2$ the value of C_1 can be determined, and we find that $\sigma(z)$ satisfies

$$\begin{aligned} \sigma(z + \omega_1) &= -\sigma(z)e^{\eta_1(z+\omega_1/2)} \\ \sigma(z + \omega_2) &= -\sigma(z)e^{\eta_2(z+\omega_2/2)}. \end{aligned} \tag{14}$$

EXERCISES

1. Show that any even elliptic function with periods ω_1, ω_2 can be expressed in the form

$$C \prod_{k=1}^{n} \frac{\wp(z) - \wp(a_k)}{\wp(z) - \wp(b_k)} \qquad (C = \text{const.})$$

provided that 0 is neither a zero nor a pole. What is the corresponding form if the function either vanishes or becomes infinite at the origin?

2. Show that any elliptic function with periods ω_1, ω_2 can be written as

$$C \prod_{k=1}^{n} \frac{\sigma(z - a_k)}{\sigma(z - b_k)} \qquad (C = \text{const.}).$$

Hint: Use (14) and Theorem 6.

3.3. The Differential Equation. By use of formula (12) it is easy to derive the Laurent expansion of $\zeta(z)$ about the origin, and differentiation will then yield the corresponding expansion of $\wp(z)$. We have first

$$\frac{1}{z - \omega} + \frac{1}{\omega} + \frac{z}{\omega^2} = -\frac{z^2}{\omega^3} - \frac{z^3}{\omega^4} - \cdots$$

and when we sum over all periods we obtain

$$\zeta(z) = \frac{1}{z} - \sum_{k=2}^{\infty} G_k z^{2k-1}$$

where we have written

$$G_k = \sum_{\omega \neq 0} \frac{1}{\omega^{2k}}.$$

Observe that the corresponding sums of odd powers of the periods are zero, as was to be expected since ζ is an odd function. Because

$$\wp(z) = -\zeta'(z)$$

we obtain further

$$\wp(z) = \frac{1}{z^2} + \sum_{k=2}^{\infty} (2k - 1)G_k z^{2k-2}.$$

In the following computation we write down only the significant terms, since it is understood that the omitted terms are of higher order:

$$\wp(z) = \frac{1}{z^2} + 3G_2 z^2 + 5G_3 z^4 + \cdots$$

$$\wp'(z) = -\frac{2}{z^3} + 6G_2 z + 20G_3 z^3 + \cdots$$

$$\wp'(z)^2 = \frac{4}{z^6} - \frac{24G_2}{z^2} - 80G_3 + \cdots$$

$$4\wp(z)^3 = \frac{4}{z^6} + \frac{36G_2}{z^2} + 60G_3 + \cdots$$

$$60G_2\wp(z) = \frac{60G_2}{z^2} + 0 + \cdots.$$

The last three lines yield

$$\wp'(z)^2 - 4\wp(z)^3 + 60G_2\wp(z) = -140G_3 + \cdots.$$

Here the left-hand side is a doubly periodic function, and the right-hand side has no poles. We may therefore conclude that

$$\wp'(z)^2 = 4\wp(z)^3 - 60G_2\wp(z) - 140G_3.$$

It is customary to set $g_2 = 60G_2$, $g_3 = 140G_3$ so that the equation becomes

$$\wp'(z)^2 = 4\wp(z)^3 - g_2\wp(z) - g_3. \tag{15}$$

This is a first-order differential equation for $w = \wp(z)$. It can be solved explicitly, namely, by the formula

$$z = \int^w \frac{dw}{\sqrt{4w^3 - g_2w - g_3}} + \text{constant},$$

which shows that $\wp(z)$ is the inverse of an elliptic integral. More accurately, this connection is expressed by the identity

$$z - z_0 = \int_{\wp(z_0)}^{\wp(z)} \frac{dw}{\sqrt{4w^3 - g_2w - g_3}}$$

where the path of integration is the image under $\wp$ of a path from z_0 to z that avoids the zeros and poles of $\wp'(z)$, and where the sign of the square root must be chosen so that it actually equals $\wp'(z)$.

We recall that we encountered the relationship between elliptic functions and elliptic integrals already in connection with the conformal mapping of rectangles and certain triangles (Chap. 6, Sec. 2).

*EXERCISES

The Weierstrass functions satisfy numerous identities which are best dealt with in an exercise section. They can be proved either by comparing two elliptic functions with the same zeros and poles (when σ-functions are involved), or by comparing elliptic functions with the same singular parts (when only $\wp$- and ζ-functions are involved). The following sequence of formulas is so arranged that we need to resort to this method only once.

1.

$$\wp(z) - \wp(u) = -\frac{\sigma(z-u)\sigma(z+u)}{\sigma(z)^2\sigma(u)^2} \tag{16}$$

(Use (14) to show that the right-hand member is a periodic function of z. Find the multiplicative constant by comparing the Laurent developments.)

2.

$$\frac{\wp'(z)}{\wp(z) - \wp(u)} = \zeta(z-u) + \zeta(z+u) - 2\zeta(z). \tag{17}$$

(Follows from (16) by taking logarithmic derivatives.)

3.

$$\zeta(z+u) = \zeta(z) + \zeta(u) + \frac{1}{2}\frac{\wp'(z) - \wp'(u)}{\wp(z) - \wp(u)}. \tag{18}$$

(This is a symmetrized version of (17).)

4. The addition theorem for the $\wp$-function:

$$\wp(z+u) = -\wp(z) - \wp(u) + \frac{1}{4}\left(\frac{\wp'(z) - \wp'(u)}{\wp(z) - \wp(u)}\right)^2. \tag{19}$$

(Differentiation of (18) leads to a formula which contains $\wp''(z)$. It can be eliminated by (15) which gives $\wp'' = 6\wp^2 - \frac{1}{2}g_2$. Symmetrization yields (19). Observe that this is an algebraic addition theorem, for $\wp'(z)$ and $\wp'(u)$ can be expressed algebraically through $\wp(z)$ and $\wp(u)$.)

5. Prove

$$\wp(2z) = \frac{1}{4}\left(\frac{\wp''(z)}{\wp'(z)}\right)^2 - 2\wp(z).$$

6. Prove $\wp'(z) = -\sigma(2z)/\sigma(z)^4$.

7. Prove that

$$\begin{vmatrix} \wp(z) & \wp'(z) & 1 \\ \wp(u) & \wp'(u) & 1 \\ \wp(u+z) & -\wp'(u+z) & 1 \end{vmatrix} = 0.$$

3.4. The Modular Function $\lambda(\tau)$. The differential equation (15) can also be written as

$$\wp'(z)^2 = 4(\wp(z) - e_1)(\wp(z) - e_2)(\wp(z) - e_3), \tag{20}$$

where e_1, e_2, e_3 are the roots of the polynomial $4w^3 - g_2w - g_3$.

To find the values of the e_k we determine the zeros of $\wp'(z)$. The symmetry and periodicity of $\wp(z)$ imply $\wp(\omega_1 - z) = \wp(z)$. Hence $\wp'(\omega_1 - z) = -\wp'(z)$, from which it follows that $\wp'(\omega_1/2) = 0$. Similarly $\wp'(\omega_2/2) = 0$, and also $\wp'((\omega_1 + \omega_2)/2) = 0$. The numbers $\omega_1/2$, $\omega_2/2$ and $(\omega_1 + \omega_2)/2$ are mutually incongruent modulo the periods. Therefore they are precisely the three zeros of $\wp'$, which is of order 3, and all the zeros are simple. When we compare with (20) it follows that we can set

$$e_1 = \wp(\omega_1/2), \qquad e_2 = \wp(\omega_2/2), \qquad e_3 = \wp((\omega_1 + \omega_2)/2). \tag{21}$$

It follows, moreover, and this is very important, that *these roots are all distinct.* Indeed, $\wp(z)$ assumes each value e_k with multiplicity 2, and if two of them were equal that value would be assumed four times in contradiction with the fact that $\wp$ is of order 2.

If we substitute $z = \omega_1/2$, $\omega_2/2$ and $(\omega_1 + \omega_2)/2$ in the definition (9) of $\wp(z)$ it is seen at once that the e_k are homogeneous of order -2 in ω_1, ω_2 (in other words, if the periods are multiplied by t, then the e_k are multiplied by t^{-2}). We conclude that the quantity

$$\lambda(\tau) = \frac{e_3 - e_2}{e_1 - e_2} \tag{22}$$

depends only on the ratio $\tau = \omega_2/\omega_1$, as indicated by our notation. It is quite clear from (9) that $\lambda(\tau)$ is the quotient of two analytic functions in the upper half plane $\operatorname{Im} \tau > 0$. Because $e_1 \neq e_2$ it is actually analytic, rather than meromorphic; because $e_2 \neq e_3$ it is never equal to 0, and because $e_1 \neq e_3$ it is never equal to 1.

We shall study the dependence on τ in greater detail. If the periods are subjected to the unimodular transformation

$$\begin{aligned} \omega_2' &= a\omega_2 + b\omega_1 \\ \omega_1' &= c\omega_2 + d\omega_1 \end{aligned} \tag{23}$$

then, first of all, the $\wp$-function does not change. Therefore, by looking at (20), the roots e_k can at most be permuted. Let us see what actually happens. It is clear from (23) that $\omega_1'/2 \equiv \omega_1/2$ and $\omega_2'/2 \equiv \omega_2/2$ if $a \equiv d \equiv 1 \pmod 2$ and $b \equiv c \equiv 0 \pmod 2$. Under this condition the e_k do not change, and we have shown that

$$\lambda\left(\frac{a\tau + b}{c\tau + d}\right) = \lambda(\tau) \qquad \text{for} \qquad \begin{pmatrix} a & b \\ c & d \end{pmatrix} \equiv \begin{pmatrix} 1 & 0 \\ 0 & 1 \end{pmatrix} \pmod 2. \tag{24}$$

The transformations which satisfy the congruence relation in (24) form a subgroup of the modular group (cf. Sec. 2.2), known as the *congruence subgroup* mod 2. Equation (24) asserts that $\lambda(\tau)$ is invariant under this subgroup. Quite generally, when an analytic or meromorphic function is invariant under a group of linear transformations, we call it an *automorphic function.* More specifically, a function which is automorphic with respect to a subgroup of the modular group is called a *modular function* (or an *elliptic modular function*).

We still have to determine the behavior of $\lambda(\tau)$ under a modular transformation that does not belong to the congruence subgroup. It is sufficient to consider matrices congruent mod 2 to $\begin{pmatrix} 1 & 1 \\ 0 & 1 \end{pmatrix}$ and $\begin{pmatrix} 0 & 1 \\ 1 & 0 \end{pmatrix}$ respectively, for all other types can be composed from these. In the first case we obtain $\omega_2'/2 = (\omega_1 + \omega_2)/2$ and $\omega_1'/2 = \omega_1/2$; this means that e_2 and e_3 are interchanged, while e_1 remains fixed, and hence λ goes over into $(e_2 - e_3)/(e_1 - e_3) = \lambda/(\lambda - 1)$. In the second case $\omega_2'/2 = \omega_1/2, \omega_1'/2 = \omega_2/2$, so that e_1 and e_2 are interchanged, and λ goes over into $1 - \lambda$. Sample transformations are $\tau \to \tau + 1$ and $\tau \to -1/\tau$. We find that $\lambda(\tau)$ satisfies the functional equations

$$\lambda(\tau + 1) = \frac{\lambda(\tau)}{\lambda(\tau) - 1}, \qquad \lambda\left(-\frac{1}{\tau}\right) = 1 - \lambda(\tau). \tag{25}$$

3.5. The Conformal Mapping by $\lambda(\tau)$. For convenience we shall henceforth use the normalization $\omega_1 = 1$, $\omega_2 = \tau$. With this choice of periods we obtain from (9) and (21)

$$\begin{aligned} e_3 - e_2 &= \sum_{m,n=-\infty}^{\infty} \left[\frac{1}{(m - \frac{1}{2} + (n + \frac{1}{2})\tau)^2} - \frac{1}{(m + (n - \frac{1}{2})\tau)^2}\right] \\ e_1 - e_2 &= \sum_{m,n=-\infty}^{\infty} \left[\frac{1}{(m - \frac{1}{2} + n\tau)^2} - \frac{1}{(m + (n - \frac{1}{2})\tau)^2}\right] \end{aligned} \tag{26}$$

where the double series are absolutely convergent. Our first observation is that these quantities are real when τ is purely imaginary (this is also true of the individual e_k). Indeed, when we replace τ by $-\tau$ the sums remain the same, except for a rearrangement of the terms. We conclude that $\lambda(\tau)$ is real on the imaginary axis.

Because $\begin{pmatrix} 1 & 2 \\ 0 & 1 \end{pmatrix}$ is in the congruence subgroup mod 2 we have $\lambda(\tau + 2) = \lambda(\tau)$. In other words, λ has period 2. As we have seen in Sec. 2, this means that $\lambda(\tau)$ can be expressed as a function of $e^{\pi i \tau}$. It would not be difficult to determine the Fourier development, but we shall be content to show that $\lambda(\tau) \to 0$ as $\operatorname{Im} \tau \to \infty$.

To evaluate (26) we sum first with respect to m. This summation can be carried out explicitly by use of the formula

$$\frac{\pi^2}{\sin^2 \pi z} = \sum_{-\infty}^{\infty} \frac{1}{(z - m)^2}$$

(Chap. 5, Sec. 2.1, (9)). We obtain at once

$$\begin{aligned} e_3 - e_2 &= \pi^2 \sum_{n=-\infty}^{\infty} \left(\frac{1}{\cos^2 \pi(n - \frac{1}{2})\tau} - \frac{1}{\sin^2 \pi(n - \frac{1}{2})\tau}\right) \\ e_1 - e_2 &= \pi^2 \sum_{n=-\infty}^{\infty} \left(\frac{1}{\cos^2 \pi n\tau} - \frac{1}{\sin^2 \pi(n - \frac{1}{2})\tau}\right). \end{aligned} \tag{27}$$

The series are strongly convergent, both for $n \to +\infty$ and $n \to -\infty$, for $|\cos n\pi\tau|$ and $|\sin n\pi\tau|$ are comparable to $e^{|n|\pi \operatorname{Im} \tau}$; the convergence is uniform for $\operatorname{Im} \tau \geqq \delta > 0$.

The limits can now be taken termwise, and we find that $e_3 - e_2 \to 0$, $e_1 - e_2 \to \pi^2$ (from the term $n = 0$). Hence $\lambda(\tau) \to 0$ as $\operatorname{Im} \tau \to \infty$, uniformly with respect to the real part of τ. It follows further by the second equation (25) that $\lambda(\tau) \to 1$ when τ approaches 0 along the imaginary axis.

We need one more piece of information, namely the order to which $\lambda(\tau)$ vanishes together with $e^{\pi i \tau}$. From (27) the leading terms in $e_3 - e_2$ are the ones corresponding to $n = 0$ and $n = 1$. The sum of these terms is

$$2\pi^2 \left[\frac{4e^{\pi i \tau}}{(1 + e^{\pi i \tau})^2} + \frac{4e^{\pi i \tau}}{(1 - e^{\pi i \tau})^2} \right]$$

and we conclude that

$$\lambda(\tau) e^{-\pi i \tau} \to 16 \tag{28}$$

for $\operatorname{Im} \tau \to \infty$.

In Fig. 36 the region Ω is bounded by the imaginary axis, the line $\operatorname{Re} \tau = 1$, and the circle $|\tau - \frac{1}{2}| = \frac{1}{2}$. The transformation $\tau + 1$ maps the imaginary axis on $\operatorname{Re} \tau = 1$, and $1 - 1/\tau$ maps $\operatorname{Re} \tau = 1$ on $|\tau - \frac{1}{2}| = \frac{1}{2}$. Since $\lambda(\tau)$ is real on the imaginary axis, it follows by virtue of the relations (25) that it is real on the whole boundary of Ω. Furthermore, $\lambda(\tau) \to 1$ as τ tends to 0 and $\lambda(\tau) \to \infty$ as τ tends to 1 inside Ω.

We apply the argument principle to determine the number of times $\lambda(\tau)$ takes a nonreal value w_0 in Ω. Cut off the corners of Ω by means of a

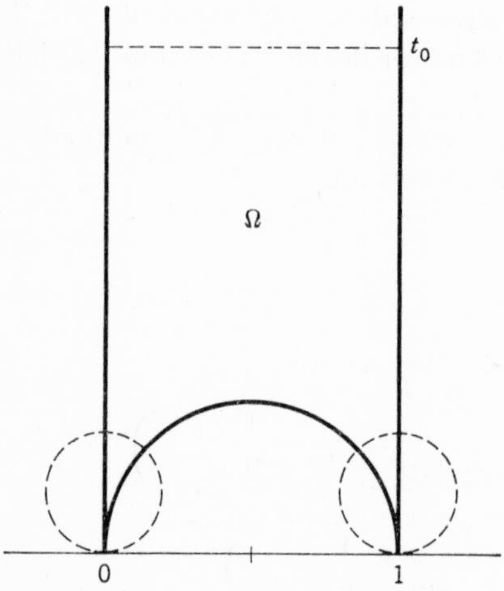

FIG. 36

horizontal line segment $\operatorname{Im} \tau = t_0$ and its images under the transformations $-1/\tau$ and $1 - 1/\tau$ (these images are circles tangent to the real axis). For sufficiently large t_0 it is clear that $\lambda(\tau) \neq w_0$ in the portions that have been cut off. The circle near $\tau = 1$ is mapped by $\lambda(\tau)$ on a curve $\lambda = \lambda(1 - 1/\tau) = 1 - 1/\lambda(\tau)$; where $\tau = s + it_0$, $0 \leqq s \leqq 1$; in view of (28) this is approximately a large semicircle in the upper half plane. It is now evident that the image of the contour of the truncated region Ω has winding number 1 about w_0 if $\operatorname{Im} w_0 > 0$, and winding number 0 if $\operatorname{Im} w_0 < 0$. As a result $\lambda(\tau)$ takes every value in the upper half plane exactly once in Ω, and no value in the lower half plane. This is also sufficient to guarantee that $\lambda(\tau)$ is monotone on the boundary of Ω. Indeed, if it were not, the derivative $\lambda'(\tau)$ would vanish at a boundary point, and it would be impossible for a full semicircular neighborhood of that boundary point to be mapped onto the upper half plane.

Theorem 7. *The modular function $\lambda(\tau)$ effects a one-to-one conformal mapping of the region Ω onto the upper half plane. The mapping extends continuously to the boundary in such a way that $\tau = 0, 1, \infty$ correspond to $\lambda = 1, \infty, 0$.*

By reflection the region Ω' that is symmetric to Ω with respect to the imaginary axis is mapped onto the lower half plane, and thus both regions together correspond to the whole plane, except for the points 0 and 1.

We shall also prove:

Theorem 8. *Every point τ in the upper half plane is equivalent under the congruence subgroup mod 2 to exactly one point in $\bar{\Omega} \cup \Omega'$.*

We refer to Fig. 37. The reader is asked to verify that the region Δ is mapped on the shaded regions in the figure by means of the linear transformations τ, $-1/\tau$, $\tau - 1$, $1/(1 - \tau)$, $(\tau - 1)/\tau$, $\tau/(1 - \tau)$ which we shall denote by $S_1, S_2, \ldots, S_6$. The matrices of the inverse transformations S_k^{-1} $(k = 1, \ldots, 6)$ are in order

$$\begin{pmatrix}1 & 0\\ 0 & 1\end{pmatrix}, \begin{pmatrix}0 & -1\\ 1 & 0\end{pmatrix}, \begin{pmatrix}1 & 1\\ 0 & 1\end{pmatrix}, \begin{pmatrix}1 & -1\\ 1 & 0\end{pmatrix}, \begin{pmatrix}0 & 1\\ -1 & 1\end{pmatrix}, \begin{pmatrix}1 & 0\\ 1 & 1\end{pmatrix}.$$

One recognizes readily that these matrices form a complete set of mutually incongruent matrices in the sense that every unimodular matrix is congruent mod 2 to exactly one of them. Precisely the same can be shown for the transformations S_k' $(k = 1, \ldots, 6)$ which map Δ' on the unshaded regions in the figure (the task of writing them down is left to the reader).

Together the 12 images of $\bar{\Delta}$ and $\bar{\Delta}'$ cover the set $\bar{\Omega} \cup \bar{\Omega}'$ (closures should be taken with respect to the open half plane).

Let τ be any point in the upper half plane. The set $\bar{\Delta} \cup \bar{\Delta}'$ can be identified with the closure of the shaded region in Fig. 34. Therefore, according to Theorem 2 there exists a modular transformation S such that $S\tau$ lies in $\bar{\Delta} \cup \bar{\Delta}'$. Suppose first that $S\tau$ is in $\bar{\Delta}$. We know that the matrix of S is congruent mod 2 to the matrix of an S_k^{-1}. It follows that the matrix of $T = S_kS$ is congruent to the identity matrix; in other words, T belongs to the congruence subgroup. Since $S\tau$ lies in $\bar{\Delta}$ we know further that $T\tau = S_k(S\tau)$ lies in $\bar{\Omega} \cup \bar{\Omega}'$. The same reasoning applies if $S\tau \in \bar{\Delta}'$. Thus there is always a $T\tau$ in $\bar{\Omega} \cup \bar{\Omega}'$, and a trivial consideration shows that it can be chosen in $\bar{\Omega} \cup \Omega'$.

The uniqueness follows readily from the fact that the S_k as well as the S_k' are mutually incongruent. We shall leave it to the reader to work out the details.

*EXERCISE

Show that the function

$$J(\tau) = \frac{4}{27}\frac{(1 - \lambda + \lambda^2)^3}{\lambda^2(1 - \lambda)^2}$$

is automorphic with respect to the full modular group. Where does it take the values 0 and 1, and with what multiplicities? Show that

$$J(\tau) = \frac{4}{27}\frac{e_1e_2 + e_2e_3 + e_3e_1}{(e_1 - e_2)^2(e_2 - e_3)^2(e_3 - e_1)^2}.$$

Show also that $J(\tau)$ maps the region Δ in Fig. 37 onto a half plane.

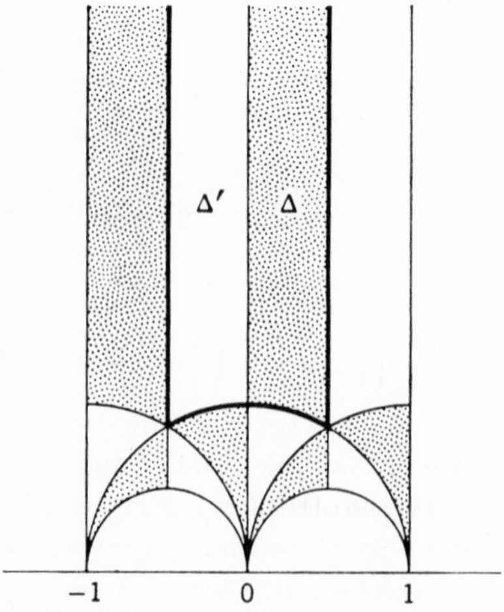

FIG 37. Fundamental region of $\lambda(\tau)$.

8 GLOBAL ANALYTIC FUNCTIONS

1. ANALYTIC CONTINUATION

In the preceding chapters we have stressed that all functions must be well defined and, therefore, single-valued. In the case of functions like $\log z$ or $\sqrt{z}$ which are not uniquely determined by their analytic expression, a special effort was needed to show that, under favorable circumstances, a single-valued branch can be selected. While this point of view answers the need for logical clarity, it does not do justice to the fact that the ambiguity of the logarithm or the square root is an essential characteristic which cannot be ignored. There is thus a clear need for a concept that emphasizes rather than circumvents multiple-valuedness.

1.1. General Analytic Functions. An analytic function $f(z)$ defined in a region Ω will constitute a *function element*, denoted by (f,Ω), and a *global analytic function* will appear as a collection of function elements which are related to each other in a prescribed manner.

Two function elements (f_1,Ω_1) and (f_2,Ω_2) are said to be *direct analytic continuations* of each other if $\Omega_1 \cap \Omega_2$ is nonempty and $f_1(z) = f_2(z)$ in $\Omega_1 \cap \Omega_2$. More specifically, (f_2,Ω_2) is called a direct analytic continuation of (f_1,Ω_1) to the region Ω_2. There need not exist any direct analytic continuation to Ω_2, but if there is one it is uniquely determined. For suppose that (f_2,Ω_2)

and (g_2,Ω_2) are two direct analytic continuations of (f_1,Ω_1); then $f_2 = g_2$ in $\Omega_1 \cap \Omega_2$, and this implies $f_2 = g_2$ throughout Ω_2. We note that if $\Omega_2 \subset \Omega_1$, then the direct analytic continuation of (f_1,Ω_1) is (f_1,Ω_2).

If (f_1,Ω_1) and (f_2,Ω_2) are direct analytic continuations of each other, it is evident that an analytic function f can be defined in $\Omega_1 \cup \Omega_2$ by setting $f = f_1$ in Ω_1 and $f = f_2$ in Ω_2. Since it had been possible to consider the function element $(f,\Omega_1 \cup \Omega_2)$ from the beginning, it would seem that nothing has been gained. Consider, however, a third function element (f_3,Ω_3) which we assume to be a direct analytic continuation of (f_2,Ω_2). Then it may well happen that Ω_3 overlaps Ω_1, but that (f_3,Ω_3) is nevertheless not a direct analytic continuation of (f_1,Ω_1). In this situation the collection (f_1,Ω_1), (f_2,Ω_2), (f_3,Ω_3) cannot be replaced by a single function element. We are thus led to a genuine broadening of the concept of function.

More generally, we shall consider chains of function elements (f_1,Ω_1), (f_2,Ω_2), . . . , (f_n,Ω_n) such that (f_k,Ω_k) is a direct analytic continuation of (f_{k-1},Ω_{k-1}). The elements in such a chain are said to be *analytic continuations* of each other. We adopt the following definition:

Definition 1. *A global analytic function is a nonvoid collection* $\mathbf{f}$ *of function elements* (f,Ω) *which is such that any two elements in* $\mathbf{f}$ *are analytic continuations of each other by way of a chain whose links are members of* $\mathbf{f}$.

A complete analytic function is a global analytic function which contains all analytic continuations of any one of its elements.

A complete analytic function is evidently *maximal* in the sense that it cannot be further extended, and it is clear that every function element belongs to a unique complete analytic function. The incomplete global analytic functions are more arbitrary, and there are many cases in which two different collections of function elements should be regarded as defining the same function. For instance, a single-valued function $f(z)$, defined in Ω, can be identified either with the collection which consists of the single function element (f,Ω), or with the collection of all (f,Ω') with $\Omega' \subset \Omega$.

A global analytic function $\mathbf{f}$ has a uniquely determined derivative $\mathbf{f}'$ defined by the function elements (f',Ω). Indeed, if (f_1,Ω_1) and (f_2,Ω_2) are direct analytic continuations of each other, so are (f_1',Ω_1) and (f_2',Ω_2). The higher derivatives $\mathbf{f}''$, $\mathbf{f}'''$, . . . can be defined in the same way.

A similar relationship may exist between any two global analytic functions $\mathbf{f}$ and $\mathbf{g}$. We assume that there is given a correspondence which to every $(f,\Omega) \in \mathbf{f}$ assigns a unique function element $(g,\Omega) \in \mathbf{g}$ in such a way that direct analytic continuations go over in direct analytic continuations. In these circumstances we agree to say that **f** is *subordinate* to **g**, and it is possible to define **f** + **g** and **fg** as collections consisting of the elements $(f + g,\Omega)$, (fg,Ω) which correspond to the elements (f,Ω) of **f**. For instance, **f** is subordinate to any entire function **h**, from which it follows that **f** + **h** and **fh** are well defined.†

We can now formulate a classical principle known as the *permanence of functional relations*. Suppose that certain global analytic functions **f**, **g**, . . . are given and that, for instance, **f** is subordinate to all the others. Let it be known that a set of corresponding function elements (f,Ω), (g,Ω), . . . satisfy a relation of the form $G(f,g, \ldots) = 0$, where the expression G is a polynomial in several variables (the proof is valid much more generally). If (f_1,Ω_1), (g_1,Ω_1), . . . is a set of direct analytic continuations, it follows at once that $G(f_1,g_1, \ldots) = 0$ in Ω_1 for the simple reason that the composite function $G(f_1(z),g_1(z), \ldots)$ is analytic in Ω_1 and vanishes in $\Omega \cap \Omega_1$. We are thus able to conclude that the relation $G(f,g, \ldots) = 0$ holds for *all* sets of corresponding function elements, a fact which may also be expressed through the equation $G(\mathbf{f},\mathbf{g}, \ldots) = 0$.

EXERCISES

1. Prove that a function element $(f,\mathbf{C})$, where **C** is the whole plane, determines a complete analytic function consisting of all function elements of the form (f,Ω).

2. Define $\sqrt{z}$ as a global analytic function by means of a finite number of function elements.

3. Suppose that (f,Ω) satisfies a differential equation of the form $P(f,f',f'', \ldots) = 0$, where P is a polynomial whose coefficients are entire functions. Prove that all function elements of the complete analytic function determined by (f,Ω) satisfy the same differential equation.

1.2. The Riemann Surface of a Function. In order to study the multiple-valued nature of a global analytic function it is convenient to introduce the notion of a *branch*.‡ Two function elements (f_1,Ω_1) and (f_2,Ω_2) are said to determine the same branch at a point $z_0 \in \Omega_1 \cap \Omega_2$ whenever $f_1 = f_2$ in a neighborhood of z_0. In order that this happen it is sufficient, but not necessary, that the function elements are direct analytic continuations of each other. They are always, however, analytic continuations of each other, for they are both direct analytic continuations of their common restriction to a neighborhood of z_0. We note that two

† We make only transient use of this notion of subordinacy which is related to but not identical with one in rather common use.

‡ The word *germ* is also commonly used.

function elements determine the same branch at z_0 if and only if they have the same Taylor development about z_0.

The relation between function elements which we have just introduced is evidently an equivalence relation. With respect to this equivalence relation the totality of function elements (f,Ω) with $z_0 \in \Omega$ falls into well-defined equivalence classes which we call the *analytic branches* at z_0. It is easy to see that they can be identified with all power series in $z - z_0$ with a positive radius of convergence. We will denote the branch at z_0 determined by the function element (f,Ω) as (f,z_0).

For a global analytic function **f** we pick out the branches (f,z_0) determined by function elements $(f,\Omega) \in \mathbf{f}$ and call them the branches of **f** at z_0. To every branch there corresponds a unique function value $f(z_0)$ as well as unique values of the derivatives $f'(z_0)$, $f''(z_0)$, ... In analogy to the construction of Riemann surfaces of elementary multiple-valued functions we introduce a set $\mathfrak{F}$ (the Riemann surface) whose elements $\mathfrak{z}$ (the points) are the branches (f,z) of **f**. We are then in a position to consider **f** as a single-valued function $\mathbf{f}(\mathfrak{z})$ on $\mathfrak{F}$. The function $z = p(\mathfrak{z})$ which to every $\mathfrak{z} = (f,z)$ assigns the uniquely determined value z is called the *projection* of $\mathfrak{F}$ into the complex plane, and z is the *trace* of $\mathfrak{z}$.

The consideration of the Riemann surface is not of much use unless we can say when a function is continuous on $\mathfrak{F}$. Since continuity can be expressed in terms of neighborhoods, it is sufficient to define neighborhoods on $\mathfrak{F}$. Given $\mathfrak{z}_0 = (f_0,z_0)$, determined by the function element $(f_0,\Omega_0) \in \mathbf{f}$, we choose a neighborhood $V \subset \Omega_0$ of z_0 and consider the set $\mathfrak{B}$ of all branches (f_0,z) with $z \in V$. By definition, $\mathfrak{B}$ will be a neighborhood of $\mathfrak{z}_0$. It follows readily that $\mathbf{f}(\mathfrak{z})$ and $p(\mathfrak{z})$ are continuous functions in the sense that there exists, for any given $\varepsilon > 0$, a neighborhood $\mathfrak{B}$ with the property that $|\mathbf{f}(\mathfrak{z}) - \mathbf{f}(\mathfrak{z}_0)| < \varepsilon$, $|p(\mathfrak{z}) - p(\mathfrak{z}_0)| < \varepsilon$ for all $\mathfrak{z} \in \mathfrak{B}$.

By the introduction of Riemann surfaces we gain a very simple interpretation of subordination. Let $\mathfrak{F}$ and $\mathfrak{G}$ be the Riemann surfaces of **f** and **g**. Then **f** is subordinate to **g** if and only if there exists a continuous mapping σ of $\mathfrak{F}$ into $\mathfrak{G}$ such that $\mathfrak{z}$ and $\sigma(\mathfrak{z})$ have the same projection z; the proof is immediate. We observe that the mapping σ is not necessarily unique, which means that **f** may be subordinate to **g** in different ways. In a language which appeals to the imagination the existence of a projection preserving mapping implies that the surface $\mathfrak{F}$ can be spread out over $\mathfrak{G}$, or that $\mathfrak{F}$ may be considered as a Riemann surface relative to $\mathfrak{G}$.

We note finally that our definition of Riemann surfaces is provisional in as far as it does not yet include the case of branch points.

1.3. Analytic Continuation Along Arcs. We consider a global analytic function **f** with the Riemann surface $\mathfrak{F}$ and an arc γ in the complex plane with the equation $z = z(t)$, $\alpha \leqq t \leqq \beta$. Suppose that there exists on $\mathfrak{F}$ an arc $\bar{\gamma}$ whose projection is γ: we mean by this that $\bar{\gamma}$ has an equation $\mathfrak{z} = \mathfrak{z}(t)$ with $p(\mathfrak{z}(t)) = z(t)$ for all t. The fundamental assumption that $\bar{\gamma}$ is an arc means of course that $\mathfrak{z}(t)$ is continuous with respect to the neighborhoods introduced on $\mathfrak{F}$.

It is desirable to give a parallel interpretation which does not refer explicitly to the Riemann surface. To each t there corresponds a $\mathfrak{z}$ with the projection $z(t)$ and, therefore, a branch of the form $(f,z(t))$. For a given t_0 this branch is determined by a function element (f_0,Ω_0) with $z(t_0) \in \Omega_0$. A neighborhood consists of branches (f_0,z), and the continuity of $z(t)$ evidently implies the existence of a $\delta > 0$ such that for $|t - t_0| < \delta$ the branch $(f,z(t))$ is determined by the function element (f_0,Ω_0). When this is the case, we shall say that the branch $(f,z(t))$ and any one of the corresponding function elements have been obtained by *continuation along the arc* γ. According to this terminology there is complete equivalence between continuations along γ and arcs $\bar{\gamma}$ on $\mathfrak{F}$ which project into γ.

The continuation along an arc corresponds to the intuitive notion of a continuously changing branch. The existence of a continuation is not guaranteed, but the following important uniqueness theorem is valid:

Theorem 1. *Two continuations $(f_1,z(t))$ and $(f_2,z(t))$ of a global analytic function* **f** *along the same arc γ are either identical, or else they differ for all t.*

Consider the subset E of the closed interval (α,β) in which

$$(f_1,z(t)) = (f_2,z(t)).$$

Choose $t_0 \in E$ and suppose that the corresponding branches are determined by function elements (f_1^0,Ω_1), (f_2^0,Ω_2). By assumption $f_1^0 = f_2^0$ in a neighborhood of $z(t_0)$. If t is sufficiently near to t_0, the point $z(t)$ lies in this neighborhood; moreover, we can choose $f_1 = f_1^0$, $f_2 = f_2^0$, and it follows that the branches $(f_1,z(t))$, $(f_2,z(t))$ are identical. This result shows that the complement of E is closed. Suppose now that t_0 is not in E. With the same notations, $f_1^0(z)$ and $f_2^0(z)$ are not identical in any neighborhood of $z(t_0)$. Consequently there exists a neighborhood Δ of $z(t_0)$ in which $f_1^0(z) \neq f_2^0(z)$, except perhaps for $z = z(t_0)$. For t sufficiently near to t_0 $z(t) \in \Delta$, and we may take $f_1 = f_1^0$, $f_2 = f_2^0$. But if $z(t) \neq z(t_0)$ the branches $(f_1^0,z(t))$ and $(f_2^0,z(t))$ are different for the simple reason that $f_1^0(z(t)) \neq f_2^0(z(t))$, and if $z(t) = z(t_0)$ they are different by assumption. It follows that E itself is closed, and since the interval is connected the theorem is proved.

By virtue of this theorem a continuation is uniquely determined for instance by its initial branch $(f_0,z(\alpha))$. We may therefore speak of *the* continuation of $\mathbf{f}$ along γ from the initial branch $(f_0,z(\alpha))$, provided only that such a continuation exists.

If γ is an arbitrary arc and $\mathbf{f}$ a global analytic function, it may well happen that $\mathbf{f}$ does not have any continuation along γ, or that a continuation exists for some initial branches, but not for all. Let us investigate the case of an initial branch $(f_0,z(\alpha))$ which cannot be continued along γ. If $t_0 > \alpha$ is sufficiently near to α, there will exist a continuation of the initial branch along the subarc corresponding to the interval (α,t_0); indeed, this is trivially the case if the subarc is contained in the region Ω_0 of the function element (f_0,Ω_0). The least upper bound of all such t_0 is a number τ which satisfies $\alpha < \tau < \beta$, and it is easily seen that the continuation will be possible for $t_0 < \tau$, impossible for $t_0 \geqq \tau$. In a certain sense the subarc corresponding to (α,τ) may be said to lead to a point at which $\mathbf{f}$ ceases to be defined. In particular, if $\mathbf{f}$ is a complete analytic function, the subarc is called a *singular path* from the given initial branch; less precisely, it is said to lead to a *singular point* of $\mathbf{f}$. The term singular point should be used only when the corresponding path is clearly indicated.

The connection between continuation along arcs and stepwise continuation by means of a chain of direct analytic continuations requires further illumination. In the first place, if $(f_1,\Omega_1), (f_2,\Omega_2), \ldots, (f_n,\Omega_n)$ is a chain of direct analytic continuations, it is always possible to connect a point $z_1 \in \Omega_1$ to a point $z_n \in \Omega_n$ by means of an arc γ such that $\mathbf{f}$ has a continuation along γ with the initial branch (f_1,z_1) and the terminal branch (f_n,z_n). Indeed, it is sufficient to let γ be composed of a subarc $\gamma_1 \subset \Omega_1$ from z_1 to a point $z_2 \in \Omega_1 \cup \Omega_2$, a second subarc $\gamma_2 \subset \Omega_2$ from z_2 to $z_3 \in \Omega_2 \cup \Omega_3$, and so on. The continuation along γ is completely defined by setting $\mathfrak{z}(t) = (f_k,z(t))$ on γ_k.

Conversely, if a continuation $\mathfrak{z}(t)$ is given, we can find a chain of direct analytic continuations which follows the arc γ in the same way as in the preceding construction, provided merely that $\mathbf{f}$ is defined by means of a sufficiently large collection of function elements. By means of Heine-Borel's lemma it is shown that the parametric interval can be subdivided into $(\alpha,t_1), (t_1,t_2), \ldots, (t_{n-1},\beta)$ such that $\mathfrak{z}(t) = (f_k,z(t))$ in (t_{k-1},t_k) for suitably chosen function elements (f_k,Ω_k). Although (f_{k-1},Ω_{k-1}) and (f_k,Ω_k) need not be direct analytic continuations of each other, they are at least direct analytic continuations of their common restriction to a neighborhood of $z(t_{k-1})$. If these restrictions are contained in the collection $\mathbf{f}$, and this is certainly the case if $\mathbf{f}$ is a complete analytic function, then we can find a chain of direct analytic continuations with the desired properties.

In order to illustrate the use of continuations along arcs we will give a definition of $\log z$ as a complete analytic function. We define it as the collection of all function elements (f,Ω) such that $e^{f(z)} = z$ in Ω. It must be proved that this collection is complete.

We have to show that any two function elements (f_1,Ω_1), (f_2,Ω_2) in the collection can be joined by a chain of direct analytic continuations. Because of the permanence of functional relations it is clear that the intermediate function elements will belong to the same collection.

Choose points $z_1 \in \Omega_1$, $z_2 \in \Omega_2$, and join them by a differentiable arc γ which does not pass through the origin. This is possible since neither z_1 nor z_2 can be 0. Consider the function

$$\varphi(t) = f_1(z_1) + \int_\alpha^t \frac{z'(t)}{z(t)}\,dt.$$

By differentiation, $z(t)e^{-\varphi(t)}$ is constant; for $t = \alpha$ the value is 1, and hence $e^{\varphi(t)} = z(t)$. For a given t there exists, in any neighborhood of $z(t)$ which does not include the origin, a uniquely determined branch $f(z)$ of $\log z$ which takes the value $\varphi(t)$ for $z = z(t)$. It is clear that $(f,z(t))$ defines a continuation along γ. The terminal branch may not coincide with f_2, but its value must differ from $f_2(z_2)$ by a multiple of $2\pi i$. In order to obtain the right value at z_2 all that remains is to continue the terminal branch along a closed curve which circles the origin a suitable number of times. Finally, the arcwise continuation can be replaced by a finite chain of direct analytic continuations, and it is proved that $\log z$ is a complete analytic function.

EXERCISES

1. Define $\log f(z)$ for a single-valued $f(z) \neq 0$.

2. If a function element is defined by a power series inside of its circle of convergence, prove that the corresponding complete analytic function has necessarily a singular path in the circle of convergence which leads to a point on the circumference. ("A power series has at least one singular point on its circle of convergence.")

1.4. Homotopic Curves. We must now study the topological properties of closed curves in a region from a point of view which is fundamental for the theory of analytic continuations. The question which interests us is the behavior of an arc under *continuous deformations.* From an intuitive standpoint this is an extremely simple notion. If γ_1 and γ_2 are two arcs with common end points, contained in a region Ω, it is very natural to ask whether γ_1 can be continuously deformed into γ_2 when the end points are kept fixed and the moving arc is confined to Ω. For instance, in Fig. 38 the arc γ_1 can be deformed into γ_2, but not into

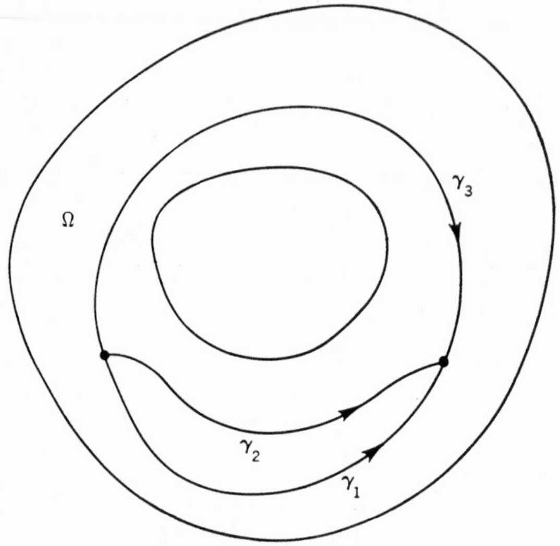

FIG. 38. Homotopic arcs.

γ_3. Two arcs which can be deformed into each other are said to be homotopic with respect to Ω. This is evidently an equivalence relation.

A precise definition must of course be given. Fortunately, the physical conception of deformation has an almost immediate interpretation in mathematical terms. It is indeed clear that a deformation of an arc can be described by means of a continuous function $z = z(t,u)$ of two variables where the point (t,u) ranges over a rectangle $\alpha \leqq t \leqq \beta$, $0 \leqq u \leqq 1$. To every fixed value $u = u_0$ there corresponds an arc $z = z(t,u_0)$, and the effect of the deformation is to change the initial arc $z = z(t,0)$ into $z = z(t,1)$. The deformation takes place within Ω if $z(t,u) \in \Omega$ for all (t,u), and it is a deformation with fixed end points if $z(\alpha,u)$ and $z(\beta,u)$ are constant. To every fixed value $t = t_0$ there corresponds an arc $z = z(t_0,u)$ with u as parameter which may be called the *deformation path* of the point corresponding to t_0. Figure 39 illustrates the effect of a deformation.

We are led to the following definition of homotopy:

Two arcs γ_1 and γ_2, defined by equations $z = z_1(t)$ and $z = z_2(t)$ over the same parametric interval $\alpha \leqq t \leqq \beta$, are said to be homotopic in Ω if there exists a continuous function $z(t,u)$ of two variables, defined for $\alpha \leqq t \leqq \beta$, $0 \leqq u \leqq 1$, with the following properties:

1. *$z(t,u) \in \Omega$ for all (t,u).*
2. *$z(t,0) = z_1(t)$, $z(t,1) = z_2(t)$ for all t.*
3. *$z(\alpha,u) = z_1(\alpha) = z_2(\alpha)$, $z(\beta,u) = z_1(\beta) = z_2(\beta)$ for all u.*

It is only for the sake of convenience that we have required the parametric intervals to be the same. If this is not the case we transform the intervals into each other by a linear change of parameter, and agree to consider the original arcs as homotopic if they are homotopic in the new parametrization.

Simple formal proofs which the reader can easily supply show that the relation of homotopy, as defined above, is an equivalence relation. We can thus divide all arcs into equivalence classes, called *homotopy classes;* the arcs in a homotopy class have common endpoints and can be deformed into each other within Ω. It deserves to be pointed out that different parametric representations of the same arc are always homotopic. Indeed, $z = z_1(t)$ is a reparametrization of $z = z_2(t)$ if and only if there is a nondecreasing function $\tau(t)$ such that $z_1(t) = z_2(\tau(t))$. The function

$$z(t,u) = z_1((1 - u)t + u\tau(t))$$

has all its values on the arc under consideration, and therefore in Ω. For $u = 0$ and $u = 1$ we obtain respectively $z(t,0) = z_1(t)$ and

$$z(t,1) = z_1(\tau(t)) = z_2(t)$$

as required, and the end points are evidently kept fixed.

If two arcs γ_1 and γ_2 are traced in succession, with γ_2 beginning at the terminal point of γ_1, they form a new arc which we will now denote by $\gamma_1\gamma_2$ in contrast to the notation $\gamma_1 + \gamma_2$ preferred in homology theory. The parametrization of $\gamma_1\gamma_2$ is not uniquely determined, but for the determination of the homotopy class this is of no importance. Very simple reasoning shows, moreover, that the homotopy class of $\gamma_1\gamma_2$ depends only on the homotopy classes of γ_1 and γ_2. By virtue of this fundamental fact we may consider the operation which leads to the homotopy class of $\gamma_1\gamma_2$ as a multiplication of homotopy classes. It is defined only when the initial point of γ_2 coincides with the terminal point of γ_1. If we restrict our attention to the homotopy classes of closed curves which begin and end at a fixed point z_0, the product is

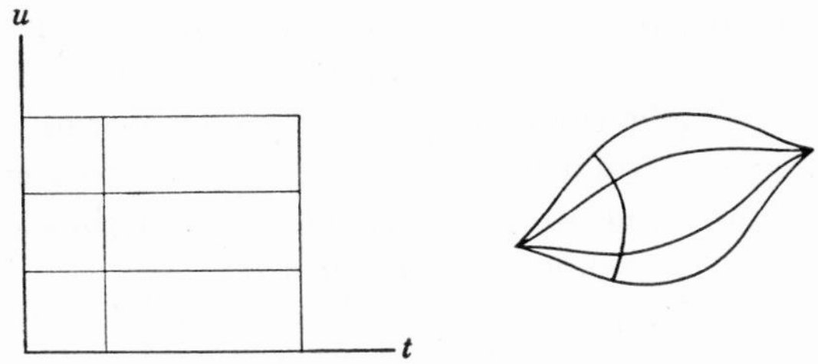

FIG. 39. Deformation.

always defined and is represented by a curve in the same family. What is more, with this definition of product the homotopy classes of closed curves from z_0, with respect to the region Ω, form a *group*. In order to prove this assertion we must establish:

1. The associative law: $(\gamma_1\gamma_2)\gamma_3$ is homotopic to $\gamma_1(\gamma_2\gamma_3)$.
2. Existence of a *unit* curve 1 such that $\gamma 1$ and 1γ are homotopic to γ.
3. Existence of an inverse γ^{-1} such that $\gamma\gamma^{-1}$ and $\gamma^{-1}\gamma$ are homotopic to 1.

The associative law is trivial since $(\gamma_1\gamma_2)\gamma_3$ is at most a reparametrization of $\gamma_1(\gamma_2\gamma_3)$. For a unit curve we can choose the constant $z = z_0$; actually, the symbol 1 may represent any closed curve which can be shrunk to the point z_0. Finally, the inverse γ^{-1} is the curve γ traced in the opposite direction. If γ is represented by $z = z(t)$, $\alpha \leqq t \leq \beta$, γ^{-1} can be represented by $z = z(2\beta - t)$, $\beta \leqq t \leqq 2\beta - \alpha$. The equation of $\gamma\gamma^{-1}$ is thus

$$\begin{aligned} z &= z(t) && \text{for } \alpha \leqq t \leqq \beta \\ z &= z(2\beta - t) && \text{for } \beta \leqq t \leqq 2\beta - \alpha. \end{aligned}$$

The curve can be shrunk to a point by means of the deformation

$$\begin{aligned} z(t,u) &= z(t) && \text{for } \alpha \leqq t \leqq u\alpha + (1 - u)\beta \\ z(t,u) &= z(u\alpha + (1 - u)\beta) && \text{for } u\alpha + (1 - u)\beta \leqq t \leqq u(\beta - \alpha) + \beta \\ z(t,u) &= z(2\beta - t) && \text{for } u(\beta - \alpha) + \beta \leqq t \leqq 2\beta - \alpha. \end{aligned}$$

The interpretation is clear: we are letting the turning point recede from $z(\beta)$ to $z(\alpha)$. Since $z(t,1) = z(\alpha) = z_0$, we have proved that $\gamma\gamma^{-1}$ is homotopic to 1. The proof is independent of the hypothesis that γ be a closed curve; thus $\gamma\gamma^{-1}$ is homotopic to 1 for any arc γ from z_0.

The group which we have constructed is called the *homotopy group*, or the *fundamental group*, of the region Ω with respect to the point z_0. As an abstract group it does not depend on the point z_0. If z_0' is another point in Ω, we join z_0 to z_0' by an arc c in Ω. To every closed curve γ' from z_0 corresponds a closed curve $\gamma = c\gamma'c^{-1}$from z_0. This correspondence is homotopy preserving and may thus be regarded as a correspondence between homotopy classes. As such it is product preserving, for $(c\gamma_1'c^{-1})(c\gamma_2'c^{-1})$ is homotopic to $c(\gamma_1'\gamma_2')c^{-1}$, by cancellation of $c^{-1}c$. Finally, the correspondence is one to one, for if γ is given we can choose $\gamma' = c^{-1}\gamma c$ and find that the corresponding curve $c\gamma'c^{-1} = (cc^{-1})\gamma(cc^{-1})$ is homotopic to γ. It is thus proved that the homotopy groups with respect to z_0 and z_0' are *isomorphic*.

If γ_1, γ_2 are any two arcs with the initial point z_0 and a common terminal point, then γ_1 is homotopic to γ_2 if and only if $\gamma_1\gamma_2^{-1}$ is homotopic to 1. For if γ_1 is homotopic to γ_2, then $\gamma_1\gamma_2^{-1}$ is homotopic to $\gamma_2\gamma_2^{-1}$, and hence to 1. Conversely, if $\gamma_1\gamma_2^{-1}$ is homotopic to 1, then

$$(\gamma_1\gamma_2^{-1})\gamma_2 = \gamma_1(\gamma_2^{-1}\gamma_2)$$

is simultaneously homotopic to γ_1 and γ_2, proving that γ_1 is homotopic to γ_2. For this reason it is sufficient to study the homotopy of closed curves.

The explicit determination of homotopy groups is simplified by the fact that the homotopy group is obviously a topological invariant. Indeed, by a topological mapping of Ω onto Ω' any deformation in Ω can be carried over to Ω' and is seen to determine a product preserving one-to-one correspondence between the homotopy classes. Topologically equivalent regions have therefore isomorphic homotopy groups.

The homotopy group of a disk reduces to the unit element; this means that any two arcs with common end points are homotopic. The proof makes use of the convexity of the disk: the arc $z = z_1(t)$ can be deformed into $z = z_2(t)$ by means of the deformation

$$z(t,u) = (1 - u)z_1(t) + uz_2(t)$$

whose deformation paths are line segments. The same proof would be valid for any convex region. In particular, the whole plane has likewise a homotopy group which reduces to the unit element.

We proved in Chap. 6, Sec. 1, that any simply connected region which is not the whole plane can be mapped conformally onto a disk. In this connection the conformality is not important, but the fact that the mapping is topological permits us to conclude that any simply connected region has a fundamental group which reduces to its unit element. We shall find that the converse is also true.

1.5. The Monodromy Theorem. Let Ω be a fixed region in the z-plane. We consider the case of a global analytic function $\mathbf{f}$ which can be continued along all arcs γ contained in Ω, starting with any branch defined at the initial point of γ. More precisely, to any arc $z = z(t)$, $\alpha \leqq t \leqq \beta$, contained in Ω, and for every function element $(f_0,\Omega_0) \in \mathbf{f}$ with $z(\alpha) \in \Omega_0$ there shall exist a continuation $\mathfrak{z}(t) = (f,z(t))$ whose initial branch is the one defined by (f_0,Ω_0).

When two arcs γ_1, γ_2 with common end points are given, we are interested to know whether a common initial branch, continued along γ_1 and γ_2, will lead to the same terminal branch. The basic theorem, known as the *monodromy theorem*, is the following:

Theorem 2. *If the arcs γ_1 and γ_2 are homotopic with respect to Ω, and if an initial branch of* $\mathbf{f}$ *can be continued along all arcs contained in Ω, then* *the continuations of this initial branch along γ_1 and γ_2 must lead to the same terminal branch.*

To begin with we note that continuation along an arc of the form $\gamma\gamma^{-1}$ will evidently lead back to the initial branch. Similarly, continuation along an arc of the form $\sigma_1(\gamma\gamma^{-1})\sigma_2$ will have the same effect as continuation along $\sigma_1\sigma_2$. For this reason, to say that the continuations along γ_1 and γ_2 lead to the same terminal branch is equivalent to saying that continuation along $\gamma_1\gamma_2^{-1}$ leads back to the initial element.

According to the assumption there exists a deformation $z(t,u)$ of γ_1 into γ_2. Every arc σ in the deformation rectangle R is carried by $z(t,u)$ into an arc $\sigma' \epsilon \Omega$, and if σ' begins at the initial point of γ_1 and γ_2 there exists a unique continuation of the given initial branch along σ'. For the sake of simplicity it will be called a continuation along σ. The theorem asserts that the continuation along the perimeter Γ of R leads back to the initial element. The sense in which Γ is described is immaterial, but should be fixed once and for all.

A simple proof can be based on the method of bisection. We begin by bisecting R horizontally, and denote by π_1 the perimeter of the lower half R_1, described from the lower left-hand corner 0 and in the direction which coincides with the direction of Γ along the common side. With the upper half R_2 we associate a curve π_2 which begins at 0, leads vertically to the lower left-hand corner of R_2, describes the perimeter of R_2 in the sense which coincides with that of Γ along the common side, and returns vertically to 0 (Fig. 40). We recognize that the curve $\pi_1\pi_2$ differs from Γ only by an intermediate arc of the form $\sigma\sigma^{-1}$. For this reason the effect of continuing along $\pi_1\pi_2$ is the same as if we continue along Γ. Consequently, if π_1 and π_2 both lead back to the initial branch, so does Γ. We make now the opposite assumption that Γ does not lead back to the initial branch. Then either π_1 or π_2 has the same property. The corre-

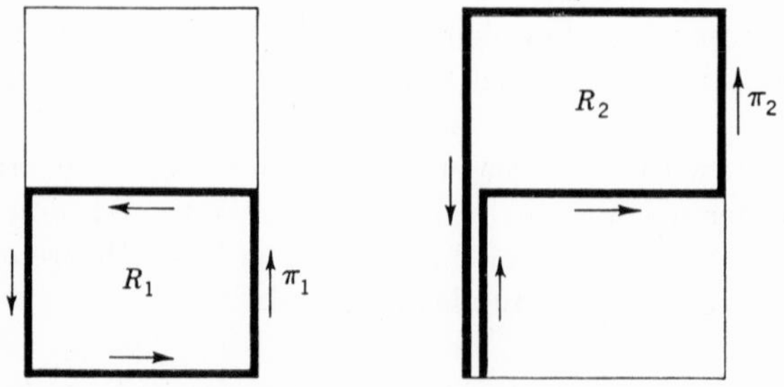

FIG. 40. The monodromy theorem.

sponding rectangle is bisected vertically, and the same reasoning is applied. When the process is repeated, we obtain a sequence of rectangles $R \supset R^{(1)} \supset R^{(2)} \supset \cdots \supset R^{(n)} \supset \cdots$ and corresponding closed curves $\pi^{(n)}$ such that the continuation of the initial branch along $\pi^{(n)}$ does *not* lead back to the same branch. Each $\pi^{(n)}$ is of the form $\sigma_n \Gamma_n \sigma_n^{-1}$ where σ_n is a well-determined polygon leading from 0 to the lower left-hand corner of $R^{(n)}$ and Γ_n denotes the perimeter of $R^{(n)}$; moreover, σ_n is a subarc of σ_{n+1}.

As $n \to \infty$ the rectangles $R^{(n)}$ converge to a point P_∞, and the polygons σ_n form, in the limit, a continuous curve σ_∞ ending at P_∞. There exists a continuation of the initial branch along σ_∞ which terminates with a branch $(f_\infty, z(P_\infty))$ at the point corresponding to P_∞. For sufficiently large n the image of Γ_n will be contained in a neighborhood Γ of $z(P_\infty)$, and the branch obtained at the terminal point of σ_n must be determined by the function element (f_∞, Δ). When this is the case, the element (f_∞, Δ) can be used to construct a continuation along $\pi^{(n)}$ which leads back to the initial branch. This contradicts the property by which $\pi^{(n)}$ was defined, and we have proved that the continuation along Γ must end with the initial branch.

The monodromy theorem implies, above all, that any global analytic function which can be continued along all arcs in a simply connected region determines one single-valued analytic function for each choice of the initial branch. This fact can also be expressed by saying that a Riemann surface (without branch points) over a simply connected region must consist of a single sheet.

We can further draw the consequence, already announced, that a region whose homotopy group reduces to the unit element must necessarily be simply connected. For suppose that Ω is multiply connected. Then there exists a bounded component E_0 of the complement of Ω, and if $z_0 \in E_0$ we know that $\log (z - z_0)$ is not single-valued in Ω. By the monodromy theorem it follows that the homotopy group of Ω cannot reduce to the unit element.

This is the last step toward proving the equivalence of the following three characterizations of simply connected regions: (1) Ω is simply connected if its complement is connected; (2) Ω is simply connected if it is homeomorphic with a disk; (3) Ω is simply connected if its fundamental group reduces to the unit element.

1.6. Branch Points. For a closer study of the singularities of multiple-valued functions it is necessary to determine, explicitly, the fundamental group of the punctured disk. Let the punctured disk be represented by $0 < |z| < 1$, and consider a fixed point, for instance the point $z_0 = r$ on the positive radius. By means of a central projection, given by

$$z(t,u) = (1 - u)z(t) + ur\frac{z(t)}{|z(t)|}$$

any closed curve $z = z(t)$ from z_0 can be deformed into a curve which lies on the circle $|z| = r$. It is thus sufficient to consider curves γ on this circle. The equation of γ will again be written as $z = z(t)$.

By continuity every t_0 has a neighborhood in which $|z(t) - z(t_0)| < r/2$; in such a neighborhood $z(t)$ cannot take both the values r and $-r$. It follows easily, by use of Heine-Borel's lemma or the method of bisection, that it is possible to write $\gamma = \gamma_1\gamma_2 \cdots \gamma_n$ where each γ_k either does not pass through r or does not pass through $-r$. For simplicity, let us refer to the points r and $-r$ by letters P_0 and P_0' (Fig. 41), and let the end points of γ_k be denoted by P_k and P_{k+1}. Since γ_k is contained in the simply connected region obtained by deleting either the positive or negative radius, it can be deformed into one of the two arcs P_kP_{k+1}. As a result γ can be deformed into a product of simple arcs with the successive end points $P_0P_1P_2 \cdots P_nP_0$. This path may in turn be replaced by $P_0P_1P_2P_0P_2P_3P_0 \cdots P_0P_{n-1}P_nP_0$ where each arc P_kP_0 and P_0P_k is, for definiteness, the one which does not contain P_0'. In fact, the new path is obtained by inserting the doubly traced arcs $P_kP_0P_k$ which we know to be homotopic to 1.

We have shown that each γ is homotopic to a product of closed curves of the form $P_0P_kP_{k+1}P_0$. If P_kP_{k+1} does not contain P_0', this curve is homotopic to 1. If, on the other hand, P_kP_{k+1} contains P_0' it is seen by enumeration of the possible cases that the curve is homotopic to C or C^{-1}, where C is the full circle. Consequently, every closed curve is homotopic to a power of C.

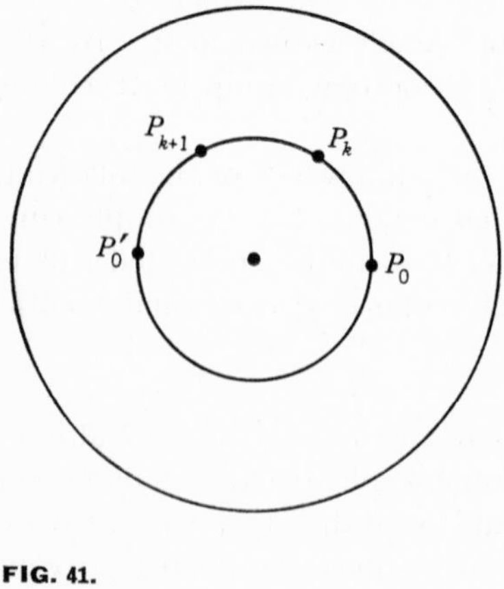

FIG. 41.

Finally, we observe that C^m is homotopic to 1 only if $m = 0$. This is seen by the fact that

$$\int_{C^m} \frac{dz}{z} = m \cdot 2\pi i,$$

while if the curve were homotopic to 1 the integral would have to vanish. From our results we conclude that the fundamental group of the punctured disk is isomorphic to the *additive group of integers*. Evidently, an arbitrary annulus has the same fundamental group.

We consider now a global analytic function **f** which can be continued along all arcs in the punctured disk $0 < |z| < 1$. We choose an initial branch at $z_0 = r$ and continue it along the curves C^m. Either the continuation never returns to the initial branch, or there exists a smallest positive integer h such that C^h leads back to the initial branch. In the latter case, set $m = qh + r$ with $0 \leqq r < h$. If C^m leads back to the initial branch, so does C^r. But since $r < h$ that is possible only if $r = 0$, and we find that C^m leads to the initial branch if and only if m is a multiple of h.

Consider the mapping $z = \zeta^h$ of $0 < |\zeta| < 1$ onto $0 < |z| < 1$. We claim that **f** can be expressed as a single-valued analytic function $F(\zeta)$ in the punctured disk of the ζ-plane. The precise sense of this statement is that there exists, for every ζ_1, $0 < |\zeta_1| < 1$, a function element $(f,\Omega) \in \mathbf{f}$ with $\zeta_1^h \in \Omega$, such that $F(\zeta) = f(\zeta^h)$ in a neighborhood of ζ_1; in particular, it is required that the function element which corresponds to the point $\zeta_0 = r^{1/h}$ determines the initial branch at z_0.

In order to construct $F(\zeta)$, we join ζ_0 to ζ by an arc γ' and continue the initial branch of **f** along the image of γ' under the mapping $z = \zeta^h$; we define $F(\zeta)$ as the terminal value obtained through this continuation. It must be proved that $F(\zeta)$ is uniquely determined. If γ_1' and γ_2' are two paths from ζ_0 to ζ, then $\gamma_1'\gamma_2'^{-1}$ can be deformed into a power C'^n of the circle through ζ_0. Consequently, the image curve $\gamma_1\gamma_2^{-1}$ can be deformed into the image of C'^n, which is C^{nh}. But C^{nh} leads back to the initial branch, and therefore γ_1 and γ_2 determine the same terminal branch. Finally, if ζ is in a neighborhood of ζ_1, we can first follow an arc γ_1' from ζ_0 to ζ_1 and then a variable arc γ' from ζ_1 to ζ which stays within the neighborhood. If the neighborhood is sufficiently restricted, the continuation along the image of γ' is determined by a single function element (f,Ω), and we have $F(\zeta) = f(\zeta^h)$ in that neighborhood.

Since $F(\zeta)$ is single-valued and analytic in a punctured neighborhood of the origin, it has a convergent Laurent development of the form

$$F(\zeta) = \sum_{-\infty}^{\infty} A_n\zeta^n.$$

The corresponding multiple-valued function of z may be said to possess the development

(1) $$f(z) = \sum_{-\infty}^{\infty} A_n z^{n/h}.$$

It must be observed that this development depends on the choice of the initial branch. Different initial branches may yield entirely different developments and, in particular, different values of h. The series(1) yields a total of h related developments obtained by choosing different initial values of $z^{1/h}$. If $\omega = e^{2\pi i/h}$, these developments are represented by

(2) $$f_\nu(z) = \sum_{-\infty}^{\infty} A_n \omega^{\nu n} z^{n/h} \qquad (\nu = 0,1, \ldots ,h - 1).$$

When the branch (f_ν,z_0) is continued along C, it leads to the branch $(f_{\nu+1},z_0)$ with the understanding that the subscript h is identified with 0.

In special cases the Laurent development may contain only a finite number of negative powers. Then $F(\zeta)$ has either a removable singularity or a pole, and the multiple-valued function $f(z)$ (or, more correctly, the global analytic function obtained by continuing the given initial branch within a punctured disk) is said to have an *algebraic singularity* or *branch point* at $z = 0$, provided of course that $h > 1$. If $F(\zeta)$ has a removable singularity, the branch point is an *ordinary* algebraic singularity, in the opposite case it is an *algebraic pole.* In either case $f(z)$ tends to a definite limit A_0 or ∞ as z tends to 0 along an arbitrary arc.

Clearly, we could just as well have studied an isolated singularity at an arbitrary point a or ∞, and the radius of the punctured disk can be as small as we wish. In the case of a finite h the correspondence between $w = f(z)$ and the independent variable z can be expressed through equations of the form

$$w = \sum_{-\infty}^{\infty} A_n \zeta^n$$

$$z = a + \zeta^h \qquad \text{or} \qquad z = \zeta^{-h}.$$

The variable ζ takes the name of *local uniformizing variable.*

In the case of an algebraic singularity it is desirable to complete the Riemann surface of **f** by the inclusion of a corresponding branch point on the surface. The projection of this point will be a, and the point itself is not determined by a branch of **f**, but by developments similar to (2). Finally, a neighborhood is formed by the branches which correspond to points ζ in a neighborhood of $\zeta = 0$. From now on it will be assumed that the Riemann surface of a global analytic function includes all such branch points.

2. ALGEBRAIC FUNCTIONS

An equation of the form $P(w,z) = 0$, where P is a polynomial in two variables, has for each z a finite number of solutions $w_1(z), \ldots, w_m(z)$. We wish to show that these roots can be interpreted as values of a global analytic function $\mathbf{f}(z)$ which is then called an *algebraic function.* Conversely, if a global analytic function is given, we want to be able to tell whether it does or does not satisfy a polynomial equation.

2.1. The Resultant of Two Polynomials. A polynomial $P(w,z)$ in two variables is *irreducible* if it cannot be expressed as the product of two polynomials none of which is constant. Two polynomials P and Q are *relatively prime* if they have no common factor except for constants.

The following theorem is algebraic in character. Because of its fundamental importance for the theory of algebraic functions we will nevertheless reproduce its proof.

Theorem 3. *If $P(w,z)$ and $Q(w,z)$ are relatively prime polynomials, there are only a finite number of values z_0 for which the equations $P(w,z_0) = 0$ and $Q(w,z_0) = 0$ have a common root.*

We suppose that P and Q are ordered according to decreasing powers of w and set $Q(w,z) = b_0(z)w^m + \cdots + b_m(z)$ where $b_0(z)$ is not identically zero. If P is divided by Q, the division algorithm yields a quotient and remainder which are polynomials in w and rational functions in z with a power of $b_0(z)$ as denominator. It is therefore possible to set up a Euclidean algorithm of the form

$$
\begin{aligned}
b_0^{r_0}P &= q_0Q + R_1 \\
b_0^{r_1}Q &= q_1R_1 + R_2 \\
b_0^{r_2}R_1 &= q_2R_2 + R_3 \\
\cdots &\cdots\cdots\cdots\cdots \\
b_0^{r_{n-1}}R_{n-2} &= q_{n-1}R_{n-1} + R_n
\end{aligned}
\tag{3}
$$

where the q_k and R_k are now polynomials and $r_0, \ldots, r_{n-1}$ denote integral exponents $\geqq 0$. The degrees in w of the R_k are decreasing, and R_n is a polynomial in z alone. If $R_n(z)$ were identically zero, the unique factorization theorem implies, by the last relation in (3), that R_{n-2} would be divisible by any irreducible factor of R_{n-1} which is of positive degree in w. The same reasoning shows, step by step, that all the R_k as well as Q and P would be divisible by the same factor. This is contrary to the assumption, for R_{n-1} is of positive degree in w and must therefore have an irreducible factor which contains w.

Suppose now that $P(w_0,z_0) = 0$ and $Q(w_0,z_0) = 0$. Substituting these values in (3) we obtain $R_1(w_0,z_0) = 0, \ldots, R_{n-1}(w_0,z_0) = 0$ and finally $R_n(z_0) = 0$. But since R_n is not identically zero, there are only a finite number of z_0 which satisfy this condition, and the theorem follows.

The polynomial $R_n(z)$ is called the *resultant* of P and Q. More precisely, if we wish the resultant to be uniquely determined, we should require that the exponents r_k in (3) are the smallest possible. Actually, we are not so interested in the resultant as in the statement of Theorem 3. The theorem will be applied to an irreducible polynomial $P(w,z)$ and its partial derivative $P_w(w,z)$ with respect to w. These polynomials are relatively prime as soon as P has positive degree in w, and the resultant of P and P_w is called the *discriminant* of P. The zeros of the discriminant are the values z_0 for which the equation $P(w,z_0) = 0$ has multiple roots.

We note, finally, that the resultant $R(z)$ of any two relatively prime polynomials P and Q can be written in the form $R = pP + qQ$ where p and q are polynomials. This follows immediately from (3).

2.2. Definition and Properties of Algebraic Functions. We begin by formulating a precise definition:

Definition 2. *A complete analytic function* $\mathbf{f}$ *is called an algebraic function if all its function elements* (f,Ω) *satisfy a relation* $P(f(z),z) = 0$ *in* Ω, *where* $P(w,z)$ *is a polynomial which does not vanish identically.*

Because of the permanence of functional relations it is sufficient to assume that one function element satisfies the equation $P(f(z),z) = 0$. The others will then automatically satisfy the same relation. Moreover, it may be assumed that $P(w,z)$ is an irreducible polynomial. Suppose indeed that $P(w,z)$ has the factorization $P = P_1P_2 \ldots P_n$ in irreducible factors. For any fixed point $z \in \Omega$ one of the equations $P_k(f(z),z) = 0$ must hold. If we consider a sequence of different points $z_n \in \Omega$ which tend to a limit in Ω, then one of the relations $P_k(f(z_n),z_n)$ must hold infinitely often. It follows that this particular relation $P_k(f(z),z) = 0$ is satisfied identically in Ω and, consequently, by all the function elements of f. We are thus free to replace P by P_k.

It is also easy to see that the irreducible polynomial P determined by an algebraic function is unique up to a constant factor. If Q is an essentially different irreducible polynomial, we can determine the resultant $R(z) = pP + qQ$. If $P(f(z),z) = 0$ and $Q(f(z),z) = 0$ for all $z \in \Omega$ we would obtain $R(z) = 0$ in Ω, contrary to the fact that $R(z)$ is not identically zero. We note that P cannot reduce to a polynomial of z alone. If it contains only w, it must be of the form $w - a$, and the function $\mathbf{f}$ reduces to the constant a.

We prove next that there exists an algebraic function corresponding to any irreducible polynomial $P(w,z)$ of positive degree in w. Suppose that

$$P(w,z) = a_0(z)w^n + a_1(z)w^{n-1} + \cdots + a_n(z).$$

If z_0 is neither a zero of the polynomial $a_0(z)$ nor a zero of the discriminant of P, the equation $P(w,z_0) = 0$ has exactly n distinct roots $w_1, w_2, \ldots, w_n$. Under this condition the following is true:

Lemma 1. *There exists an open disk Δ, containing z_0, and n function elements $(f_1,\Delta), (f_2,\Delta), \ldots, (f_n,\Delta)$ with these properties:*

(a) $P(f_i(z),z) = 0$ *in* Δ;
(b) $f_i(z_0) = w_i$;
(c) *if* $P(w,z) = 0$, $z \in \Delta$, *then* $w = f_i(z)$ *for some* i.

The polynomial $P(w,z_0)$ has simple zeros at $w = w_i$. We determine $\varepsilon > 0$ so that the disks $|w - w_i| \leqq \varepsilon$ do not overlap and denote the circles $|w - w_i| = \varepsilon$ by C_i. Then $P(w,z_0) \neq 0$ on C_i, and by the argument principle

$$\frac{1}{2\pi i}\int_{C_i} \frac{P_w(w,z_0)}{P(w,z_0)}\,dw = 1.$$

If z_0 is replaced by z, the integrals become well-defined continuous functions of z in a neighborhood of z_0. Since they can only take integer values, there exists a neighborhood Δ such that

$$\frac{1}{2\pi i}\int_{C_i} \frac{P_w(w,z)}{P(w,z)}\,dw = 1$$

for all $z \in \Delta$. This means that the equation $P(w,z) = 0$ has exactly one root in the disk $|w - w_i| < \varepsilon$; we denote this root by $f_i(z)$. By the residue calculus its value is given by

$$f_i(z) = \frac{1}{2\pi i}\int_{C_i} w\,\frac{P_w(w,z)}{P(w,z)}\,dw.$$

This representation shows that $f_i(z)$ is analytic. Moreover, $f_i(z_0) = w_i$, and (c) follows from the fact that we have exhibited n roots of the equation $P(w,z) = 0$, and it can have no more.

The lemma implies at once that there exists an algebraic function **f** corresponding to the polynomial P; in fact, we can choose **f** to be the complete analytic function determined by the element (f_1,Δ) for any z_0 which does not coincide with one of the finitely many excluded points.

We will show, moreover, that all such function elements belong to the same complete analytic function; this will also prove that the function **f** which corresponds to P is unique. Let (f,Ω) be one of these function elements. There must exist a $z_0 \in \Omega$ which is not one of the excluded points; we determine a corresponding Δ. Since $P(f(z),z) = 0$ for $z \in \Omega$, it follows by (c) that $f(z)$ equals some $f_i(z)$ at each point of $\Delta\Omega$. But then $f(z)$ equals the same $f_i(z)$ at infinitely many points in any neighborhood of z_0, and hence (f,Ω) belongs to the complete analytic function determined by (f_i,Δ).

Let the excluded points be denoted by $c_1, c_2, \ldots, c_m$. We wish to show that a function element (f,Ω) which satisfies $P(f(z),z) = 0$ can be continued along any arc which does not pass through a point c_k. If this were not so there would exist an arc $z = z(t)$, $\alpha \leqq t \leqq \beta$, such that a given initial branch can be continued along all subarcs $\alpha \leqq t \leqq \tau < \beta$, but not along the whole arc. Set $z_0 = z(\beta)$, determine Δ according to Lemma 1, and choose τ so that $z(t) \in \Delta$ for $\tau \leqq t \leqq \beta$. The same reasoning as above shows that the branch $(f,z(\tau))$ obtained by the continuation must be determined by one of the function elements (f_i,Δ). But then it can be continued all the way to β, and we have reached a contradiction.

It has not yet been proved that all elements (f_i,Δ) belong to the same global analytic function. For this part of the proof it is necessary to study the behavior at the critical points c_k in greater detail.

2.3. Behavior at the Critical Points. The points c_0 which so far have been excluded from our considerations were the zeros of the first coefficient $a_0(z)$ of P, and the zeros of the discriminant. Let δ be chosen so that the disk $|z - c_k| \leqq \delta$ contains no other critical points than c_k. We fix a point $z_0 \neq c_k$ in this disk and select one of the branches $f_i(z)$ at that point. This branch can be continued along all arcs in the punctured disk. Moreover, if it is continued along the circle C of center c_k through z_0, we must return with a branch $f_i(z)$. Since there is only a finite number of such branches, it follows easily that there must exist a smallest positive integer $h \leqq n$ with the property that continuation along C^h leads back to the initial branch $f_i(z)$. By the fundamental result of Sec. 1.6 we can write

$$f_i(z) = \sum_{\nu=-\infty}^{\infty} A_\nu (z - c_k)^{\nu/h}. \tag{4}$$

Suppose first that c_k is not a zero of $a_0(z)$. Then $f_i(z)$ remains bounded as z tends to c_k. Indeed, as soon as $f_i(z) \neq 0$, the equation $P(f_i(z),z) = 0$ can be written in the form

$$a_0(z) + a_1(z)f_i(z)^{-1} + \cdots + a_n(z)f_i(z)^{-n} = 0. \tag{5}$$

If $f_i(z)$ were unbounded, there would exist points $z_n \to c_k$ with $f_i(z_n) \to \infty$. Substitution in (5) would yield $a_0(z_n) \to 0$, contrary to the assumption $a_0(c_k) \neq 0$. It follows that the development (4) contains only positive powers, and the branch $f_i(z)$ has an ordinary algebraic singularity at c_k.

We consider now the case where $a_0(c_k) = 0$. If the multiplicity of the zero is denoted by m, we know that $\lim\limits_{z \to c_k} a_0(z)(z - c_k)^{-m} \neq 0$. From (5) we obtain

$$a_0(z)(z - c_k)^{-m} + a_1(z)(z - c_k)^{-m}f_i(z)^{-1} + \cdots + a_n(z)(z - c_k)^{-m}f_i(z)^{-n} = 0.$$

If the expression $f_i(z)(z - c_k)^m$ were unbounded, we would again be led to a contradiction. As in Sec. 1.6 we write

$$F(\zeta) = \sum_{-\infty}^{\infty} A_\nu \zeta^\nu$$

and find that $F(\zeta)\zeta^{mh}$ is bounded. Consequently $F(\zeta)$ has a pole of at most order mh, and the branch $f_i(z)$ has an algebraic pole at c_k or, in special cases, an ordinary algebraic singularity.

Finally, the behavior at $z = \infty$ needs also to be discussed. It is clear that we have a development of the form

$$f_i(z) = \sum_{-\infty}^{\infty} A_\nu z^{\nu/h},$$

valid in a neighborhood of ∞. Suppose that the polynomial $a_i(z)$ is of degree r_i (the coefficients which vanish identically will be left out of consideration). Choose an integer m such that

$$m > \frac{1}{k}(r_k - r_0) \tag{6}$$

for $k = 1, \ldots, n$. We contend that $f_i(z)z^{-m}$ must be bounded as $z \to \infty$. If this were not so we would have $f_i(z)^{-1}z^m \to 0$ for a sequence tending to ∞. This would imply $f_i(z)^{-k}z^{mk} \to 0$ and, by (6), $f_i(z)^{-k}z^{r_k - r_0} \to 0$ for $k \geqq 1$. If (5) is multiplied by z^{-r_0} it follows that all terms except the first tend to zero. This is a contradiction, and we may conclude that $f_i(z)$ has at most an algebraic pole at infinity.

To sum up, we have proved that an algebraic function has at most algebraic singularities in the extended plane. We will now prove a converse of this statement. In order to obtain a converse it is essential to add an assumption which implies that there are only a finite number of branches at a given point.

Let **f** be a complete analytic function. For each c we assume the existence of a punctured disk Δ, centered at c, such that all branches of **f** which are defined at a point $z_0 \in \Delta$ can be continued along all arcs in Δ and show algebraic character at c. The assumption shall be satisfied also for $c = \infty$, in which case Δ is the exterior of a circle. Moreover, for one Δ it must be assumed that the number of different branches at z_0 is finite.

Since the extended plane can be covered by a finite number of disks Δ, the center included, it follows that only a finite number of points c can be effective singularities; we denote these points by c_k. It is easy to prove that the number of branches at any point $z \neq c_k$ is constant. For every such point has a neighborhood in which all branches of **f** are single-valued and can be continued throughout the neighborhood. It follows that the set of points z with exactly n branches is open (n can be finite or infinite). Since the extended plane minus the points c_k is connected, only one of these sets is nonempty. Hence n is constant, by assumption it cannot be infinite, and it cannot be zero since in that case **f** would be an empty collection of function elements.

The branches at any point $z \neq c_k$ may now be denoted as $f_1(z), \ldots, f_n(z)$, except that the ordering remains indeterminate. We form now the elementary symmetric functions of the $f_i(z)$, that is to say the coefficients of the polynomial

$$(w - f_1(z))(w - f_2(z)) \cdots (w - f_n(z)).$$

These coefficients are well-defined functions of z, and obviously analytic except for possible isolated singularities at the points c_k. As z approaches c_k we know that each $f_i(z)$ may grow toward infinity at most like a negative power of $|z - c_k|$. The same is hence true of the elementary symmetric functions. We conclude that the isolated singularities, including the one at infinity, are at most poles, and consequently the elementary symmetric functions are rational functions of z. If their common denominator is denoted by $a_0(z)$, we find that all branches $f_i(z)$ must satisfy a polynomial equation

$$a_0(z)w^n + a_1(z)w^{n-1} + \cdots + a_n(z) = 0,$$

and it is proved that **f** is algebraic.

It is now easy to settle the point which was left open in Sec. 2.2. Suppose that the function element (f,Ω) satisfies the equation $P(f(z),z) = 0$ where P is irreducible and of degree n in w. Then the corresponding complete analytic function **f** has only algebraic singularities and a finite number of branches. According to what we have just shown **f** will satisfy a polynomial equation *whose degree is equal to the number of branches.* It will hence satisfy an irreducible equation whose degree is not higher. But the only irreducible equation it can satisfy is $P(w,z) = 0$, and its degree is n. Therefore the number of branches is exactly n, and we have shown that all solutions of $P(w,z) = 0$ are branches of the same analytic function.

It remains only to collect the results:

Theorem 4. *An analytic function is an algebraic function if it has a finite number of branches and at most algebraic singularities. Every algebraic function* $w = \mathbf{f}(z)$ *satisfies an irreducible equation* $P(w,z) = 0$, *unique up to a constant factor, and every such equation determines a corresponding algebraic function uniquely.*

It is also customary to say that an irreducible equation $P(w,z) = 0$ defines an *algebraic curve.* The theory of algebraic curves is a highly developed branch of algebra and function theory. We have been able to develop only the most elementary part of the function theoretic aspect.

EXERCISE

Determine the position and nature of the singularities of the algebraic function defined by $w^3 - 3wz + 2z^3 = 0$.

3. PICARD'S THEOREM

In this section we shall prove the celebrated theorem of Picard, which asserts that an entire function omits at most one finite value. We shall prove it as an application of the monodromy theorem (Sec. 1.5), using the modular function $\lambda(\tau)$ (Chap. 7, Sec. 3.5) in an essential way. This is Picard's own proof. Many other proofs have been given which are more elementary in that they need less preparation, but none is as penetrating as the original proof.

3.1. Lacunary Values. A complex number a is said to be a *lacunary value* of a function $f(z)$ if $f(z) \neq a$ in the region where f is defined. For instance, 0 is a lacunary value of e^z in the whole plane.

Theorem 5 (Picard). *An entire function with more than one finite lacunary value reduces to a constant.*

We recall that an entire function $f(z)$ is one which is analytic in the whole plane. If a and b are distinct finite values and if $f(z)$ is different from a and b for all z, we are required to show that $f(z)$ is constant.

Consider $f_1(z) = (f(z) - a)/(b - a)$. This function is entire and $\neq 0$ and 1. If f_1 is constant, so is f. Therefore it is no restriction to assume from the beginning that $a = 0$, $b = 1$.

We shall define a global analytic function $\mathbf{h}$ whose function elements (h,Ω) share the following property: Im $h(z) > 0$, and $\lambda(h(z)) = f(z)$ for $z \in \Omega$. Here $\lambda(\tau)$ is the modular function defined in Chap. 7, Sec. 3.5. It will be shown that $\mathbf{h}$ can be continued along all paths. Since the plane is simply connected it will follow by the monodromy theorem that $\mathbf{h}$ defines an entire function $h(z)$. Because $h(z)$ has all its values in the upper half plane, e^{ih} is bounded. By Liouville's theorem h must reduce to a constant, and so does $f(z) = \lambda(h(z))$.

By Theorem 7 of Chap. 7 there exists a point τ_0 in the upper half plane such that $\lambda(\tau_0) = f(0)$. Because $\lambda'(\tau_0) \neq 0$, by the same theorem, there exists a local inverse of λ, defined in a neighborhood Δ_0 of $f(0)$ and denoted by λ_0^{-1}, characterized by the conditions $\lambda(\lambda_0^{-1}(w)) = w$ in Δ_0 and

$$\lambda_0^{-1}(f(0)) = \tau_0.$$

By continuity there is a neighborhood Ω_0 of the origin in which $f(z) \in \Delta_0$, and we can therefore define $h(z) = \lambda_0^{-1}(f(z))$ in Ω_0. We shall let $\mathbf{h}$ be the complete analytic function obtained by continuing the function element (h,Ω_0) in all possible ways.

We have to show that the element (h,Ω_0) can be continued along all paths, and that Im h remains positive. If this were not true we could find a path $z = z(t)$, $0 \leqq t \leqq t_1$, such that h can be continued and Im h remains positive up to any $t < t_1$, while either h cannot be continued up to t_1, or else Im $h(z(t))$ tends to 0 for $t \to t_1$. We can determine a value τ_1 with $\lambda(\tau_1) = f(z(t_1))$ and a local inverse λ_1^{-1} with $\lambda_1^{-1}(f(z(t_1))) = \tau_1$, defined in a neighborhood Δ_1 of $f(z(t_1))$. Let Ω_1 be a neighborhood of $z(t_1)$ in which $f(z) \in \Delta_1$, and choose $t_2 < t_1$ so that $z(t) \in \Delta_1$ for $t_2 \leqq t \leqq t_1$. We know that $\lambda(\tau)$ has the same value $f(z(t_2))$ at $\tau = h(z(t_2))$ and at $\tau = \lambda_1^{-1}(f(z(t_2)))$. Hence, by Theorem 8 of Chap. 7, there exists a modular transformation S in the congruence subgroup mod 2 such that

$$S[\lambda_1^{-1}(f(z(t_2)))] = h(z(t_2)).$$

We now define h_1 in Ω_1 by $h_1(z) = S[\lambda_1^{-1}(f(z))]$. It is evident that (h_1,Ω_1) is a continuation of $\mathbf{h}$ up to t_1 which satisfies $\lambda(h_1(z)) = f(z)$ and Im $h_1 > 0$. We conclude that $\mathbf{h}$ can indeed be continued along all paths, and as we have pointed out, Picard's theorem follows at once.

We have carried out the proof in such painstaking detail in an effort to convince the reader that the monodromy theorem plays as essential a role in the proof as the modular function.

4. LINEAR DIFFERENTIAL EQUATIONS

The theory of global analytic functions makes it possible to study, with a great degree of generality, the complex solutions of ordinary differential equations. Of all differential equations the linear ones are the simplest, and also the most important. A linear equation of order n has the form

$$(7) \quad a_0(z)\frac{d^n w}{dz^n} + a_1(z)\frac{d^{n-1}w}{bz^{n-1}} + \cdots + a_{n-1}(z)\frac{dw}{dz} + a_n(z)w = b(z)$$

where the coefficients $a_k(z)$ and the right-hand member $b(z)$ are single-valued analytic functions. In order to simplify the treatment we restrict our attention to the case where these functions are defined in the whole plane; they are thus assumed to be entire functions. A *solution* of (7) is a global analytic function $\mathbf{f}$ which satisfies the identity

$$(8) \qquad a_0\mathbf{f}^{(n)} + a_1\mathbf{f}^{(n-1)} + \cdots + a_{n-1}\mathbf{f}' + a_n\mathbf{f} = b.$$

We have already remarked that this is a meaningful equation and that it is fulfilled as soon as a function element (f,Ω) of $\mathbf{f}$ satisfies the corresponding equation with $\mathbf{f}$ replaced by f. A function element with this property will be called a *local solution.*

The reader who is familiar with the real case will expect the equation (8) to have n linearly independent solutions. This is so as far as local solutions are concerned, but we must be prepared to find that different local solutions can be elements of the same global analytic function. In other words, in the complex case part of the problem is to find out to what extent the local solutions are analytic continuations of each other.

The equation (7) is *homogeneous* if $b(z)$ is identically zero. This is the most important case, and it is the only one we will treat. Furthermore, we can assume that the coefficients $a_k(z)$ have no common zeros; in fact, if z_0 were a common zero we could divide all coefficients by $z - z_0$, and the solutions would remain the same. As a matter of fact, if we are willing to consider meromorphic coefficients we may divide (7) by $a_0(z)$ from the beginning. Conversely, if an equation with meromorphic coefficients is given, each coefficient can be written as a quotient of two entire functions; after multiplication with the common denominator we obtain an equivalent equation with entire coefficients. It is thus irrelevant whether we do or do not allow the coefficients to have poles.

In the case $n = 1$ the equation (7) has the explicit solution

$$w = e^{-\int \frac{a_1(z)}{a_0(z)}dz}.$$

The only problem is thus to determine the multiple-valued character of the integral, a question which has already been treated. On the other hand, the case $n = 2$ is found to have all the characteristic features of the general case. For this reason we find it sufficient to deal with homogeneous linear differential equations of the second order.

4.1. *Ordinary Points.* A point z_0 is called an *ordinary point* for the differential equation

$$a_0(z)w'' + a_1(z)w' + a_2(z)w = 0 \tag{9}$$

if and only if $a_0(z_0) \neq 0$. The central theorem to be proved is the following:

Theorem 6. *If z_0 is an ordinary point for the equation* (9), *there exists a local solution (f,Ω), $z_0 \in \Omega$, with arbitrarily described values $f(z_0) = b_0$ and $f'(z_0) = b_1$. The branch (f,z_0) is uniquely determined.*

We prefer to write (9) in the form

$$w'' = p(z)w' + q(z)w \tag{10}$$

where $p(z) = -a_1/a_0$, $q(z) = -a_2/a_0$. The assumption means that $p(z)$ and $q(z)$ are analytic in a neighborhood of z_0; for convenience we may take $z_0 = 0$. Let

$$\begin{aligned} p(z) &= p_0 + p_1z + \cdots + p_nz^n + \cdots \\ q(z) &= q_0 + q_1z + \cdots + q_nz^n + \cdots \end{aligned} \tag{11}$$

be the Taylor developments of $p(z)$ and $q(z)$.

In order to solve (10) we use the method of indeterminate coefficients. If the theorem is true, the solution $w = f(z)$ must have a Taylor development

$$f(z) = b_0 + b_1z + \cdots + b_nz^n + \cdots \tag{12}$$

whose coefficients satisfy the conditions

$$\begin{aligned} 2b_2 &= b_1p_0 + b_0q_0 \\ 6b_3 &= 2b_2p_0 + b_1p_1 + b_1q_0 + b_0q_1 \\ &\cdots\cdots\cdots\cdots\cdots \\ n(n-1)b_n &= (n-1)b_{n-1}p_0 + (n-2)b_{n-2}p_1 + \cdots + b_1p_{n-2} \\ &\quad + b_{n-2}q_0 + b_{n-3}q_1 + \cdots + b_0q_{n-2} \\ &\cdots\cdots\cdots\cdots\cdots \end{aligned} \tag{13}$$

This already proves the uniqueness. All that remains to prove is that the equations (13) lead to a power series (12) with a positive radius of convergence. It will then follow by permissible operations of term-wise differentiation, multiplication, and rearrangement that (12) is a solution of the equation with desired initial values of f and f'.

Since the series (11) have positive radii of convergence, there exist, by the Cauchy inequalities, constants M_0 and $r_0 > 0$ such that

$$|p_n| \leqq M_0 r_0^{-n} \qquad |q_n| \leqq M_0 r_0^{-n}. \tag{14}$$

In order to show that (12) has likewise a positive radius of convergence, is is sufficient to prove similar inequalities

$$|b_n| \leqq M r^{-n} \tag{15}$$

for a suitable choice of M and r.

The natural idea is to prove (15) by induction on n. In the first place (15) must hold for $n = 0$ and $n = 1$; this leads to the preliminary conditions $|b_0| \leqq M$, $|b_1| \leqq Mr^{-1}$ which are satisfied for sufficiently large M and sufficiently small r. Assume (15) to be valid for all subscripts $<n$. In order to simplify the computations we choose $r < r_0$; then the general equation (13) leads at once to the estimate

$$\begin{aligned} n(n-1)|b_n| &\leqq MM_0[(1 + 2 + \cdots + (n-1))r^{1-n} + (n-1)r^{2-n}] \\ &= MM_0\left[\frac{n(n-1)}{2}\,r + (n-1)r^2\right]r^{-n}. \end{aligned}$$

We have thus

$$|b_n| \leqq MM_0\left(\frac{r}{2} + \frac{r^2}{n}\right)r^{-n} \leqq MM_0\left(\frac{r}{2} + r^2\right)r^{-n}$$

and (15) follows, provided that $M_0(r/2 + r^2) \leqq 1$. It is clear that this and the preceding requirements are fulfilled for all sufficiently small r. The proof is complete.

There exist, in particular, local solutions $f_0(z)$ and $f_1(z)$ which satisfy the conditions $f_0(z_0) = 1$, $f_0'(z_0) = 0$ and $f_1(z_0) = 0$, $f_1'(z_0) = 1$. Because of the uniqueness the solution with the initial values b_0, b_1 must be $f(z) = b_0 f_0(z) + b_1 f_1(z)$. Hence every local solution is a linear combination of $f_0(z)$ and $f_1(z)$. Moreover, the solutions $f_0(z)$ and $f_1(z)$ are linearly independent, for if $b_0 f_0(z) + b_1 f_1(z) = 0$ we obtain first $b_0 = 0$ by substituting $z = z_0$, and subsequently $b_1 = 0$ since $f_1(z)$ cannot be identically zero.

EXERCISES

1. Find the power-series developments about the origin of two linearly independent solutions of $w'' = zw$.

2. The Hermite polynomials are defined by

$$H_n(z) = (-1)^n e^{z^2} \frac{d^n}{dz^n} (e^{-z^2}).$$

Prove that $H_n(z)$ is a solution of $w'' - 2zw' + 2nw = 0$.

4.2. Regular Singular Points. Any point z_0 such that $a_0(z_0) = 0$ is called a *singular point* of the equation (9). If the equation is written in the form (10), the assumption means that either $p(z)$ or $q(z)$ has a pole at z_0, for we continue to exclude the case of common zeros of all the coefficients in (9).

There are different kinds of singular points. We begin by a preliminary study of the simplest case which occurs when $a_0(z)$ has a simple zero. Under this hypothesis the functions $p(z)$ and $q(z)$ have at most simple poles, and if we choose $z_0 = 0$ the Laurent developments are of the form

$$p(z) = \frac{p_{-1}}{z} + p_0 + p_1 z + \cdots$$

$$q(z) = \frac{q_{-1}}{z} + q_0 + q_1 z + \cdots .$$

This time, if we substitute

$$w = b_0 + b_1 z + b_2 z^2 + \cdots$$

in (10), the comparison of coefficients yields

$$\begin{aligned} -p_{-1}b_1 &= b_0 q_{-1} \\ 2(1 - p_{-1})b_2 &= b_1 p_0 + b_1 q_{-1} + b_0 q_0 \\ &\cdots\cdots\cdots \\ n(n - 1 - p_{-1})b_n &= (n-1)b_{n-1}p_0 + (n-2)b_{n-2}p_1 + \cdots \\ &\quad + b_1 p_{n-2} + b_{n-1}q_{-1} + b_{n-2}q_0 + \cdots + b_0 q_{n-2} \\ &\cdots\cdots\cdots \end{aligned} \tag{16}$$

This system of relations is essentially different from (13). In the first place, only b_0 can be chosen arbitrarily, and hence the method yields at most one linearly independent solution. Secondly, if p_{-1} is zero or a positive integer, the system (16) has either no solution or one of the b_n can be chosen arbitrarily.

Assuming that p_{-1} is not zero or a positive integer we will show that the resulting power series has a positive radius of convergence. As before we use the estimates (14), choose $M \geqq |b_0|$, and assume (15) for subscripts $<n$. Under the auxiliary hypothesis $r \leqq r_0$ we obtain

$$n|n - 1 - p_{-1}| \cdot |b_n| \leqq Mr^{-n}\left\{M_0\left[\frac{n(n-1)}{2}r + (n-1)r^2\right] + |q_{-1}|r\right\}.$$

Inasmuch as $(n - 1)/|n - 1 - p_{-1}|$ is bounded, an inequality of the form

$$|b_n| \leqq Mr^{-n}(Ar + Br^2)$$

will hold for all n. For sufficiently small r this is stronger than (15), and the convergence follows.

As already indicated, the result is of a preliminary nature. Our real object is to solve (10) in the presence of a *regular singularity* at z_0. This terminology is used to indicate that $p(z)$ has at most a simple and $q(z)$ at most a double pole at z_0.

Under these circumstances it turns out that there are solutions of the form $w = z^\alpha g(z)$ where $g(z)$ is analytic and $\neq 0$ at $z_0(= 0)$. We make this substitution in (10) and find, after brief computation, that $g(z)$ must satisfy the differential equation

$$g'' = \left(p - \frac{2\alpha}{z}\right)g' + \left(q + \frac{\alpha p}{z} - \frac{\alpha(\alpha - 1)}{z^2}\right)g. \tag{17}$$

For arbitrary α this is of the same type as the original equation, and nothing has been gained. We may, however, choose α so that the coefficient of g has only a simple pole. If $q(z)$ has the development

$$q(z) = \frac{q_{-2}}{z^2} + \cdots$$

this will be the case if α satisfies the quadratic equation

$$\alpha(\alpha - 1) - p_{-1}\alpha - q_{-2} = 0, \tag{18}$$

known as the *indicial equation*. For such α our preliminary result shows that (10) has a solution of the form $z^\alpha g(z)$, $g(0) \neq 0$, provided that $p_{-1} - 2\alpha$ is not a nonnegative integer.

Let the roots of (18) be denoted by α_1 and α_2. Then

$$\alpha_1 + \alpha_2 = p_{-1} + 1$$

or $\alpha_2 - \alpha_1 = p_{-1} - 2\alpha_1 + 1$. Hence α_1 is exceptional if and only if $\alpha_2 - \alpha_1$ is a positive integer. Consequently, if the roots of the indicial equations do not differ by an integer, we obtain two solutions $z^{\alpha_1}g_1(z)$ and $z^{\alpha_2}g_2(z)$ which are obviously linearly independent. If the roots are equal or differ by an integer, the method yields only one solution.

Theorem 7. *If z_0 is a regular singular point for the equation (9), there exist linearly independent solutions of the form $(z - z_0)^{\alpha_1}g_1(z)$ and $(z - z_0)^{\alpha_2}g_2(z)$ with $g_1(0),\ g_2(0) \neq 0$ corresponding to the roots of the indicial equation, provided that $\alpha_2 - \alpha_1$ is not an integer. In the case of an integral difference $\alpha_2 - \alpha_1 \geqq 0$ the existence of a solution corresponding to α_2 can still be asserted.*

If one solution is known it is not difficult to find another, linearly independent of the first. The methods which lead to a second solution belong more properly in a textbook on differential equations. It is also impossible to treat the case of irregular singularities in this book.

EXERCISES

1. Show that the equation $(1 - z^2)w'' - 2zw' + n(n + 1)w = 0$, where n is a nonnegative integer, has the Legendre polynomials

$$P_n(z) = \frac{1}{2^n n!} \cdot \frac{d^n}{dz^n}(z^2 - 1)^n$$

as solutions.

2. Determine two linearly independent solutions of the equation

$$z^2(z + 1)w'' - z^2w' + w = 0$$

near 0 and one near -1.

3. Show that Bessel's equation $zw'' + w' + zw = 0$ has a solution which is an integral function. Determine its power-series development.

4.3. Solutions at Infinity. If $a_0(z)$, $a_1(z)$, $a_2(z)$ are polynomials, it is natural to ask how the solutions behave in the neighborhood of ∞. The most convenient way to treat this question is to make the variable transformation $z = 1/Z$. Since

$$\frac{dw}{dz} = -Z^2\frac{dw}{dZ}$$
$$\frac{d^2w}{dz^2} = 2Z^3\frac{dw}{dZ} + Z^4\frac{d^2w}{dZ^2}$$

equation (10) takes the form

$$\frac{d^2w}{dZ^2} = -\left(2Z^{-1} + Z^{-2}p\left(\frac{1}{Z}\right)\right)\frac{dw}{dZ} + Z^{-4}q\left(\frac{1}{Z}\right)w. \tag{19}$$

We say of course that ∞ is an ordinary point or a regular singularity for the equation (10) if the point $Z = 0$ has the corresponding character for

(19). Thus ∞ is an ordinary point if the coefficients in (10) have a removable singularity at $Z = 0$; this is the same, by definition, as saying that $-(2z + z^2p(z))$ and $z^4q(z)$ have removable singularities at ∞. Similarly, ∞ is a regular singularity if these functions have, respectively, at most a simple and a double pole at ∞.

It is interesting to determine the equations with the fewest singularities. If ∞ is to be an ordinary point, $q(z)$ must have at least four poles, unless it vanishes identically. In the latter case $p(z)$ can have as few as one pole, and if the pole is placed at the origin we must have $p(z) = -2/z$. The corresponding equation

$$\frac{d^2w}{dz^2} = -\frac{2}{z}\frac{dw}{dz}$$

has the general solution $w = az^{-1} + b$.

If $q(z)$ is not identically zero, there can be as few as two regular singularities. It is evidently easiest to place the singularities at 0 and ∞, and for this reason we turn immediately to the case where ∞ is a regular singularity. If there is to be only one finite singularity, placed at the origin, we must have $p(z) = A/z$, $q(z) = B/z^2$. With another choice of constants the equation can be written in the form

$$z^2w'' - (\alpha + \beta - 1)zw' + \alpha\beta w = 0. \tag{20}$$

It has the solutions $w = z^\alpha$ and $w = z^\beta$, where α and β are obviously the roots of the indicial equation. If $\alpha = \beta$, there must be another solution. To find it we write (20) in the symbolic form

$$\left(z\frac{d}{dz} - \alpha\right)^2 w = 0$$

and substitute $w = z^\alpha W$. We obtain

$$\left(z\frac{d}{dz} - \alpha\right) z^\alpha W = z^\alpha \cdot z\frac{dW}{dz}$$

$$\left(z\frac{d}{dz} - \alpha\right)^2 z^\alpha W = z^\alpha \cdot z\frac{d}{dz}\left(z\frac{dW}{dz}\right).$$

The equation $\left(z\dfrac{d}{dz}\right)^2 W = 0$ has the obvious solution $W = \log z$, and hence the desired solution of (20) is $w = z^\alpha \log z$.

4.4. *The Hypergeometric Differential Equation.* We have just seen that differential equations with one or two regular singularities have trivial solutions. It is only with the introduction of a third singularity that we obtain a new and interesting class of analytic functions.

It is quite clear that a linear transformation of the variable transforms a second-order linear differential equation into one of the same type and that the character of the singularities remains the same. We can therefore elect to place the three singularities at prescribed points, and it is simplest to choose them at 0, 1, and ∞.

If the equation

$$w'' = p(z)w' + q(z)$$

is to have finite regular singularities only at 0 and 1, we must have

$$p(z) = \frac{A}{z} + \frac{B}{z-1} + P(z)$$
$$q(z) = \frac{C}{z^2} + \frac{D}{z} + \frac{E}{(z-1)^2} + \frac{F}{z-1} + Q(z)$$

where $P(z)$ and $Q(z)$ are polynomials. In order to make the singularity at ∞ regular, $2z + z^2p(z)$ must have at most a simple pole at ∞ and $z^4q(z)$ must have at most a double pole. In view of these conditions $P(z)$ and $Q(z)$ must be identically zero, and the relation $D + F = 0$ must hold. These are evidently the only conditions, and we can rewrite the expressions for $p(z)$ and $q(z)$ in the form

$$p(z) = \frac{A}{z} + \frac{B}{z-1}$$
$$q(z) = \frac{C}{z^2} - \frac{D}{z(z-1)} + \frac{E}{(z-1)^2}.$$

The indicial equation at the origin reads

$$\alpha(\alpha - 1) = A\alpha + C.$$

So if its roots are denoted by α_1, α_2 we obtain $A = \alpha_1 + \alpha_2 - 1$, $C = -\alpha_1\alpha_2$. Similarly, $B = \beta_1 + \beta_2 - 1$ and $E = -\beta_1\beta_2$, where β_1, β_2 are the roots of the indicial equation at 1. In order to write down the indicial equation at ∞ we note that the leading coefficients of $-2z - z^2p(z)$ and $z^4q(z)$ are $-(2 + A + B)$ and $C - D + E$, respectively. Hence the roots γ_1, γ_2 satisfy $\gamma_1 + \gamma_2 = -A - B - 1$ and

$$\gamma_1\gamma_2 = -C + D - E.$$

We conclude at the relation

$$\alpha_1 + \alpha_2 + \beta_1 + \beta_2 + \gamma_1 + \gamma_2 = 1, \tag{21}$$

and we find that the equation can be written in the form

$$(22)\quad w'' + \left(\frac{1 - \alpha_1 - \alpha_2}{z} + \frac{1 - \beta_1 - \beta_2}{z - 1}\right) w' + \left(\frac{\alpha_1\alpha_2}{z^2} - \frac{\alpha_1\alpha_2 + \beta_1\beta_2 - \gamma_1\gamma_2}{z(z-1)} + \frac{\beta_1\beta_2}{(z-1)^2}\right) w = 0.$$

In order to avoid the exceptional cases we will now assume that none of the differences $\alpha_2 - \alpha_1$, $\beta_2 - \beta_1$, $\gamma_2 - \gamma_1$ is an integer. Our next step is to simplify the equation (22). In Sec. 3.2 we have already shown that the substitution $w = z^\alpha g(z)$ determines for $g(z)$ a similar differential equation, namely, the equation (17). Since the original equation has solutions of the form $w = z^{\alpha_1} g_1(z)$, $w = z^{\alpha_2} g_2(z)$, we conclude that the transformed equation (17) must have solutions of the form $g(z) = z^{\alpha_1 - \alpha} g_1(z)$ and $g(z) = z^{\alpha_2 - \alpha} g_2(z)$. Hence the indicial equation of (17) has the roots $\alpha_1 - \alpha$, $\alpha_2 - \alpha$, as can also be verified by computation. Simultaneously, the roots which correspond to the singularity at ∞ change from γ_1, γ_2 to $\gamma_1 + \alpha$, $\gamma_2 + \alpha$. In exactly the same way we can separate a factor $(z - 1)^\beta$ and find that the resulting equation has exponents which are smaller by β at 1 and larger by β at ∞. The natural choice is to take $\alpha = \alpha_1$, $\beta = \beta_1$. In the final equation the six exponents are then 0, $\alpha_2 - \alpha_1$, 0, $\beta_2 - \beta_1$, $\gamma_1 + \alpha_1 + \beta_1$, $\gamma_2 + \alpha_1 + \beta_1$, respectively. In order to comply with time-honored conventions we will write $a = \alpha_1 + \beta_1 + \gamma_1$, $b = \alpha_1 + \beta_1 + \gamma_2$, $c = 1 + \alpha_1 - \alpha_2$. Because of the relation (21) we get $c - a - b = \beta_2 - \beta_1$. Accordingly, the new differential equation will be of the form

$$w'' + \left(\frac{c}{z} + \frac{1 - c + a + b}{z - 1}\right) w' + \frac{ab}{z(z-1)} w = 0$$

or, after simplification,

$$(23)\qquad z(1 - z)w'' + [c - (a + b + 1)z]w' - abw = 0.$$

This is called the *hypergeometric differential equation*, and we have proved that the solutions of (22) are equal to the solutions of (23) multiplied by $z^{\alpha_1}(z - 1)^{\beta_1}$. It is assumed that none of the exponent differences $c - 1$, $a - b$, $a + b - c$ is an integer.

According to the theory, equation (23) has a solution of the form $w = \sum_{n=0}^{\infty} A_n z^n$. If this power series is substituted in (23), we find with very little computation that the coefficients must satisfy the recursive relations

$$(n + 1)(n + c)A_{n+1} = (n + a)(n + b)A_n.$$

The extremely simple form of this relation makes it possible to write down the solution explicitly. With the choice $A_0 = 1$ we find that the hypergeometric equation is satisfied by the function

$$F(a,b,c,z) = 1 + \frac{a \cdot b}{1 \cdot c} z + \frac{a(a+1) \cdot b(b+1)}{1 \cdot 2 \cdot c(c+1)} z^2 + \frac{a(a+1)(a+2) \cdot b(b+1)(b+2)}{1 \cdot 2 \cdot 3 \cdot c(c+1)(c+2)} z^3 + \cdots,$$

known as the *hypergeometric function.* It is defined as soon as c is not zero or a negative integer.

The radius of convergence of the hypergeometric series can easily be found by computation, but it is more instructive to use pure reasoning. In the first place, we know that $F(a,b,c,z)$ can be continued analytically along any path which does not pass through the point 1 and does not return to the origin. Hence a single-valued branch of $F(a,b,c,z)$ can be defined in the unit disk $|z| < 1$ (because the disk is simply connected), and it follows that the radius of convergence is at least equal to one. If it is greater than one, $F(a,b,c,z)$ will be an entire function. Near infinity it must be a linear combination of the solutions $z^{-a}g_1(z)$, $z^{-b}g_2(z)$ known to exist in a neighborhood of ∞. But it is clear that a linear combination can be single-valued only if a or b is an integer. If a is an integer b is not, by assumption, and $F(a,b,c,z)$ is a multiple of $z^{-a}g_1(z)$. By Liouville's theorem, if a were positive $F(a,b,c,z)$ would vanish identically, which is not the case. The only case in which the radius of convergence is infinite is thus when a (or b) is a negative integer or zero, and then the hypergeometric series reduces trivially to a polynomial.

In a neighborhood of the origin there is also a solution of the form $z^{1-c}g(z)$. Here $g(z)$ satisfies a hypergeometric differential equation with the six exponents $\alpha_2 - \alpha_1$, 0, 0, $\beta_2 - \beta_1$, $\gamma_1 + \alpha_2 + \beta_1$, $\gamma_2 + \alpha_2 + \beta_1$. It follows at once that we can set $g(z) = F(1 + a - c, 1 + b - c, 2 - c, z)$. We have proved that two linearly independent solutions near the origin are $F(a,b,c,z)$ and $z^{1-c}F(1 + a - c, 1 + b - c, 2 - c, z)$, respectively.

The solutions near 1 can be determined in exactly the same manner. It is easier, however, to replace z by $1 - z$ and interchange the α's and β's. As a result we find that the functions $F(a,b,1 + a + b - c, 1 - z)$ and $(1 - z)^{c-a-b}F(c - b, c - a, 1 - a - b + c, 1 - z)$ are linearly independent solutions in a neighborhood of 1. The solutions near ∞ can be found similarly.

We have demonstrated that the most general linear second-order differential equation with three regular singularities can be solved explicitly by means of the hypergeometric function. It is evidently also possible, although somewhat laborious, to determine the complete multiple-valued structure of the solutions.

EXERCISES

1. Show that $(1 - z)^{-\alpha} = F(\alpha,\beta,\beta,z)$ and $\log 1/(1 - z) = zF(1,1,2,z)$.
2. Express the derivative of $F(a,b,c,z)$ as a hypergeometric function.
3. Derive the integral representation

$$F(a,b,c,z) = \frac{\Gamma(c)}{\Gamma(b)\Gamma(c-b)} \int_0^1 t^{b-1}(1-t)^{c-b-1}(1-zt)^{-a}\,dt.$$

4. If w_1 and w_2 are linearly independent solutions of the differential equation $w'' = pw' + qw$, prove that the quotient $\eta = w_2/w_1$ satisfies

$$\frac{d}{dz}\left(\frac{\eta''}{\eta'}\right) - \frac{1}{2}\left(\frac{\eta''}{\eta'}\right)^2 = -2q - \frac{1}{2}p^2 + p'.$$

4.5. Riemann's Point of View. Riemann was a strong proponent of the idea that an analytic function can be defined by its singularities and general properties just as well as or perhaps better than through an explicit expression. A trivial example is the determination of a rational function by the singular parts connected with its poles.

We will show, with Riemann, that the solutions of a hypergeometric differential equation can be characterized by properties of this nature. We consider in the following a collection $\mathbf{F}$ of function elements (f,Ω) with certain characteristic features which we proceed to enumerate.

1. The collection $\mathbf{F}$ is *complete* in the sense that it contains all analytic continuations of any $(f,\Omega) \in \mathbf{F}$. It is *not* required that any two function elements in $\mathbf{F}$ be analytic continuations of each other, and hence $\mathbf{F}$ may consist of several complete analytic functions.

2. The collection is *linear.* This means that $(f_1,\Omega) \in \mathbf{F}$, $(f_2,\Omega) \in \mathbf{F}$ implies $(c_1f_1 + c_2f_2,\Omega) \in \mathbf{F}$ for all constant c_1, c_2. Moreover, any three elements (f_1,Ω), (f_2,Ω), $(f_3,\Omega) \in \mathbf{F}$ with the same Ω shall satisfy an identical relation $c_1f_1 + c_2f_2 + c_3f_3 = 0$ in Ω with constant coefficients, not all zero. In other words, $\mathbf{F}$ shall be at most *two dimensional.*

3. The only finite singularities of the functions in $\mathbf{F}$ shall be at the points 0 and 1; in addition, the point ∞ is also counted as a singularity. More precisely, it is required that any $(f,\Omega) \in \mathbf{F}$ can be continued along all arcs in the finite plane which do not pass through the points 0 and 1.

4. As to the behavior at the singular points we assume that there are functions in $\mathbf{F}$ which behave like prescribed powers z^{α_1} and z^{α_2} near 0, like $(z-1)^{\beta_1}$ and $(z-1)^{\beta_2}$ near 1, and like $z^{-\gamma_1}$ and $z^{-\gamma_2}$ near ∞. In precise terms, there shall exist certain analytic functions $g_1(z)$ and $g_2(z)$

defined in a neighborhood Δ of 0 and different from zero at that point; for a simply connected subregion Ω of Δ which does not contain the origin function elements $(z^{\alpha_1}g_1(z),\Omega)$, $(z^{\alpha_2}g_2(z),\Omega)$ can be defined, and it is required that they belong to **F**. The corresponding assumptions for the points 1 and ∞ can be formulated in analogous manner.

The reader will have recognized that the solutions of the differential equation (22) have just these properties, provided that none of the differences $\alpha_2 - \alpha_1$, $\beta_2 - \beta_1$, $\gamma_2 - \gamma_1$ is an integer. In addition, the relation $\alpha_1 + \alpha_2 + \beta_1 + \beta_2 + \gamma_1 + \gamma_2 = 1$ is satisfied. We make both assumptions and prove, under these restrictions, that there exists one and only one collection **F** with the properties 1 to 4. Accordingly, **F** will be identical with the collection of local solutions of the differential equation (22).

Riemann denotes any function element in **F** by the symbol

$$P\begin{Bmatrix} 0 & 1 & \infty & \\ \alpha_1 & \beta_1 & \gamma_1, & z \\ \alpha_2 & \beta_2 & \gamma_2 & \end{Bmatrix}.$$

Thus P does not stand for an individual function, but this is evidently of little importance. Once the uniqueness is established such identities as

$$P\begin{Bmatrix} 0 & 1 & \infty & \\ \alpha_1 & \beta_1 & \gamma_1, & z \\ \alpha_2 & \beta_2 & \gamma_2 & \end{Bmatrix} = z^{\alpha}(z-1)^{\beta}\, P\begin{Bmatrix} 0 & 1 & \infty & \\ \alpha_1 - \alpha & \beta_1 - \beta & \gamma_1 + \alpha + \beta, & z \\ \alpha_2 - \alpha & \beta_2 - \beta & \gamma_2 + \alpha + \beta & \end{Bmatrix}$$

or

$$P\begin{Bmatrix} 0 & 1 & \infty & \\ \alpha_1 & \beta_1 & \gamma_1, & z \\ \alpha_2 & \beta_2 & \gamma_2 & \end{Bmatrix} = P\begin{Bmatrix} 0 & 1 & \infty & \\ \beta_1 & \alpha_1 & \gamma_1, & 1-z \\ \beta_2 & \alpha_2 & \gamma_2 & \end{Bmatrix}$$

follow immediately provided that some care is given to their proper interpretation. The fact that such relationships, some of them quite elaborate, can be so easily recognized is one of the motivations for Riemann's point of view.

In order to prove the uniqueness, consider two linearly independent function elements (f_1,Ω), $(f_2,\Omega) \in$ **F**, defined in a simply connected region Ω which does not contain 0 or 1. There are such function elements in any Ω, for the functions $z^{\alpha_1}g_1(z)$ and $z^{\alpha_2}g_2(z)$ are linearly independent in their region of definition; they can be continued along an arc which ends in Ω and determine linearly independent function elements. If (f,Ω) is a third function element in **F**, the identities

$$\begin{aligned} cf + c_1f_1 + c_2f_2 &= 0 \\ cf' + c_1f_1' + c_2f_2' &= 0 \\ cf'' + c_1f_1'' + c_2f_2'' &= 0 \end{aligned}$$

imply

$$\begin{vmatrix} f & f_1 & f_2 \\ f' & f_1' & f_2' \\ f'' & f_1'' & f_2'' \end{vmatrix} = 0.$$

We write this equation in the form

$$f'' = p(z)f' + q(z)f$$

with

$$p(z) = \frac{f_1f_2'' - f_2f_1''}{f_1f_2' - f_2f_1'}, \qquad q(z) = -\frac{f_1'f_2'' - f_2'f_1''}{f_1f_2' - f_2f_1'}. \tag{24}$$

Here the denominator is not identically zero, for that would mean that f_1 and f_2 were linearly dependent.

We make now the observation that the expressions (24) remain invariant if f_1 and f_2 are subjected to a nonsingular linear transformation, *i.e.*, if they are replaced by $c_{11}f_1 + c_{12}f_2$, $c_{21}f_1 + c_{22}f_2$ with $c_{11}c_{22} - c_{12}c_{21} \neq 0$. This means that $p(z)$ and $q(z)$ will be the same for any choice of f_1 and f_2; hence they are well-determined *single-valued* functions in the whole plane minus the points 0 and 1.

In order to determine the behavior of $p(z)$ and $q(z)$ near the origin, we choose $f_1 = z^{\alpha_1}g_1(z)$, $f_2 = z^{\alpha_2}g_2(z)$. Simple calculations give

$$\begin{aligned} f_1f_2' - f_2f_1' &= (\alpha_2 - \alpha_1)z^{\alpha_1+\alpha_2-1}(C + \cdots) \\ f_1f_2'' - f_2f_1'' &= (\alpha_2 - \alpha_1)(\alpha_1 + \alpha_2 - 1)z^{\alpha_1+\alpha_2-2}(C + \cdots) \\ f_1'f_2'' - f_2'f_1'' &= \alpha_1\alpha_2(\alpha_2 - \alpha_1)z^{\alpha_1+\alpha_2-3}(C + \cdots) \end{aligned}$$

where the parentheses stand for analytic functions with the common value $C = g_1(0)g_2(0)$ at the origin. We conclude that $p(z)$ has a simple pole with the residue $\alpha_1 + \alpha_2 - 1$ while the Laurent development of $q(z)$ begins with the term $-\alpha_1\alpha_2/z^2$. Similar results hold for the points 1 and ∞. We infer that

$$p(z) = \frac{\alpha_1 + \alpha_2 - 1}{z} + \frac{\beta_1 + \beta_2 - 1}{z - 1} + p_0(z)$$

where $p_0(z)$ is free from poles at 0 and 1. On the other hand, the development of $p(z)$ at ∞ must begin with the term $-(\gamma_1 + \gamma_2 + 1)/z$. According to its definition (24), $p(z)$ is a logarithmic derivative. As such it has, in the finite plane, only simple poles with positive integers as residues. In view of the relation $(\alpha_1 + \alpha_2 - 1) + (\beta_1 + \beta_2 - 1) = -(\gamma_1 + \gamma_2 + 1)$, it follows that $p_0(z)$ can have no poles at all and must, in fact, vanish identically.

Since $f_1f_2' - f_2f_1'$ is thus $\neq 0$ except at 0 and 1, we conclude that $q(z)$ is of the form

$$q(z) = -\frac{\alpha_1\alpha_2}{z^2} - \frac{\beta_1\beta_2}{(z-1)^2} + \frac{A}{z} + \frac{B}{z-1} + q_0(z)$$

where $q_0(z)$ is a polynomial. At ∞ the development must begin with $-\gamma_1\gamma_2/z^2$. We find that $q_0(z)$ must be identically zero while

$$A = -B = -(\alpha_1\alpha_2 + \beta_1\beta_2 - \gamma_1\gamma_2).$$

Collecting the results we conclude that f satisfies the equation

$$w'' + \left(\frac{1-\alpha_1-\alpha_2}{z} + \frac{1-\beta_1-\beta_2}{z-1}\right)w' + \left(\frac{\alpha_1\alpha_2}{z^2} - \frac{\alpha_1\alpha_2+\beta_1\beta_2-\gamma_1\gamma_2}{z(z-1)} + \frac{\gamma_1\gamma_2}{(z-1)^2}\right)w = 0$$

which is just the equation (22).

This completes the uniqueness proofs, for it follows now that any collection $\mathbf{F}$ which satisfies 1 to 4 must be a subcollection of the family $\mathbf{F}_0$ of local solutions of (22). For any simply connected Ω which does not contain 0 or 1 we know that there are two linearly independent function elements (f_1,Ω), (f_2,Ω) in $\mathbf{F}$. Every $(f,\Omega) \in \mathbf{F}_0$ is of the form $(c_1f_1 + c_2f_2,\Omega)$ and is consequently contained in $\mathbf{F}$. Finally, if Ω is not simply connected, then $(f,\Omega) \in \mathbf{F}_0$ is the analytic continuation of a restriction to a simply connected subregion of Ω, and since the restriction belongs to $\mathbf{F}$ so does (f,Ω) because of the property 1.

INDEX